CENTURY'S CHILD

A Novel of an American Family's Cold War Years
by

Walter D. Rodgers

First copy of First Edition
Walter D. Rodgers

Printed in Victoria, Canada

National Library of Canada Cataloguing in Publication

Rodgers, Walter D., 1936-
Century's child / Walter D. Rodgers.
ISBN 1-55369-338-8
I. Title.
PS3618.O34C45 2002 813'.6 C2002-901353-4

TRAFFORD

This book was published *on-demand* in cooperation with Trafford Publishing.
On-demand publishing is a unique process and service of making a book available for retail sale to the public taking advantage of on-demand manufacturing and Internet marketing. **On-demand publishing** includes promotions, retail sales, manufacturing, order fulfilment, accounting and collecting royalties on behalf of the author.

Suite 6E, 2333 Government St., Victoria, B.C. V8T 4P4, CANADA
Phone 250-383-6864 Toll-free 1-888-232-4444 (Canada & US)
Fax 250-383-6804 E-mail sales@trafford.com
Web site www.trafford.com TRAFFORD PUBLISHING IS A DIVISION OF TRAFFORD HOLDINGS LTD.
Trafford Catalogue #02-0151 www.trafford.com/robots/02-0151.html

10 9 8 7 6 5 4

To Mickey, who put up with me as I tried to write a first novel, and to Freddie, who forged the base metal into steel.

WDR
29 May 2001.

* * *

Foreword

The following is a work of fiction.

References to actual historical persons have used the actual names and ranks in effect at the time.

References to everyone else in this novel are totally based on the author's imagination. They are not intended to portray any actual human being, living or dead. Many of the incidents described are based on combinations of the experiences of several men, with no intent to portray any one of the sources.

Place names, with the exception of those of a few military bases and camps have not been changed or disguised in any way.

All other references to persons and events in this novel are absolutely fictitious, as are the names, dates, and times of military operations.

The author recommends the reader review the Glossary first, particularly if he or she has a limited military background, and also the map of Vietnam which follows page 225.

WDR

Illustrations

Great-grandfather John R. Vogelsong..........................28
Alf, Kenny, and Coe Richards, Senior, 1916..................30
Freddie, 1895...33
Doll Vogelsong, 1895...35
Kansas City in the 1930s 59
Grandfather A.G. Reidl..65
Mary Grace Reidl..67
Unit Shoulder Patch, Carrier-Pigeon Division,
Army Signal Corps........................108
Amy 122
Battalion Area of Operations 172
Northwestern III Corps, 30 Jan 1968 215
Southeastern Indochina 141
II Corps...156
Battalion Rear Layout, 2/502...178
The March from the Airfield, Phuoc Binh...........................189
Bu Gia Map, 30 Jan 1968..194
The Big-Game Hunters, Phuoc Binh...............................192
Northern I Corps, Diagram..215
Khe Sanh Area..207
Fire Support Base (FSB) Bastogne..220
FSB Ridge...227
Cache, Thua Thien Province 229
FSB Boston..236
Glossary... ..302

"....To him (Mark Twain) English was always a *spoken* tongue; he wrote as he *talked*.... He imparted to the printed page the vivacity of the spoken word, its swiftness and its unpremeditated ease."

"Mark Twain and the Art of Writing,"
Brander Matthews,
Harper's Weekly, October 1920.

* * *

"Strike the tent."

The last words of GEN Robert E. Lee.

1July 1916

Ruins of Thiepval, 8 Miles West Of Bapaume
Somme Area, Department du Nord, France

In 1888, a few of Grandpa Clair's uncles and their children, his older cousins, had followed the lumber north to Labrador. They settled there, some migrating further east to the Crown Colony of Newfoundland, not yet a part of the Dominion of Canada. They became permanent residents there, and, as the trees played out, worked the cod fisheries at sea, or the packing plants ashore.

Some recent historians would say that on this day in 1916 the Twentieth century was less than two years old, having begun on 7 August 1914.

At the outbreak of the Great War in August 1914, six of the youngest of the Richards cousins joined Newfoundland regiments of the British Army, and after some training in Home County Barracks, were sent to England for further "lessons-learned" instruction. That consisted of a distillation of the hard experiences of the Battle of the Frontiers, in which 400,000 Allied soldiers died between 7 August and 15 November1914, and the also-ruinously-costly Gallipoli Campaign of 1915.

From there, the boys were allocated to separate companies, and moved to France for their final field training. They were then rotated through the trenches by company for three or four days at a time, to develop an introduction to actual combat survival skills.

One of the cousins lost a leg to a stray German rifle bullet on 2 May 1916, and was invalided home later that same month. He developed deep vein thrombosis, followed by septicemia, and died at sea during his return voyage to Newfoundland.

On the morning of 1 July 1916, after four days' artillery bombardment of the German trench positions, and closely following a diversionary French attack before Verdun, the Newfoundlanders launched their assault. They left their trenches, and advanced in open order, shining Lee-Enfield Short Model rifles at high port, bayonets fixed, with the men dressed right, and uncovered front-to-rear. They walked away from the low ridgeline marking their field fortifications, keeping a twelve-foot interval between men, down into the shallow valley to their front, and then up the slope of the opposite low hill toward the shell-torn German earthworks.

Only a few of them made it as far as the German wire, though rare individuals and understrength sections did actually get into *the enemy's positions.*

In most places along the line, however, the Germans climbed quickly up, out of their untouched 20-foot-deep dugouts, carrying G1898 long Mauser rifles and Maxim machine guns, took their pre-assigned, if battered, positions and shot the advancing khaki waves to pieces. The Newfoundlanders were knocked down in windrows before most of them had even reached the halfway point of their assault.

The five Richards cousins were never seen again; doubtless they were among the 20% of the dead who were not identifiable, and were buried behind the battlefield among the 27,000 others who died there, all in less than two hours.

None of the American relatives heard about this episode at the time. I discovered it while researching the emigrant branch of The Family in 1988. Only then was it possible to tell the few surviving American Richards what had happened to their older cousins seventy-two years before.

Their graves are still there, not five hundred yards from the places that they died, among those of their comrades-in-arms and -in-death.

No Newfoundland Territorial unit, even at the height of World War Two, *twenty-eight years later, has been deployed to a combat zone since that morning in 1916.*

We few, we happy few, we band of brothers;
For he to-day that sheds his blood with me
Shall be my brother............
And gentlemen in England now abed
Shall think themselves accurs'd they were not here,
And hold their manhood cheap whiles any speaks
That fought with us upon Saint Crispin's day.

Shakespeare,
Henry the Fifth.

1.

Christmas Week, 1990, Ayun Airfield, North-Central Arabia

O, Mankind! Call upon your Lord humbly and in secret. Lo! He loveth not the aggressor!

The Glorious Koran
Surah vii, 55.
Marmaduke Pickthall, Translator.

* * *

I stood in the long shadow of a five-ton truck, watching the 645th Medical Clearing Company unload in Arabia, 111 officers and enlisted men and women in all, in two C-130s. Each was heavily loaded, carrying a full duffel bag, an M-16 rifle and a stuffed ALICE pack. Their load-bearing equipment (LBE) was Army Green, Shade AG-44.

I spoke to their advance-party executive officer: "They look good. You must have trained them well."

"We think so," he responded. "They were all MOS-qualified before they were alerted to deploy, and we've had five weeks to give them a final polish."

The men and women seemed dazzled by the late afternoon sun after being closeted in the relative darkness of the C-130s' cargo bays. They were wide-eyed and skittish, frequently looking toward the north as though expecting the rumble of distant artillery fire, unusual in green troops.

The advance party counted off the troops into smaller quartering groups, and then led them into a pre-placed tent village consisting of twelve GP Medium tents, and a line of eight U.S. Government-leased light-blue civilian Porta-Potties which would not have been out of place on any stateside construction site.

As I reflected on it, I'd spent a lot of Christmas seasons away from home. The first one, long past for me, is the most difficult.

That morning, early, I'd finished the first of the 68 letters home that I'd write from the Middle East. Any Old Soldier will tell you that the time to do any personal task is the half-hour before or following breakfast, whether it's writing home, taking a dump, or cleaning your weapon; you're not likely to have any other time to do it that day. Admittedly, I wrote home less often than I had from Vietnam, thanks to the development of satellite telephone communication in the interim.

The scene this December 20th was of a wide view, one of a light beige powdery sand, lit by brilliant white sunlight, and of sharp black shadows. There wasn't a cloud in the huge sky. In fact, that was the usual case in Arabia.

No plant life was visible in any direction.
The air was dry, with a faintly incense-like odor. One whiff, and your nasal passages were wide open for the duration.
The debarkees were wearing desert camouflage, khaki battle dress uniforms (BDU), with black markings placed irregularly to break up their outlines.
The 645th's personnel made up the first element of many more units due to follow, up to and including general hospitals, the Army's largest treating facilities.
I remember thinking that it would be the newcomers' first night in a combat zone, though hardly mine. Over the next few months, they'd be exposed to modern warfare, and, if they survived it, would never again be the people they were that evening.
I knew. I'd been through it all, 23 years before.

* * *

On Christmas day, an instructor team from Central Command (CENTCOM), driving Dodge pickup trucks, pulled up at 7AM. All personnel located nearby were to be trained intensively for nine clock hours on the one-man-fired AT-4 Karl Gustav antitank rocket launcher, a very effective Swedish design that an American manufacturer built under license. It was a disposable four-foot-long single-use 84mm-diameter (thus, its caliber) fiberglass tube, containing the entire firing unit: rocket, propellant/fuel, and electrical ignition system.
Everyone fell into formation for class, no exceptions, private to full colonel. I couldn't help thinking back over the decades I'd served since 1954, and of the Army's failure to design or adopt anything even remotely like the Karl-Gustav after it dropped the 3.5-inch rocket launcher around 1960. Yes, we *had* a one-man launcher, but it was too light to stop a tank. And yes, we had heavier rockets that would do the job, but they were too heavy for one man to carry and then fire. Nothing against the AT-4, mind you, I just wondered why *we* (who used to be the foremost country on earth when it came to innovation) didn't develop it or a facsimile.
There hadn't been time for actual firing practice in the states, so CENTCOM was making it a very high priority in-country.
We practiced firing the weapon with a 9mm subcaliber device (really a *model* of the launcher fitted with an internal 9mm carbine barrel that fired a standard pistol bullet) until we were proficient with it at a range of 75 meters, our targets being cardboard rectangles a little smaller than a tank hull. The target range wasn't marked out on the ground; it was simply miles of desert, with a low dune half a mile distant as our backstop
Let me backtrack to correct myself on one point: We *did* have one individually-fired anti-tank missile that was wire-guided, which required the gunner to stand upright on a modern battlefield for 11 seconds, to guide it home. Whoever approved that weapon for issue to troops had surely never been under

small-arms fire. Eleven seconds is about three mens' lifetimes when the bullets are flying.

All through the day-long class, the rumble of passing 25-ton semis only let up between serials of what looked like one everlasting convoy, heading north along the excellent Saudi highway system, all newly-built since (the oil-price hike of) 1974. It was the advance party of the 24th Infantry Division (Mechanized). The heavy trailers were loaded with either one tank, plus miscellaneous cargo, or with two Bradley armored fighting vehicles. Both were admittedly overloads, but time was of the essence.

The lightly-armed 82d Airborne Division was already in its over-watch/screening positions just south of the border with Kuwait. They had been there since August; being a very light infantry force they were (and are now) the unit of first resort for rapid overseas deployment. However, airborne units are too lightly armed to resist an armored or mechanized attack for long. So, a stronger defensive posture had to be put in place quickly, lest the Iraqis decide to head south, with their hundreds of Soviet-made T-55s and T-72s, once they'd consolidated their forces inside Kuwait.

In retrospect, even ten years after the fact, I can't understand why they didn't do just that, after taking twelve hours or so to regroup and consolidate in Kuwait City. They'd probably have used captured commercial gas stations to refuel, and then struck south into Arabia before even the 82d, our most mobile force, could arrive from CONUS. The Iraqis could have, no, *should* have, seized most of Arabia's oil fields in 72 hours, tops.

Even after the U.S./Coalition force buildup was completed several weeks later, the Iraqi army had over three times the number of tanks that we did, and twice the number of artillery tubes. It was reasonable to expect that there'd be at least some breakthroughs into our rear areas, where the medical units would be located. This mandatory training would give us some small chance to defend against them.

There would be no place for the medics to run, and no place to hide for them, nor for their helpless, unarmed charges.

So, as the Geneva Convention states: "Medical personnel are specifically permitted to fight to defend themselves and/or their patients."

Saddam Hussein had promised us "The Mother of All Battles," and I believed him; couldn't really afford not to. I just hoped that the heavyweight 2d Armored Division could get here from Germany before it started.

I was working for the Theater Surgeon's office in this war. I couldn't go back to the 101st, though they were beginning to arrive in-theater. I was too old, and too high-ranked; my old airborne division had no place for me. Even the XVIII Airborne Corps, when it finally arrived, was up to strength and had no vacancies.

When I imagined what Saddam's promised clash of armies would be like, I visualized a repeat of a freewheeling, widespread, weeks-long 1943 replay of the Battle of Kursk, spread over a hundred-mile-diameter vortex of desert. The open terrain, and the numbers and composition of the opposing forces was about equivalent to the Russians' and Germans' in 1943. We'd have played the Germans' role of the smaller force, though the one possessing a degree of technological superiority.

However, the Germans *had* lost the Battle of Kursk.

* * *

23 February 1991
Four Miles South of An Nasiriah, Iraq

The bloated bluebottle fly circled the feed slowly. Sensing a quiet area with no movement detectable by her compound eyes, she tightened the radius of her turn, banking left as she did so.

She landed, then paused, motionless herself for three seconds.

Seeing no threat, she walked across the dead Iraqi mortar crewman's lower lid, onto the surface of his open eye, sucking up the precious water.

Maternal egg-laying could wait, for a few minutes.

The mortar crew had set up their weapon and its 360-degree firing position 800 meters west of a battery of Soviet-made 130mm guns. All four men had been wounded by a stray submunition ejected from one of the Americans' Multiple Launch Rocket System missiles, as a volley of twenty-four rounds fell, enveloping the battery area with hundreds of the grenade-sized bomblets.

This crewman had died instantly, and two others in less than five pain-racked minutes, trying to reach help where there was none.

The fourth member of the crew is still unaccounted-for.

That was these soldiers' share of Saddam Hussein's "Mother of All Battles."

* * *

Cousin David Reidl
2 February 1969.

When I had been back from Vietnam about six weeks, I heard through the Family Grapevine that David had gotten *his* orders to go, in three weeks.

I made it a point to go see him at his parents' house, near where I'd lived when I was in high school. He looked well, and appeared to be in good physical condition. He said he'd just made PFC, four weeks out of Advanced Individual Training (AIT).

Even after the Ia Drang Valley, Khe Sanh, Tet and Mini-Tet, he wasn't afraid. He was overconfident; I think his training had been *too* good.

He was eager to get to Vietnam, now that it was certain that he *was* going, and get on with his life after his Army service.

We must have talked for an hour or so. I warned him in no uncertain terms: "Don't underestimate the North Vietnamese Army (NVA). Their soldiers are at least as accomplished as ours, man for man, or perhaps even a little better. Our big advantage lies in our having almost unlimited firepower and superior sustainment of our side by rapid resupply."

There were details I thought might help him in the year to come that I had learned by experiences not covered in the Army's training manuals. Like: carry a 4-by-4-inch sponge instead of a washcloth. You can bathe in much less water that way. In a pinch, you can use it in lieu of a towel, too. And carry a lady's pocket mirror, as small as you can find, to shave in. And don't be taken prisoner. Don't even think of surrendering to a nonwhite soldier. It's better to die quickly, rather than by inches. As it turned out, he went, even as I had, to a separate brigade, the First Brigade of the Fifth Mechanized Division, which had assumed responsibility for the northernmost extremity of South Vietnam, along the 1954 Demilitarized Zone (DMZ). The Brigade song was even a parody of the Dinah Shore TV commercial:

"See the *DMZ*
In your *APC* (armored personnel carrier);
America is
Asking you to *Die*."

As David and I visited, the family dog came in, and was all over me in less than a second, wagging his tail and trying to lick my face. It was Boots, *our* family dog, who remembered me from my adolescence, 15 years before. I'd thought of him as long-dead, but he had been boarding with David's family for all those years. He recalled me by odor, from a dog's-lifetime-old molecular imprint, stored in his olfactory cortex, as if all that time apart had just been overnight.

The encounter caused a welling-up of *something* large in my chest, and I couldn't talk for two or three minutes. I covered it up (as The Family is wont to do) by turning away from David, petting and hugging Boots.

A year later, David was back, uninjured, not even scratched.

I found out years later from his older brother that he had been awarded a Silver Star for valor above and beyond the call of duty.

David wouldn't (and won't) even discuss it.

He would be the last of The Family to deploy, at least to that war.

Our family, and thousands like it, carried this country through three world wars in the 20th century, if you'll allow me the license to count Korea, Vietnam, and the Cold War combined as one global conflict.

It took us seventy-two years, but we won.

2.

Present Day

Men are attracted to war. Always have been, and probably always will be. And, later, they usually regret it, once they've been sufficiently terrified, or are wounded, or develop their first case of malaria, dengue, or dysentery. Somehow, war loses its adventure and/or nobility somewhere along that continuum.

I contend that any story can begin at the beginning, the middle, or the end.

My name is Richards. I go by my middle name, Coe, because I've never liked "John" or "Jack," and "J.C." in adolescence at least, was synonymous with the initials of Our Lord and Savior, world without end, amen. The adolescent humor resulting from those initials was also without end.

And this story, The Family's, begins in the middle.

I can't choose to start at the end of the story, because the end, though near, isn't here quite yet. I can't remember the early part well, so I suspect that starting there would be pretty chaotic. That eaves the middle as a starting point, so, by default, that's where I'll have to begin.

As this Twenty-first century begins, I'm in my mid-sixties.

I've experienced nearly two-thirds of the Twentieth Century. There was never a dull moment. Unless you count the eight Eisenhower years, 1952-1960.

My current diagnosis is Alzheimer's disease, early stage. There, for the first time I've written it down and watched it bounce between the page and my eyes, back and forth, back and forth, at least 20 times. It's a chronic form, and my prognosis is good, which is to say that I will live several more years, possibly more. I do *not* mention this as a cheap attempt to garner sympathy; everyone dies, in my not-inconsiderable experience. But blackjack is my hobby, and percentages rule in that game, as they do in life.

So, let me emphasize that I am under the press of time. Either way, long odds or short, I've never written a book before, so I'd better get on with it. With luck, I'll finish the book before I finish, period.

And let me warn you in advance: you're going to get The Family's story warts and all; it will be as real as I can make it. How it impresses you is a secondary consideration. If it's too blunt (or obtuse) or offends, I'm sorry. However, you will never wonder what I *meant* by a particular sentence; *that* will be crystal-clear.

Try not to trip over all the details; as you progress through our story, their purpose will become more understandable.

Just stay with me and it will all fall into place.

Romance has seized me by the scruff of the neck three times, and has temporarily shaken me loose from whatever common sense I had. "As the heart fills, the brain empties," according to that great modern philosopher, Dr. Laura Schlesinger. Each time, by the time that rational thought and behavior had returned, the first two relationships had gone stale, and I devoutly wished that the one that resulted in marriage, finally, could have been *first* in line.

I have two grown children. The less I say about them, the less confusion I'll introduce. They are busy wasting their lives, and to that extent have been a great disappointment to me. It probably isn't entirely their fault. The children of compulsively-successful men often *don't* do well. By most standards, they're nice kids, typical of their generation, but they aren't major players in this narrative.

I'd hoped to be the founder of a *dynastic* family along the lines of the fictional Canadian Whiteoaks, in the serial novels of Mazo de la Roche. Possibly, I even had the potential to be the originator of a *physician* family dynasty modeled on the Mayo Brothers' or the Menningers'. Those large families, though they doubtless had their internal conflicts, each presented a united, even monolithic face to the outside world.

To that extent, I've failed.

In the family for which I am (half) responsible, the members just don't have a consistent sense of cohesion nor the individual discipline to commit to the concept. On the other hand, neither do all of the Boston Kennedys, who are *the* penultimate modern American dynasty.

Once Old Joe had had a stroke, and stopped functioning as the central controller, it, too, began to fray around the edges, and did so in full public view. So, long before the deteriorating cerebral grey cells finally even threatened to take out my cognition, the Whiteoaks-like-family fantasy had ended.

And, anyway, our two children were too young to have any part in The Family's encounter with the Cold War.

* * *

Many men, as they sense their mortal years as being finite, (and I do mean *men*; I've never seen a woman do it, unless you count the last-minute suicide note, which doesn't count in this context) write some sort of testament or life-history. In my line of work, you see them written in ball-point, pencil, even crayon, on all kinds of paper, by people who had never written *anything* before, so far as their survivors knew, and sometimes they'd sit down to record it before they'd even been diagnosed as being seriously ill. My suspicion is that, consciously or not, it's an effort made to ensure that they won't be forgotten.

So, that may explain what this story is about.

That, and the phenomenon of individual change. Especially in the sense that a bad start, even a *really* bad start, need not equate to failure.

In fact, individuals and families, in their tens of thousands, may even win a half-century-long Cold War.

You may fairly charge that war makes up an inordinate amount of the subject matter of this narrative. Perhaps it does. I can only justify it by stating three opinions about war:

One: It appears to be a recurring, vicious human behavior. Net result: negative.

Two: In spite of the tremendous waste and even misuse of human and material resources, it accelerates progress in every field of science known to man. Net result: positive.

Three: It brings out the best and worst in human beings, and does it rapidly. After first-hand exposure to it, there can be no question in your mind about who *you* are. And the people around you can never again convince you that they're anything that they're not. That's a contribution to both personal insight and to understanding of our fellow-man. Net result: positive.

The positives outnumber the negative by two to one.

3.

27 December 1990

"...instead of a single definitive (surgical-*WDR*) operation that focuses on anatomical reconstruction, the damage control strategy uses a staged approach that focuses on restoration of patient stability while temporarily sacrificing anatomical integrity.

"...the first key issue is patient selection.

"...Thus, careful triage and mature surgical judgement...are required to avoid expending extremely limited surgical resources, personnel and time on these most seriously (i.e. *multiply*(WDR))- injured patients."

LTC John B. Holcomb, MC, USA:
" Military, Civilian, and Rural Application
of the Damage Control Philosophy,"
Military Medicine, p. 490, vol. 166, June 2001.

* * *

Half the estimated 35,000 casualties expected for Operation Desert Storm would probably have occurred during the first phase of that incredibly violent battle that we had been promised by Saddam Hussein, if it developed according to prior estimates.

The rest would be accounted for by the projected nine-month-long slog west-northwest. That phase of the campaign would have been characterized by a well-organized defense of every terrain feature in our path, until their army was "attritted-down" to a force too weak to hold us off, Baghdad fell, and Saddam Hussein was killed, was exiled somewhere out of our reach, or captured.

The medical support of the American force could be based on the assumption that of those 35,000, a fourth would die of wounds outright or would be unsalvageable. Another fourth or so would sustain minor wounds, which could easily wait 24 hours for definitive treatment. Of the half remaining, 2/3 would require surgical treatment in 4 hours or so to survive. The final 1/3 would require surgical treatment in 2 hours or less to have any chance at all.

That's a simplified, some might say grossly *over*-simplified, explanation of the concept of triage, the sorting of patients to assign priority of surgical treatment. It's necessary any time that demand for medical treatment exceeds the supply, even temporarily.

Nearly all the wounded would be generated (what an unparalleled euphemism!) in the first few hours, if not *the* first hour after engagement. That would, in turn, saturate first the treatment facilities and then, unless strict medical regulating procedures were followed, the evacuation systems, in that order. Once saturation occurs, all patient traffic stops. Anyone with a wound who was not already in a hospital would be unlikely to reach one.

That situation could not be allowed to develop.

Where would the very best surgeons be? Operating?

Not on your life.

No, they would be *sorting* the wounded at every level of treatment, at least partly to siphon off that one-fourth to one-third who would be hopeless cases, the so-called "Expectant" category (*expect*-ed not to make it).

Evacuation of those patients would be stopped where they were. They'd be placed to one side, made as comfortable as was humanly possible, be given very close nursing attention, receive aggressive palliative care, pastoral attention, and let slip away, quietly.

Those same senior surgeons would also decide who could only survive with prompt, relatively-brief surgical treatment, and place them at the head of the line.

Since 1916 it's been standard practice to *triage* (not to be confused with the activity of a civilian "triage nurse," a functionary, who bears *no* resemblance to a true prioritizer of treatment) in just this way, the large numbers of near-simultaneous battlefield casualties. The most experienced surgeon on-site is the best choice to actually make the hard decisions. In this way, the surgical backlog (expressed in hours) is minimized, more of the salvageable wounded survive, or put another way, the greatest good for the greatest number is achieved.

At least, that was the plan. *Our* plan.

On paper.

29 January 1968
Phuoc Binh, South Vietnam

Parachutes were carefully inspected, and then packed. Unit equipment was given a final cleaning, then packaged for air-drop under the watchful eyes of officer and NCO jumpmasters.

Individual gear was then subjected to the same scrutiny.

Defects and shortages were noted, and each man was sent to his company supply room to exchange defective items for new ones, or to draw replacement equipment for whatever shortages had been found.

Unlike my peacetime experience, there was no hassle over articles lost in a combat zone; they were simply replaced without question or comment.

The only items not on hand were explosives and ammunition, which would be issued on the airfield, immediately before the jump.

Fire support plans were finalized, to include air strikes if required.

We planned to jump onto a disused airfield, the classic target of airborne troops, chase the VC away, secure it, and then use it to receive reinforcements.

From that point on, what we did would be governed by the enemy's reaction.

* * *

29 November 1990

My reaction to being activated (on Thanksgiving Day, 1990) was: "Well, here we go again; it's not the first time," but with a difference. I made it a point to return to Kansas City from Arizona to see all my relatives, just as I had in 1967, but not because I expected to be out of touch for a year; not *this* time.

It was my considered opinion that, while the United States and Coalition Forces would win the war, with Iraq's history of using poison gas and of utilizing Soviet armored doctrine, against a numerically smaller force, *my* surviving this episode would be unlikely.

What I was doing, what I was *expected* to do, was to say "Goodbye," to everyone I loved and who loved me deeply, while seeming to say "Hello, again. Just thought I'd drop by." Though I live 1300 miles away.

That's how The Family operates: You *say* something superficial, even trivial, but *mean* something else, profound.

* * *

After all my misgivings that fall and winter of 1990, I was never to hear a shot fired in anger; the Iraqi Army disintegrated, and surrendered after 90 hours of continuous attack by a smaller but vastly more capable Coalition force.

* * *

This country is subjected to a never-ending litany of efforts to define the "Me Generation", the people born between 1944 and 1954. There are about forty million of them. Subtracting the women, we are left with about twenty million men who were of military age during the time window of 1965 to 1973, the Vietnam years.

About ten million of them successfully avoided service in the armed forces during that period. As a result, most of them lived, and went on to become the leaders of today's United States.

At the time, they were easy to spot.

In their early lives, they were the ones who refused to take out the garbage.

A few years later, they flaunted their non-conformity by slavishly conforming *to* the bizarre appearance of hippie or rocker styles (long hair, or shaved heads, or even initials shaved into their tresses.) Part of that image, too, was smoking, injecting, or snorting all manner of pharmaceuticals, often killing themselves, or at least their cerebral cortices.

Their greatest heroes were and are two prominent people of the last half of the Twentieth century, Lady Diana Spencer and William Jefferson Clinton, holders of high offices who, when the chips were down, had publicly refused to do *their* public duty, too.

This is the story of one family which represents the *other* ten million, the half that powers the United States.

That half of the "Me Generation" and the three generations that preceded and formed it also deserves to have *its* story told.

While living normal civilian lives, they left their jobs, schools and families, and saved Western civilization. They did it by:

1. Fighting the Vietnam War, and only being prevented from winning it partly by the whores of the Liberal Left, with the help of the stateside, obstructionist activities of the *other* half of the "Me Generation;"
2. Making up the force-in-being that held the Cold War at (at least) a tie for 45 years, till their adversary collapsed;
3. Thus winning the Cold War in its 45th year, topping it off by:
4. Fighting and winning the Second Gulf War (1991) in three and a half days.

They can be spotted in a crowd, even at this advanced age, by these characteristics:

1. Their hair isn't styled; it's *cut*. And they have shaved today.
2. They aren't whiners, and can't abide people who are.
3. They tend to be gainfully employed, whether or not they suffer mentally or physically (as many do) from the after-effects of war.

4. They're the half of the population that votes.

5. They attend their own funerals covered with an American flag, a national color, symbolic of their pride in their service and sacrifices.

This is *their* story.

* * *

Bring the good old bugle, boys, we'll sing another song;
Sing it with a spirit that will start the world along.
Sing it as we used to sing it, sixty thousand strong,
While we were marching through Georgia!

Chorus:
Hurrah! Hurrah! We bring the jubilee!
Hurrah! Hurrah! The flag that makes you free!
So we sang the chorus from Atlanta to the sea,
While we were marching through Georgia!

Song: *Marching Through Georgia.*
(Best sung with a banjo and cornet accompaniment).

* * *

17 November 1864
0530

Breakfast had been brief. The cooking fires were out, and the faint beginning of a cold sunrise was lighting the clear sky to the east. Stars gleamed brightly in the black sky overhead.

The three battalion drummers began the Long Roll, and the men, in march order, began to assemble four-deep, facing south on the east-west road that now lies a foot beneath the surface of the westbound lane of Interstate Highway 18.

Company F, 199th New York Volunteers, chilled to the bone, their feet cased in damp, heavy-duty ankle-high black brogans, formed up in the cold, and waited for their companies' First Sergeants.

Each man carried a shiny, new .58-caliber muzzle-loading Enfield model 1861 rifled musket and a socket-lug bayonet, forty cartridges, a blanket, canvas shelter-half, three days' ration of flour, bacon and coffee beans, and a metal canteen. Every man carried about one-fourth of the cooking equipment used by his four-man mess.

They were identically dressed in dusty sky-blue kersey trousers, and equally-dusty dark blue woolen jackets on which the brass Federal buttons still shone with some degree of their original luster.

The 199th was a newly-raised regiment from the area around Elmira, and was made up mostly of farm boys. By today's standards, they had received only minimal combat training before entraining for Chattanooga four months before. The Regiment was also new to the Army of the Tennessee, to which it was assigned, and new to combat. It had marched in pursuit of the already-withdrawing Confederate forces from Chattanooga to Atlanta, seeing action only in the last two days of the Battle of Atlanta. They had taken no casualties during that light contact, pushing the weakened Rebels away, to the south and west of the city.

The upcoming operation would involve the troops' leaving all unit trains behind, even down to company level quartermaster- and cook-wagons, to catch up with the riflemen if and when they could. Medical supplies were limited to whatever the surgeons could carry in their saddlebags and on pack mules.

Captain Wahl, the Company Commander, posted the First Sergeant and addressed his 115-man Company, once it was dressed right, and covered down (aligned) front to rear by its sergeants:

"We will be moving east along this road as fast as we can, as far as we can every day, until we come to salt-water and can't march any further. Be on the lookout for Reb bushwhackers. Stay together, and stay on the road. Above all, don't straggle. Keep up with the company.

"First Sergeant!"

The First moved forward and saluted, facing Captain Wahl. He then about-faced, taking the commander's position. Captain Wahl strode rapidly to the Company's left flank.

The First Sergeant then roared: "Private Vogelsong, move out on the double to the Right Guide position." He paused to allow the soldier time to get there. Then: "Compane...e...e, Left, FACE!" Another pause. "Forwar...r...r...d, MARCH!"

As the company moved past his post, the First Sergeant double-timed to his march position at the rear of the main body.

So, with the captain at what had now become the head of Company F, and the First Sergeant in its trail, Great-grandfather John R. Vogelsong stepped off on his left foot, away from the smoldering ashes of Atlanta, away from his company's support elements, the right guide of a flying column that would bisect the Confederacy, make military history, introduce the concept of total war to the world, and change America forever, all before he turned eighteen.

John R. Vogelsong

Uncle Kenney

Kenneth C. Richards was the oldest of three boys, and was, by all accounts except hers, his mother's favorite. He could draw well, and did well in school. He graduated from Northeast High School in June 1926, unlike my father who didn't graduate. Then, he went to work in a union shop as an apprentice electrician.

The family's workers were all strong union men, and after 1929, strong Democrats.

Honesty compels this description of Kenney: he was a drunk. There's no better way to say it. He wasn't the type of alcoholic who is loaded all the time. He'd work sober for months, and then overdo it, sober up days but keep up the heavy nightly drinking, start drinking earlier after work, then start *at* work for a while, then finally would stop drinking for months at a time again, and then repeat the cycle, again and again.

In my childhood, I only remember seeing him visibly intoxicated once, and Grandma Richards ordering him out of her house, to return only when he was sober. He never sought professional help. It's just as well, because Alcoholics Anonymous, an effective approach, didn't even start until the late 1930s. The medical profession didn't know its ass from third base about the disease, and what they *did* teach (alcoholism as a character/behavior disorder) was totally incorrect. That deficiency of knowledge went largely uncorrected until the 1970s.

Kenney started drinking before he was twenty-one, and after he reached 21, and he became legal, started drinking too much.

He married, fathered a daughter, lived in the Northeast neighborhood (near Freddie, his mother), and made it work for a while. Then, in 1932, his wife divorced him, and moved to Cleveland, taking their daughter with her. He deteriorated a little during the later part of the Depression, but kept work as well as some, and better than most. Still, he was on a downhill slide, and I think he knew it.

When I read *The Studs Lonigan Trilogy* by James T. Farrell, I thought of Kenney. He had fit the image of Studs pretty closely. He meant well, worked hard, always tried to do the right thing, and with the assistance of alcohol succeeded in ruining everything important in his life.

The day after Pearl Harbor he was waiting on the front steps when the Navy Recruiting Office opened. Though he was very nearly over-age, the Navy took him, and for four years he stayed sober, at least while he was at sea, in the Pacific. He served on an eight-inch-gun light cruiser, and took part in just about every South Pacific battle and most of the naval actions in the Central Pacific after his transfer to the Fleet on New Years Day, 1943.

He may have had a mean side (as did the fictional *Studs*),but if he did, I never saw it. He was as good to me as any adult I've ever known. He went out of his way to entertain me, and taught me to like potato soup on a cold winter day, to play marbles indoors on a carpet when it was raining, how to take long walks in the cold and talk to someone, and to light-and-throw firecrackers with one continuous swing of the right arm.

Alf Dad Kenney
October, 1916

He had married again in the late 1930s, to a woman who would put up with him, and was independent enough to not really need him much, though during the war years she did accompany Kenney around the country whenever he was ashore. I didn't get to know her well, though they lived only seven blocks from me....and from his mother, Freddie.

After the war, Kenney drank himself to death, slowly. It took him until 1962, when he developed terminal cirrhosis with hepatic failure and ascites, complicated by splenomegaly, hypersplenism, and renal failure.

His mother outlived him. If she showed any emotion at all when he died, I didn't see it. Of course, in The Family, emotions, whether love, affection, grief, or dislike were *never* suitable for public view.

One was expected to, at worst, excuse oneself, and deal with it in private, funeral or not.

He had been his own worst enemy, and had been unable to cut the apron strings that held him to the house where he'd been born, and the neighborhood where he'd grown up. All those things about Kenney, good and bad, influenced me throughout my childhood.

I miss him.

* * *

5 December 1967

I stared into the super-dark, even Stygian, night of Vietnam, my first in the field. I hadn't yet learned the trick of off-center vision using starlight, to see a little in darkness.

How did I get out here? Was I like Kenney, escaping from my responsibilities?

Or would I turn out to be a war lover, who needed this kind of life? I doubted the last; I felt the collective absence of Joan, our son, home and Kansas City already.

Grandmother Freddie

Her three sons called her "Freddie", and she hated it.

I called her "Grandma Richards".

She was scandalized by hearing any member of a younger generation address an older relative by his first name. That showed a complete lack of respect, she said, and was totally inappropriate.

She had been born Elfrieda Vogelsong in 1881, in Paola, Kansas. Her father was a prominent man in that Victorian community, being part-owner of a grain mill. He had fought in the Civil War as a seventeen-year-old boy, and had been on Sherman's March to the Sea, from the ashes of Atlanta to Savannah, Georgia, in late 1864.

Freddie was never pretty, as her sisters (Dolly was a knockout) had been, but was quite plain, perhaps even homely. Even at that, her family felt (and often said) that by settling for a match with a common carpenter, that she had married beneath herself.

She and Clair C. Richards, my grandfather, met around 1900, and were married in 1901. His family, and shortly thereafter the newly-married couple, moved 45 miles north-northeast to that Paris of the Plains, Kansas City, Missouri. He and his father built two houses on Lawndale Avenue, on spec, and sold them. He bought the third lot, beside the first two and, between 1902 and 1903 built the house, room by room, where Freddie would live until her death in the spring of 1964.

The couple carefully left native black walnut trees in place on the two adjacent lots; every autumn Freddie and her sons would gather, clean (the stain took weeks to wear off your hands) and store the nuts for use in baked dishes through the winter to follow. When I was old enough, I was expected to take part, too.

As soon as the house at 346 South Lawndale was habitable, the couple moved in. I suspect that it smelled of furniture polish from the first day.

Since Freddie stood only four-feet-eleven, her husband had custom-built her kitchen for a very short person. When my cousins and I were children, we delighted in visiting it, because we could reach everything; it was sized just right for *us*, too.

Grandpa Clair then built a large carpenter's shop (called, not surprisingly, The Shop) from property line to property line, across the back yard, fronting onto the alley in back. It had two huge freight doors that opened and closed from side to side on overhead rollers. For years afterward, he had some small (as compared to a residential or commercial building) job going out there. Typically, it would be a boat for himself or someone else, a set of furniture for repair or refinishing, or a piece of custom-built cabinetry, or often all three at once.

Her sons were born in 1907, 1909, and 1914, all of them at home, as was customary at the time for all except society's homeless and most destitute women. Only in the late Twenties did hospitals become acceptable places for labor and delivery of respectable women, as a matter of routine.

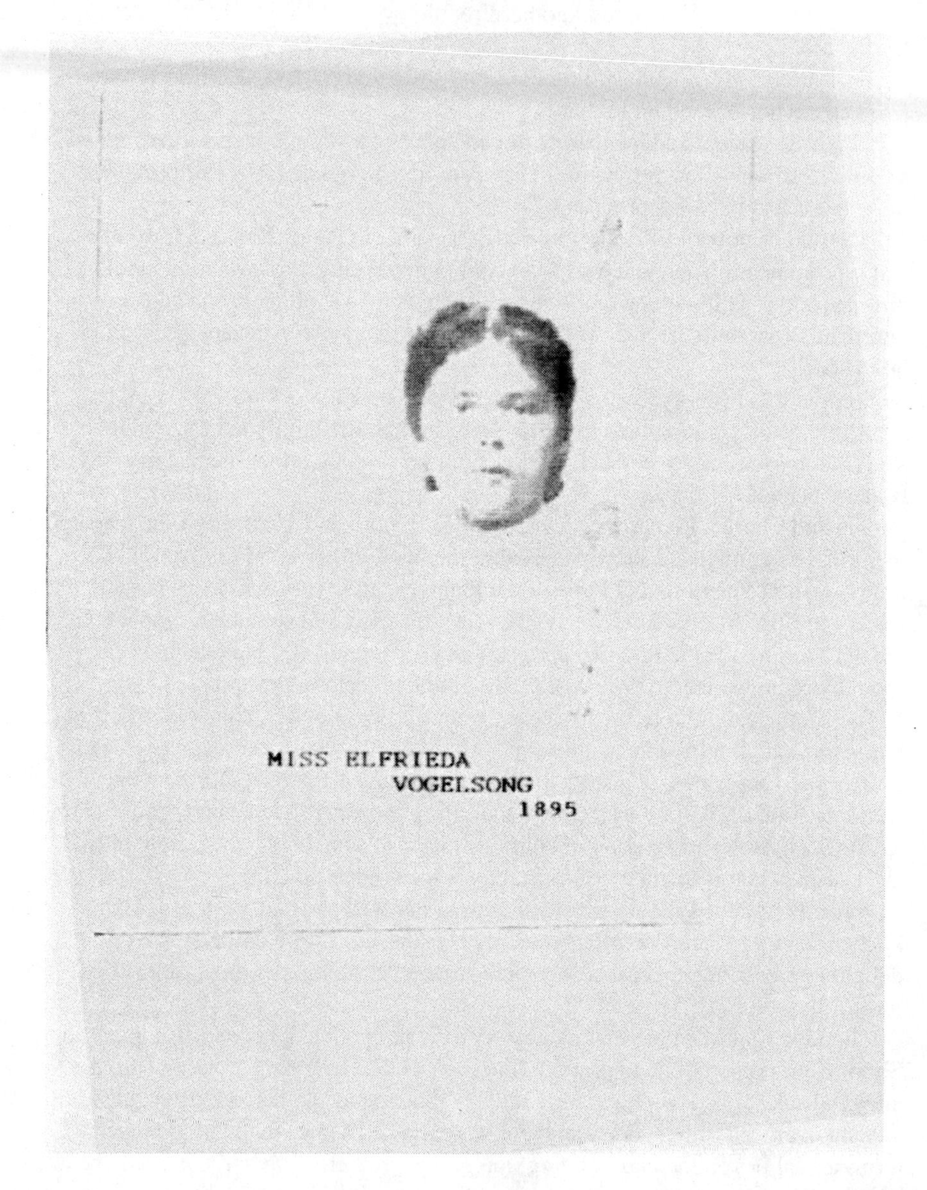

My uncles used to tell me how she would take them on trips back to Paola, Kansas, to visit her family, traveling in a dignified manner (and that's how she approached *everything*), forty-five miles by train (she never learned to drive) several times a year. When they arrived, they'd run to their grandfather's mill and throw themselves onto piles of milled wheat, rolling in and on it, burrowing into it, and sifting it through their fingers.

It was some time in the late 1920s that the house next door, one of the three that Grandpa Clair and his father had built, came onto the market, and Freddie insisted that they buy it, split it into two share-the-bathroom apartments, and rent them out. He had preferred not to have the responsibility for the property, because he'd rather have used his spare time for hunting, fishing, or working at his own pace in The Shop.

As was the usual circumstance, Freddie prevailed, and the house came into our family (it wasn't The Family; not yet). She planted a cherry tree in back of the new property, I think as a symbol of ownership. In our springs together, she'd walk me through blossoming, fruit development, ripening and picking.

Her husband died unexpectedly in the winter of 1934, under circumstances that are less than clear. He'd gone to his cabin near Liberty, Missouri, to go fishing. After he left the Lawndale house, Freddie never saw him again.

Miss Doll Vogelsong, 1895

His boat was found adrift in the Missouri River a few days later, but his body was never recovered.

Widowhood in those days of one-wage-earner families was bad enough. For it to have occurred in the middle of a depression compounded it into a real disaster. Grandma Richards had always been careful with money. Now, she became downright closefisted, of necessity. Yet, what does not kill us makes us stronger, and in this case, it did just that.

She split the house at 346 South Lawndale into two shotgun apartments, and continued to manage the two in 348, giving her the income from three furnished apartments in two adjacent houses, plus giving her a place to live in the fourth and largest apartment.

About all that Grandpa Clair's death left her for a contemporary support system was her older sister, Bess, who lived at 350 South Lawndale, the corner house of the three that my Richards great-grandfather and his sons had built between 1900 and 1901.

Bess had a small Boston black-and-white bull terrier, Nosy, who took the opportunity to bite me every time that he got the chance.

My father was the youngest of Freddie's three boys. He married my mother in 1934. I was born in 1936. They often left me with Freddie, first in the late 1930s when their marriage was going well, and then in the '40s, when it wasn't. That gave her a second shot at raising a boy (or dare I say, a son?).

She made it a point to let me sleep late on Saturday mornings. She'd listen to KCMO, until she heard the theme music from "*Let's Pretend*," a network radio series of dramatized fairy tales. She would advance the radio's volume gradually and slowly, until it woke me. The next day, she would take me to church and Sunday school at the White Avenue Methodist Church, the same one where she had taken her sons twenty years earlier, and where she was remembered with a memorial service twenty years later.

Her house was filled with the debris of the Edwardian Age, contrasting sharply with a prominently-displayed framed print of a middle-aged Douglas MacArthur as a four-star general.

Her bookcase over the gas log was filled with two layers of books from the late Victorian and the Edwardian years. There were several years' hard-covered editions of faux-marble-paper-bound *Illustrated Stories from Blackwood*, which I didn't find out until college was a popular literary magazine of the time.

The collection of books also held a 1912 edition of the complete twenty-volume *Book of Knowledge*, which I read, as had her sons, in their consecutive childhoods. And all 23 volumes of the *Tom Swift* adventure series, a treasure in itself.

There was a stand-up, wind-up Victrola set obliquely in one corner of the living room, which contained a huge assortment of 78-rpm records (including some Enrico Caruso first cuts for Victor) with dates of issue that ran from around 1900 to 1932. She also had an extensive collection of the performances of Sir Harry Lauder on 78s, and some irreplaceable original Kansas City jazz recordings on the Brunswick label.

There was a front, east-facing sun-room which we children never used. We had to be happy with the child-sized kitchen.

Grandma Richards' household also consisted of a series of large, gray tomcats, all named "Tommy," who without exception demonstrated to me that cats are hard-wired to be unable to ignore the end of a string pulled along the ground, or fail to stalk the odd gray mouse among the petunias and pansies planted alongside and between the houses. She was the adult who showed me fireflies, and how one could easily spend a whole evening watching them.

Grandma Richards was the best cook I've ever known. Her "Glorified Potatoes," mashed together with riced onion and carrot, covered with cream gravy, and served with fried chicken or minute steak were, to a hungry eight-year-old, close to Christmas, if only for an hour.

She was an Anglophile. She made it a point to instruct me about England, and the King, Queen, and the two little princesses, Elizabeth and Margaret, the royal family of a country then fighting for its life.

She would tell me about Germany, and how Hitler was destroying a society that she once had admired, which had led the world with its scientific and medical achievements for the preceding hundred years.

During the war years, a standard "We Have a Man in the Service" flag was displayed in a front window, a white field with a red border, and three blue stars up the center line, indicating the number of sons she'd sent to war. It was sort of like the Parable of The Widow's Mite. She gave all that she had, and never mentioned it. The *banner* did the talking to anyone passing by (incidentally, *my* wife put up a World War II one-star flag for me in 1990-91, during Desert Shield. She'd never tell me where she had found it).

On special occasions, every two or three weeks, the two of us would take a bus downtown to shop, see a movie in one of those awesome temples to the cinema left over from the Twenties, resplendent in dark oak, with red and gold trim. We'd stop for lunch at Wolferman's cafeteria for (an exotic choice!) chow mein. At that time, downtowns were still business centers of cities. People *lived* in cities, not the suburbs, and the best merchandise was to be found at large, locally-owned city-center department stores.

As I write, the memories flood back: Watching the automatic doughnut-maker at Woolworths, chili dogs at Kresge's lunch counter, seeing the large, wet, twenty-degree Midwest snowflakes fall, stick, and melt against the warmth of 346's windowpanes, listening to after-school radio serials on her table-model RCA radio the size of one of today's personal computers, and many more.

When I enter an unfamiliar place, the smell of O-Cedar furniture polish is guaranteed to flash me back to 1944.

I don't believe that it's over-dramatizing to say that she formed me more than anyone else except perhaps my own mother, and it may even have been a tie between the two.

To her, life was a serious business; I cannot, even once, remember seeing her laugh.

She loved us all, and never once *said* it to any of us, nor to anyone else. She saw her duty not in expressing affection, but by demonstrating it in her behavior; showing us who we were, and that we could (and should) always improve on whatever life handed us, or upon whatever *we* did in response to it.

She was absolutely correct.

Mary and John Coe Richards, Senior

My parents met while they were in high school in northeast Kansas City.

Mom graduated; he didn't.

When Dad wasn't working, he played a wicked game of tennis, I'm told. From time to time during my childhood we moved in and out of their old neighborhood, where Grandmother Freddie and my late Uncle Kenneth lived, and where my 92-year-old Uncle Alfred *still* lives, in the house he bought for $2400 in 1934.

I have few pleasant memories of grammar school. It was the same one that my father and uncles had attended. I was a slow learner, and now that I can verbalize it, I see that I tended (and still do) to think in concrete terms better than in abstractions, which made the development of conceptual thinking difficult. It's even possible that I had attention deficit disorder; I was (and am) distractible enough to qualify at least on that diagnostic axis. Not that any one in our public school system ever put it into *those* terms; not in the Forties.

Math was a bitch dating from Day One of Year One, in September 1942. By sixth grade, I was nearly phobic about it.

My parents' marriage was not going well, either, and World War II finished it once and for all.

Dad wasn't a drinker. Women were *his* weakness.

In the third year of the war, he was in a bit of a bind, which is to say that he'd knocked up an 18 year-old-girl (he was thirty) named Dolores, who worked near him at the local North American Aviation plant, building B-25s. when he got his "Greetings from the Your Friends and Neighbors," summoning him into the Armed Forces.

* * *

Mom, ever-charitable, let Dolores stay with the two of us for a few weeks, until she could arrange to travel home to Alabama (no abortion-on-demand in those days, and travel priorities were tight).

My father had been drafted into the Marine Corps at the worst possible time, in the spring of 1944, as a replacement for the horrendous casualties of 1942 and 1943, and for worse ones (quite rightly) expected in 1945. He was no soldier, had stayed out of the service as long as he could, and served a short and undistinguished tour; I was ashamed of him for that, though in spite of it, I loved him more than I ever told him.

It wasn't our family's way to discuss feelings, real emotions, like that.

He was medically discharged in early 1945. He had been involved in a short but intense campaign on the island of Guam, and had developed combat exhaustion.

From my selfish point of view, it is fortunate that he did.

His regiment, the 26th Marines, was one of the three from the Fifth Marine Division (5 Mar Div) that landed at Iwo Jima a few months later. The Marine Corps took a full quarter of *all* its dead in the Pacific War as its men tried to wade inland, shin-deep in the black volcanic grit of Iwo.

Had he survived that, and the subsequent refit in Hawaii, Okinawa was scheduled next, also a costly affair. And, if he had been among the few that made it through *both* battles, the 26th was scheduled for Operation Olympic in October 1945.

That was to have been the invasion of the Japanese home islands, in his case an amphibious assault across the beach just south of the bomb-ruined town of Kushikino.

What were his chances of ever seeing the United States again? Ten per cent? Probably less.

So, thank God for the invasion of Guam, for Dad's combat fatigue, and for The Bomb, which all came together, and allowed him to live to see his grandchildren.

And it just occurred to me: I have a half-brother or half-sister out there somewhere. I wonder what he or she looks like? Will he or she recognize himself or herself if he or she reads this? And what would they think of this older half-brother of theirs, after reading about the rest of The Family?

I can never know for certain; it wasn't Our Family's way (or that *era's* way) to discuss incidents like that.

* * *

Mom went to work in a defense plant.

I became one of the hundreds of thousands of latch-key children in the wartime United States. And that role, too, in its own way, was *my* contribution to the war effort. Or, you might say, the two of us were mobilized, too.

Our apartment was across the street from a branch library, a place of quiet, that was clean, safe, and whose books introduced me to a way to escape long hours of the unpleasant here-and-now of a broken home, absent parent(s) and the mant opportunities for trouble in the streets outside school hours.

It was many years before I found out that the library *wasn't* named for a man whose full name was Louis George Branch.

* * *

4.

I graduated from Raytown High School in 1954.

High school, too, was an unpleasant time. I was not good at any sport except boxing (I was a lightweight), and we didn't have a boxing team. At Raytown, socially, if you weren't what Coach Basswood called a "football boy," you weren't shit. I tried out for the team, even the "B" team (second-best), but I was too light for the line and too slow for backfield. As far as my striking appearance, I had thick lips. Some of the kids made fun of them, and I'm still sensitive about their appearance even though they've evolved contrariwise, and been *thin* for over forty years.

My classmates in that Age of Conformity wore what was almost a uniform: blue (there was no other color) jeans and plaid shirts for boys. Girls wore medium gray very heavy flannel skirts, with or without an embroidered poodle, with a light-colored blouse.

If I hadn't been a pathological reader, there's no way of telling how bad my grades would have been. As it was, bored silly most of the time, and shooting pool most afternoons, my grades were only a little above averagI vaguely thought that I wanted to go to college, but had no plans beyond that.

We took mandatory Physical Education Monday, Wednesday and Friday all four years. I detested it, but have to admit that mandatory PE and its accompanying self-discipline probably did build character. Its absence as a have-to subject might explain at least part of what's missing in today's Gen-X-ers.

We also took mandatory Fine Arts all four years; I believe that *that* helped some of us appreciate them, too, i.e., that fraction of the class that would otherwise have been lost to the complex of country-and-western-music/color-TV as their sole concept of classy entertainment.

And I owe this to Raytown High School: I first heard of a college education there, and also ascertained that it represented a ticket on The Upward Mobility Railroad.

Now, *that* got my attention.

But it put me into an awkward position. I loved and respected my family, but an attempt to break away from the blue-collar mind-set and its expected behavior ("You've graduated from high school. Get a job.") was certain to disappoint at least some of them, Grandma Freddie probably most of all.

My immediate family didn't have a clue about higher education.

In fact, my mother and stepfather lived what one might charitably call a subsistence existence. Whatever money they earned was spent with no thought for a future beyond the next payday, *before* the next payday.

"Sure, go to collidge," they said, "and get educated. *We* can't help you, but hey, you're eighteen. We wish you well."

So I gave it the old college (sorry for the pun) try.

My life went much like this: City bus to Kansas City Junior College (all I could afford) year-round, including the Summer Session. Start classes at 8AM (seven in the summer) and attend till 2PM. Haul ass to work on the bus. Study on the bus. Work 3PM to midnight, usually including weekends. Study on the bus home or at the lighted bus stops in the often-ten-below-zero Kansas City winter nights. National Guard every Wednesday night, seven PM to 11 PM. Study college work or required military science during breaks. Study on the bus home. National Guard Annual Training ("Send a boy to camp this summer.") for two weeks every year. Study *there* in free time. Work a little overtime on weekends.

With few changes, and rare exceptions, from June 1954 to July 1967, that was it.

Every fucking day.

My most prominent memory of that time is one of being tired very nearly all the time.

That might explain why I'm such a lazy, self-indulgent bastard when I *do* have some free time, and why I partied as hard I did when I could (or when I shouldn't) find the time. And why I failed so miserably that catastrophic summer halfway through what I fondly call Debacle One.

Dewey

Staff Sergeant James A. Garfield Dewey was the Machine Gun Sergeant of Battery B, 128th Field Artillery, of the Missouri National Guard, from 1956 to 1958. All anyone ever called him was "Dewey," at his request. I was a corporal then, and we were tent-mates. I served on a gun crew, feeding shells into a 105mm howitzer.

He was 59 in 1956, and had been in combat in both World Wars. Then, he farmed a little place near Sedalia. He stood five feet four, and couldn't have weighed over 130 pounds. He had a thin, almost a hatchet-face, that was heavily wrinkled, and eyes that looked as if they had seen too much.

What I learned from him by osmosis, because I can never recall his teaching anything formally, was how to survive in a field environment, in the sense that, as he often said, "Any damn' fool can live out (doors) and be miserable. The trick is to do it and be comfortable enough so's you can do your job."

Instead of a bayonet, unlike every other enlisted man, he carried a short bolo machete with a 13-inch blade. He could clear and ditch a pup-tent site with it in 30 seconds flat. In rocky terrain, he knew how to place the rocks so that they conformed to the body's natural curves, and so sleep more restfully. He could pitch a pup tent perfectly in thirteen minutes, not an easy task.

He showed me how to get into the chow line early, so that I could finish eating, lie down, elevate my feet and rest until the afternoon Work Call.

He always seemed to be able to find a cup of hot coffee in those pre-heat-tab days.

Wherever you are now, thanks, Dewey.

* * *

5.

1 July 1956

The classes of the General Arts and Science Program at Kansas City Junior College (KCJC) were more like a roadway (or a dirt track), and that track stretched away into the far future, In fact, it extended so far that I couldn't see an end to it. At that time I was working as a four P.M.-to-one A.M. clerk in the sporting goods and paint departments at Katz' Super Store in North Kansas City.

It occurred to me after long thought that I had no *defined* goal, and that at the rate I was going, it would take seven years, minimum, to get a degree. And then, a degree in *what*? I'd had a close friend in high school, R.T. O'Riley, who'd announced for pre-medical (hereafter abbreviated pre-med) even that early in his career. He had a plan, was unquestionably smarter than I was, and I needed advice, so I called him. We talked, and he guided me onto the pre-med trail (or perhaps it was *rails* since it was so inflexible).

As I recall, *deciding* to get in touch wasn't enough. My impression now is that in those days I was accustomed to not having ready access to a telephone; just calling R.T. was a major project. Nowadays, audio communication is universal, almost a God-given right.

Our family and social circle were carpenters and electricians. We didn't do white collar. Certainly, I knew next to nothing about higher education until I got to high school. And post-graduate work? At home, to my immediate family, that was totally *terra incognita.*

Later, I got some flak from a few carping family members for seeking advice from a peer; we were the same age, what could he know that I didn't? Well, who else was there? My father? Right. My stepfather? Worse. My uncles who were completely unfamiliar with any occupation or lives other than their own? Sorry, but no.

Still, I had seen *some* doctors in action, in the course of my many three-PM-to-eleven-PM careers, as a sometime hospital orderly. I thought that I could do the work, perhaps better than some that I'd observed could, or at least were doing.

And I could keep my mouth shut, and wasn't a liar or a thief, as a few of my exemplars *had* been. And further, thought that if I could, that I should.

What else was a Land of Opportunity about?

Logically, if I worked well with the public now, why *not* be a doctor, that most intimate of the public's servants? At that
time there were too few physicians, so unemployment wasn't likely in the foreseeable future, and it paid well. Why not, indeed, aim high??

Like the reward of a trapeze artist changing moving bars in midair, the payoff, if I could do it, would be incomparable.

If I missed, the fall (or hard landing) would last for a lifetime.

* * *

I had always (mistakenly) believed that I was smarter than I am.

I'll clarify and elaborate on that point later.

Another almost-fatal item on my list of weak points was that I fell in love too easily, to quote Sinatra (and R.T.).

I spent more time (time that I didn't have) winning, losing, chasing or catering to girls (successfully and not so successfully) than I should have. It wasn't just that I was hornier than an elk herd, though I was, or that I couldn't keep my fly zipped.

I needed to be loved.

Not once in my life have I had sex with a girl or woman that I didn't know well, respect, trust and *like*. For me, that's the most pleasurable part *of* sex. Casual sex, let alone (God forbid) commercial sex, even when offered, has never appealed to me. In fact, the diversion itself gives me satisfaction only because I'm *giving* pleasure to someone to whom I'm close and I like. If that makes me some sort of pervert (what Dewey called a *pre*-vert), so be it. It certainly wasn't--and never has been-- sex for the sake of self-gratification.

Sorry if it disappoints you, but that's all I intend to say about the subject. .

Except that the time expended in that pursuit probably cost me half a grade point on my undergraduate transcript.

Still, an irresistible impulse *is* irresistible.

* * *

Wanda Marie Wallace was a high school classmate.

I was smitten, glassy-eyed and weak-kneed, the first time that I met her in 1951, when she transferred to Raytown from a high school in Los Angeles.

Her father quite rightly discouraged my seeing too much of her; we were too young for anything like a steady relationship to be allowed to develop. That would come later. I loved her then, and probably do now. We were on-and-off, and then really ON for seven years, time, proximity, and geography permitting. I think that the attraction stemmed partly from my realization that under that 1950s conventional exterior that girls of the time manifested, she had a first-class mind, and I let her know that I appreciated her for it.

And, then, we both had more than our share of hormones.

As we kept running into each other, two young people genuinely fond of each other, exploring the adult world, first on one campus, and then on another, the close association of like seeking out like was probably inevitable.

Milton's Place

There's a famous (or notorious) club, or dive, at 39th and Broadway in my hometown. It's called Milton's. It's also called a jazz club, though I *wouldn't call it that. It's been there since the middle 1930s. No* live *music, jazz or any other, has been heard there since the mid-1940s. At that time, legend has it, Milton, the owner, decided to gamble with a concept at least 15 years ahead of its time.*

He replaced all the lights in the place with dimly glow-lit baseboards around the walls, leaving only the bar, against the south wall, illuminated as before. The windows were painted over with two coats of medium-dark brown paint, so that (also legendary), the habitué's sense of time was totally interrupted. Whether it was day or night outside, inside, you were just at Milton's. *To top off the change, there was a huge jukebox with 200 selections available, hard-wired (with the electrical cord of an earlier time than now) into multiple huge speakers, comprising a primitive, low-tech, devastatingly effective even today, stereo/surround system. The furniture was dark leather, low-slung, and comfortable.*

Drinks were, and still are, excellent and relatively cheap.

Some of the music was jazz, from the schools of New Orleans, Chicago, Memphis, and Kansas City. More, though, were modern renditions of songs introduced during the twenties and thirties, but sung by modern artists, thus changing their presentation in a profound way.

Wanda Marie loved the place. So did I.

My own favorites, guaranteed to return me to 1958 Kansas City in one second or less, are the show tunes of Rodgers and Hart, particularly "Little Girl Blue," or "Dancing on the Ceiling."

"Sit there
And count the rain-drops
Fall-ing on you;
Poor girl, you're through.
All you can count on are your fingers,
Un-happy Little Girl Blue."

Jumbo, *Richard Rodgers*
and Lorenz Hart, 1928

The time shift is completely entangled with being twenty-one, with being in love, and with being completely oblivious to several serious rough spots in the road ahead. For some reason, the current rendition of "My One and Only Love," as performed by Sting takes me back, also. I can't say why. Perhaps it's the 1930-ish arrangement. And, honestly, I don't care why.

The fact that it does *is enough.*

6.

Enlisted men are stupid, but extremely sly and cunning, and bear watching.

The Army Officer's Guide, 1894.

I'd been chasing Reserve commissioned officer status for seven years, balancing the requirements against a pre-med curriculum, the aforementioned woman trouble, and several full-time jobs. Each time I completed the course work, the standards were raised. It was like trying to walk up a "down" escalator.

After missing my step the third time (part-time courses in 1956, 1958, and 1960), the Army decreed that the only way open was to go full-time to Officer Candidate School, and thus head off that next escalation. God knows what *it* would have been. A master's degree? West Point graduates only? Both? At the time I was a buck sergeant in a National Guard artillery firing battery (really, was *trapped* there by the location of my pre-med colleges and the paucity of Guard units). No real career aim or avocation pushed toward The Artillery School; regulations limited me to applying only there because of my unit of origin.

On 27 May 1961 I reported in to the now-defunct Robinson Barracks, the Artillery and Missile School's Officer Candidate School, at Fort Sill, Oklahoma.

A little corner of hell on earth called "Zero Week."

And there we must stop, and go back for a bit.

The events leading *to* Zero Week need some explaining.

I told you before that this was at least partly a story about change, and that about the best I could do would be to *approximate* beginning at the beginning.

* * *

I was (and remain) the child of a nation at war.

The tail-end of the Great Depression is a vague series of visual impressions that resemble black-and-white snapshots, and freeze-frames, of dust, dirty clothes, and one horrendous lightning-and-thunderstorm with torrential rain and flooding of the streets, over the tops of the curbstones.

There's a (small-) childhood memory of being attacked and flogged by a waist-high white rooster, which was, I now know, only defending his territory.

All the cars were black with silver-bright (probably nickel-steel, not chrome) bumpers; that probably made them Model "A" Fords.

My first recollections of the war years are alternately black-and-white and in color, mostly olive drab and Marine green.

And the red-white-and-blue serviceman flags, like Freddie's, in all the windows.

In grade school, in 1943 and 1944, you could look up and see planes, or planes towing gliders, hundreds of them, in a miles-wide stream, flying from the western to the eastern horizon. This railroad in the sky seemed never to end, at least during recess period.

Christmas, 1943, we broke our prewar blown-glass treetop ornament and had to replace it with a crummy silvered wartime cardboard five-pointed star. Not that I'm complaining; it could have been worse. Ask someone who was a child in Stalingrad, Essen or Coventry at that time.

* * *

The First World War and its huge European war debts at least partially caused the Depression, when I was born.

The Great War of 1914-1918 also precipitated the Russian Revolution *prematurely* and, because of the war-learned behavior of the Reds *and* the Whites, more violently than is likely, had it occurred in peacetime. The Revolution in turn caused the formation of the Comintern. From *its* first day, it committed itself to wars of national liberation, such as Korea (missed it by a year) and Vietnam (bingo).

Some fringe historians maintain that the World War was the defining event of this century, and that the (foreshortened) Twentieth century really began in August, 1914 and ended in 1989, with the collapse of the USSR, as opposed to the more conventional parentheses of 1900-1999.

There are even a few super-fringe thinkers who say that the First World War didn't end until 1945. It *paused* for 21 years, and then, at least partly as vengeance against the provisions of the Treaty of Versailles, was reactivated in 1939, when I was three.

During my childhood, The Great War was called "the last war," with the implication that its resolution had been unsatisfactory, or at best, incomplete.

Even now, with World War II long past, I cut the ends out of cans and rinse them clean, remove the labels, and mash them flat to save space, though I know that the steel makers don't need them to make tanks anymore. I hesitate to discard foil, though no one needs it to build B-29s, now. I still save waste kitchen grease till I realize that no one wants it to manufacture explosives, and then have to dispose of a month's supply all at once. As I write this, there's a six-pound mass of congealed bacon grease in the kitchen, lurking in a fruit juice can, waiting for disposal.

Growing up didn't involve *wanting* to be a soldier, as much as it seemed inevitable that it would be required of me, in fact of *all* of us boys. The enemy might change, but that expectation (fixation?) never did.

Men born since 1965 simply do not, *cannot* understand the effect of a childhood lived in wartime, nor in the certainty of compulsory military service, probably to involve at least some hostile activity, with some foreigner or other earnestly trying to separate your body and soul. It colored our every action from about age 14 on. For example, we didn't even try to get permanent jobs before serving. No one would hire us anyway. Basic training filtered out society's unusables and saved employers the trouble.

It also spared them the need to hold our jobs open for two years. There were very few early marriages then. You can't support a wife on a private's pay. Also, we were allowed a couple of years to learn to cope with the concept and requirements of adulthood. That may explain the low drop-out rate of those college students who used the GI Bill.

In addition, the absence of most or all male relatives between 18 and 44 years of age for most of five years during our childhood years *must* have influenced our development in some way.

* * *

Present Day:

The Antagonists
(A Few Words About the Red Menace)

First, most Americans didn't know a god-damned thing about it, start to finish. They paid it antipathetic lip service, almost as an article of faith.

Understanding it, however, was another matter. That required a degree of study and the development of insight similar to that taught in Jesuit theology. And most Americans were (and are) too dumb or too lazy to bother learning anything factual about it. They remained at their (low) set-points, intellectually, usually where they were placed by their family backgrounds.

That same set-point also explains why communism as a formal political system never really had a chance to take root in the United States, even during the depths of the Great Depression, when it seemed that the country itself was finished. The population couldn't grasp the concept.

Adoption of the Party's philosophy involved becoming an activist. That, in turn, required both the level of comprehension that I described, plus a degree of personal commitment to conversion that Catholicism did, involving the willingness to suffer, to die, or to kill (singly as in assassination, or indiscriminately, as in terrorism) in order to further the Party's interests. The single exception to that ideology involved those few pitiful wealthy dupes (and I met four married couples of them) who naively believed that if they helped the Party financially *now*, that they would be allowed to keep what they had, once the Revolution triumphed.

I choose Catholicism as an analogy for a reason: Communism was never a political system. *It was a religion*, and demanded a religious way of life. And it has, like every other theocratic system, failed miserably everywhere that it has been tried in modern times. At least a limited degree of private enterprise was adopted almost immediately by the ruling (priestly?) classes, since they were vitally interested in the population that supported them not starving to death. In those countries that were the keepers of the Stalinist flame such as North Korea, Albania, and Bulgaria, famine *was* a frequent and familiar visitor.

At a State Republican Convention, I once shared adjacent urinals with David Horowitz, a reformed, now-conservative former Red-Diaper-Baby. "Start to finish, it was a system for losers," he opined to me.

So *their* religion, armed to the teeth, was actively trying to defeat *our* (relatively) democratic way of life in Asia, in Eastern Europe, and on the post-colonial African continent. And if that's *not* a world war, even if the actual shooting was intermittent, you'll have to give me a better definition, and even then you're unlikely to convince me.

27 April 1959

East Rifle Range, Fort Leonard Wood, Missouri

I was a corporal, then.

The battery mess section was feeding 160 men and officers, in that order, on a line of serving tables next to their 2 ½-ton mess truck.

Just as I passed through the open-air chow line, the low clouds burst and it really started to pour.

There wasn't a scrap of shelter for any of us, officer or EM.

I'd slung my M1 rifle muzzle-down when the morning had become cloudy, to keep the bore dry, just in case. It and my glasses, sheltered under the front flange of the steel helmet that we wore in those days were all that was spared. Every other piece of equipment and clothing that I, that we all, wore, was as soaked as if we'd jumped or marched into a pond, and climbed out again.

I grabbed one of my two pork chops and stuck it between my teeth. The mashed potatoes, pound cake and bread were a total loss. The canned green beans were awash, in my mess kit brim-full of water, but were salvageable. That brings me to Rule One of Military Life: Things are never so bad that they can't get worse.

It can always start raining.

* * *

To get through pre-med quickly, I had elected the option of serving eight years in the National Guard to satisfy my military obligation. Then, I'd projected, when I finished medical school, I'd have no *pressing* military duty, and could choose a branch of service, or even defer more military service indefinitely. 95% of graduating MDs faced a random doctor draft; I'd be spared that.

Once the KCJC phase was finished, I transferred to Central Missouri State College to finish the three-year prescribed pre-med course, again, all that I could afford. Next-best again, out of many next-best-things I'd experience (and gladly settle for) over the next fifteen years.

While I was enrolled there, I performed reasonably well, staying in the upper 12% of my pre-med class, but should have had a hint of The Wrath to Come: *Beware ye the flunked-out medical student who's your obligatory Ph.D. pre-med advisor.* And if she's an old maid, as was Dr. Mathilde Knauss, really beware, if you're male. Oddly enough, Dr. Knauss treated male *non*-pre-meds well. That interaction was my first experience with The Established Social Order, which had a vested interest in keeping the blue-collar class right where it was. It was most assuredly not to be my last. The Establishment's great strengths were its incumbency and its lack of accountability outside its own boundaries.

Nonetheless, in December 1957, I applied to Midwest State University Medical

School, and was accepted less than two weeks later. Perhaps they knew Dr. Knauss well, and hadn't paid much attention to her opinion of me.

My Midwest, 1.

The farm country extended further into the much-smaller cities' edges forty-five years ago.

The leaves turn about October first, maple-red, elm-yellow, and oak-rust-colored. In about three weeks they fall, and are burned in great piles. You can smell the smoke for miles.

College at Central Missouri State, and the whole world to be embraced lay before me.

This was as close to contentment as I had come in my life up until that time.

* * *

As I said earlier, I didn't join the Army outright at seventeen, nor did I wait to be drafted. Eight years in the Guard, with simultaneous pre-med schooling seemed an excellent way to deal with both requirements.

However, in 1957, as soon as I heard of the Israeli system of national defense, I was thunderstruck, and thereafter held in its thrall. *This*, I thought, was the way it *should* be done. Men (and some women) are in the Active Reserve from age 18 till age 54. No way out of it. It's a sacred obligation. Being in the Active Reserve meant that you were liable for up to a year's active duty per year in peacetime. And in wartime, all bets were off. Everyone reported in. A man quite simply owed his life and his life*time* to his country.

So, since I take pride in putting my money where my mouth is, in 1961, I decided to stay a reservist as long as they'd have me.

7.

1 April 1958

I'd been in love (there he goes, again) during my pre-med years, with a girl who would probably count as the love of my life. I'd known her in high school, and been crazy about her even then. For another three years we were inseparable on campus. I'd even started wearing a mustache at her urging, in the late 1950s, before it was fashionable. I had introduced her to my mother, grandmother and Uncle Alf.

The best I could get out of her when the subject of marriage came up was: "Probably."

Then, at the end of March 1958, having found a man that she liked better, possibly someone with a less labile mood, and *his* family, whom she preferred ("More European," she said) to mine, she dumped me.

I don't know what became of her. I hope that her destiny was the best of everything that comes with a happy life.

I never tried to contact her again. I wasn't about to become one of those pitiful schlumpfs who follow the shadow of an old love, hoping that what *was* might be again. And it never is. Anyway, medical school was less than six months away, and I had to make some money, fast.

I found a job as a hospital orderly working five thirteen-hour days a week, with overtime on days six or seven if I wanted them. It was at a private psychiatric hospital (The wealthy are eccentric; only the poor are crazy.).

Again, I saw licensed MDs in action; I knew that I could do a better job than *that.*

I hadn't recovered from Wanda by September.

It may be that I still haven't. Furthermore, this was a time that I absolutely did not need distractions.

But need 'em or not, my baggage held quite a number.

8.

6 September 1958

The physical plant of the med school's basic science building was so new that it still had the raw smell of fresh concrete. That odor even overcame the phenolic glycerin fumes from the Gross Anatomy Lab.

The usual academic load in pre-med was (and is) 16 or 17 semester hours. I could usually get by at that level with a "B" average by repetition and sheer persistence. In medical school, it was *25* hours a semester.

I'd borrowed a small monthly allowance from Grandmother Freddie, who was vocally dubious about the whole idea. I found out in 1999 that if Uncle Alf had not advised her to extend the loan, my illustrious shot at the Nobel in Medicine would have ended right there, in 1958.

Other than that, and my corporal's pay in the National Guard, I was broke (there were no Federal Student Loan programs then). I was able to find a part-time job (conduct strictly forbidden by the Med School Administration) at the end of my first year.

I had been able to find a cheap (and hot) attic room the day before Orientation.

In addition to those three millstones (being a dump-ee, no money, and a hellacious academic load) around my neck, I'd had endogenous depression since childhood, which though blatantly obvious (and treatable), had gone unrecognized, though I was in daily contact with professionals who *should* have noticed the rather-obvious signs. The one person who can't make the diagnosis is (surprise!) the patient himself. Both options, of diagnostic counseling and of drug treatment if appropriate, are offered to today's medical students without prejudice, incidentally.

But, then, I was taught by Our Family, there were either crazy people, or normal people like us.

Right.

Many years after these events, when I had the money and insight to have myself tested psychometrically, I found that I had a dysthymic depressive personality.

No surprise there.

However, I *also* was diagnosed with a learning disability, and probably a moderately severe case of attention deficit disorder, both of which *were* unexpected. Together, the three explain quite a lot.

In today's medical schools, all kinds of accommodation is given to students with these problems, such as taking exams alone to diminish "test anxiety," giving them extra time to complete examinations, and even free tutoring in some cases.

Now, knowing about those recently-improved conditions, I have to laugh. To paraphrase Abraham Lincoln, if I *didn't* laugh, I'd cry.

* * *

The first hour of the first day of classes was a lecture by the Dean. He advised us that we were expected to redress the shortage of general practice and family doctors in the state. Then he mentioned that the work would be hard, and that a 10% attrition rate the first year, and a similar percentage the second was not unusual.

I wondered if this had any similarity to the French Army's 1914-1918 practice of unit punishment by shooting every tenth man, *pour encourager les autres* (to encourage the others).

As it turned out, it did.

Our clinical professors thought that they were Marine Corps drill instructors, and acted out the role. They manifested an abysmal ignorance of any aspect of life or the world outside that of their departments. Their method of instruction consisted of rapid-firing questions until the unfortunate target missed one, and then heaping ridicule upon him. That passed for teaching medicine.

"Mr. Richards, what cell are we looking at here?"

"That's a lymphocyte, Dr. Marr."

"Mr. Dunbar, what is its function?"

"Uh"...produces antibodies?'

"NO. NO. NO!!! Have you read the assignment (We all had.)? *Can* you read? Been to any lectures lately (Just seven so far today, Sir.)? Anyone know the answer? The *right* answer?" Poor Dunbar was progressively shrinking in height, as if he were being driven into the floor with an oversized tent-pitching maul.

And so on.

And the kicker is that *most* of what they taught us was incomplete, based on what we know today (there are several *dozen* types of lymphocytes, and they perform thousands of functions each). That's forgivable; science, after all, marches on. What we know now is always an advance over what we knew then. What is *not* forgivable is the impression of absolute certainty that what we were being given was Holy Writ. I can't recall a single episode where this phrase was used: "We *think* that the function of so-and-so is such-and-such, but there is some work indicating that the opposite may be true. Or that both may be wrong."

Not once. Not at MSU Med.

* * *

So much for my professors.

After 33 years of being a family practitioner, it is my considered opinion that not one of those guys would have survived ten minutes in the real world of private medical practice.

They probably didn't know it, but they were *hiding out* in medical school, which was good for them and for the ailing public who were spared contact with them, though not so good for our class. Nor was it a fate to be desired for those hapless teaching patients unable to escape their ministrations (no Medicare or Medicaid, yet, to give patients a choice).

As a less-than happy alternative to them, with only two exceptions that I can remember, we had multiple PhD basic science instructors who walked apart much like little emperors, their relative ranks inversely proportional to their respective amount of direct student contact.

At this point, I learned my final lesson about my antagonist, The Established Order: they're easy to spot in a crowd. Just watch how they interact with or treat anyone who is unable to retaliate. Oh, and I almost forgot: because they're the Establishment, therefore Authority, and so *they make the rules*. And they're not above changing them in the middle of the game.

* * *

Words simply cannot convey the massive difficulty inherent in taking and passing exams where the right answers weren't always right, but rather what we'd been told was the *expected* answer by these pukes. Any other response that might actually *be* correct was marked as wrong.

Figures that I collected in 1975 revealed the following results: no more than 15% of that class went into general practice, and only half of those stayed in the state whose taxpayers and tax dollars had paid for their education. I make that a hit-to-target-miss ratio of 1 to 13. I wonder if the Dean ever had to explain the shortfall. I hope so, but doubt it. There was no accountability at the top, as far as I could see. Just at the bottom. Us.

In addition, in contrast with the Dean's admission remarks, the clinical faculty deprecated general practice, verbally and viciously, on a daily basis.

My Midwest, 2.

Kansas City is the best-planned city of any size I have ever seen.

It's equally as true today as it was in my childhood.

Not only was the city laid out on a 90-degree, top-is-north grid, but great attention had been paid to having more than enough green belts, parks ranging in size from one acre to over two thousand acres in size, and trees placed so that, at maturity, they'd completely overarch the streets of the residential neighborhoods. Driving through them in spring and summer was like navigating a series of long, green, sun-dappled tunnels.

The architectural style of its public buildings runs all the way from Doric Greek Classical to art nouveau.

The place is practically covered with statuary, of concrete, limestone, or bronze, everywhere you turn.

When I was in grammar school, we were required to study the city's history, to include who had designed what, and the details of the city's infrastructure. Then we were taken on field trips as part of the course. I can only remember visiting the Museum of Art, The City Museum, Union Station complete with a short train ride, the Park System with its large and small shelter houses, and the Country Club Plaza (the world's first suburban shopping center). Oh, yes, and the Zoo, which had to put up with a mob of eight-year-olds before the usual opening hour. Think of it, a whole zoo, all to ourselves.

The museums and their generously-proportioned grounds, plus the large and small expanses of the Park System allowed a pervasive odor of fresh-cut grass throughout the city seven months a year.

Union Station, Kansas City.

Shelter House, Swope Park, Kansas City, Mo.

It was, in short, a neighborhood from Tacoma alternating with one from Second Empire Paris, again and again, over eighty square miles. You'd never guess I miss it to the heart, even now, would you?

* * *

6 October 1958

The MSU Med Class of '62 was almost a cohort (same age, same sex, same education, same color) of 21- and 22-year olds. We also had two women, a few older men, no blacks, and no Latins.

There are a few recollections of my classmates which stay with me to this day, because, short of marriage, the enforced intimate prolonged contact, under extreme pressure, made us closer than any group I can think of, at least in civilian life.

There was The Giraffe, who was tall, thin, and so named because, in spite of the threat of instant dismissal for cheating, could and did look over the shoulders of the guys next to him during exams. I honestly can't be sure he couldn't see as far as two students over, right and left, giving him his choice of four answers other than his own. He was a likable guy, otherwise.

I *still* wonder if he had clavicles.

Also prominent in the crew was The Dolt, a small-towner with no imagination and no extra-scholastic experience whatever. He literally could not think deductively. He gave the impression of an "Aw, shucks," approach to the world, so that it was impossible to hold any deficiency, including a pathological naiveté, against him. I didn't dislike him. Quite the contrary, I was and remain always happy to see him. But, just as was case with Uncle Kenney, affection would be no excuse for dishonesty in describing him.

The Mega-Dolt was a fat, clumsy oaf, with no sense whatever. He couldn't think, either, and was guaranteed to completely fuck up any manual task he approached not on the first, but on the first *three* tries. How had he gotten into, and how would he get through medical school? Easy. High grades in pre-med and med school. The guy was an objective-test-taking machine. He had a photographic memory; that had been enough. Did he comprehend what he had read/photographed? I don't think so.

The Genius was quiet, withdrawn, and absolutely unflappable. He knew at the outset that if his grades were high (and they would be) he could get away with anything short of a felony arrest. And then, for the next four years, he did.

The Sociopath was... What can I say? A sociopathic personality. He was charming, personable, and intelligent. Sociopaths usually are. Motivated by sheer self-interest, he graduated in the lower third of the Class of '62, without incident. Well, until twelve years later when he surrendered his Ohio medical license, for reasons unknown, at least to the general public. There was also a man with a similar personality, too, who as yet hasn't tripped over his moral imbecility, and is practicing psychiatry in suburban Los Angeles.

The kid we called Harpo, because of his facial resemblance to the Marx brother, was a cheerful, invariably pleasant young man, remarkable in this crowd for his lack of pathology, and I remember him with only fond recollections.

All the rest of the men and women were what I can only call the Smart Guys. They kept their heads down, their mouths shut, followed instructions, and made it through.

* * *

Mary Grace Reidl

11 March 1918 - 23 December 1997

Mom died at the age of 79. The cause of her death: cigarette use since the age of fifteen.

She couldn't keep her blood pressure down with medications. I've found over the years that a heavy smoker *can't*; the constant hits of nicotine override the medications and raise blood pressure. The older the patient, the higher it goes. It *stays* higher, longer, too.

I believe, and tried to tell her at the time, that if she had stopped smoking after her first small stroke, that it was likely to have been her last one. She could have probably avoided the others, the last five, that wrecked her basilar-vertebral arterial tissue distribution, tiny hemorrhages that happened, one by one, each added to the past ones, killing her by inches.

She died rather suddenly on December 23d, 1997. I couldn't get a plane ticket at that time of year. Anyway, there was nothing I could have done that would have made a difference.

The last thing she told me about her half of The Family was that she thought that they (and we) were Jews. Her father had certainly looked the part. Her side of the family originated and lived in the Upper Rhineland, probably for hundreds of years. I'd be surprised if there *wasn't* a Jew or two (or even ten) in the genetic line.

Grandfather Anton George Reidl was grossly racist and vocally anti-Semitic. He was also a practicing Roman Catholic; the two were not exclusive in 1947, the year that he died of a ruptured left
ventricular aneurysm following a classic myocardial infarction. He had been sixty-three.

Two years younger than I am *now.*

Mom was from Kansas City, originally, the next-to-youngest of six children, four of them girls.

I grew up with her, usually just the two of us living together. She and my father were together and not, together and not, and then, while he was in the Marines and I was eight, not ever again. To her credit, she never once said a word against him, at least to me.

When I was ten, and she was 28, she remarried.

My stepfather, Roy, was eight years older than she was, a farm boy from north-central Missouri, a carpenter (Mom seemed to be attracted to them) who was viciously racist. He had had a savagely mean father and a pugnaciously-religious, strict mother. The traits of both showed in their son.

His first wife had died of pneumonia five years before.

I was ready to love him, but *he* wasn't ready. I wonder if he ever had been, at least up until that time.

Grandfather Anton George Reidl, 1928

Current nomenclature would classify Roy as a Type A Dominant Male.

I'd tend to modify that to this extent: he *wanted* to be the Dominant Male in a group, but among adults, he didn't have a hope in hell of making it. With his kids, though, he was an A, however overbearing or even brutal he had to be to make it stick.

He brought two sons to our family unit, who had been in a City orphanage for two years; they were both older than I. I often wonder if he really hated the three of us, or if I only misunderstand his behavior. For whatever reason, he was not a pleasant man to be near. I would find excuses not to be around the house, for as many waking hours every day as I could possibly manage.

The two other boys each fled, and joined the Navy at seventeen, before graduating from high school. Roy and I had it out when I turned seventeen. He had slapped me across the face, hard, for showing silent disrespect/contempt. Being unarmed, I then faced right and prepared to guard left, go for the eyes, and counterpunch with my right. Mom stepped in and stopped us. Then she and I left.

We stayed away for two years.

It was that, or one of us, he or I, would have killed the other. I don't know if he knew that I'd become a pretty good lightweight boxer, or not. When he saw my copy of the *British Commando Combat Manual, Unarmed and Use of the Fairbairn Knife,* and the switchblade I'd started carrying during my freshman year (both to deal with the Seniors' hazing), he knew that my days of tolerating his abuse were over, and that if he swung on me, it might well be his last swing at anyone.

And I'd be writing a very different story from a cell in Jefferson City, instead of a third-floor office overlooking the Puget Sound and part of a half-million square miles of conifer forest.

So, we were close, my mother and I, the two of us against the world.

When I went to college, she and Roy reconciled.

And then when I was 25 and married, and Mom was 42, she turned up pregnant for the first time since 1936. All concerned were surprised, to put it mildly.

My half-sister was born the next year. Her parents spoiled her rotten. We all did. A late child such as she was *is* something special.

When my son was born three years later, everyone, including my sister, spoiled him. And he and my stepfather, Roy, adored each other. Any overt personal dislike that I harbored toward Roy couldn't survive that.

I lost my closeness to my mother then, though it was more of a slow, evolutionary process than any sudden estrangement.

The only real sorrow and loss I feel is not so much that she is dead, but that it need not have happened *then.* Except for her hypertension, she was in excellent health.

Without the cigarettes, she'd probably be alive today.

* * *

Mary Grace Reidl, 1945

Binion's Horseshoe Casino
Las Vegas
A Week Ago, Sunday.

First Hand out of a six-deck shoe: It's a twenty-five-dollar blackjack table. There are five players, and the dealer. The five players will get two cards up, and the dealer will get one down and then one up. From one to five, in order of play, it's ten-four, blackjack, a pair of queens, nine-three, deuce-three.

The dealer has a five up.

Next round, the ten-four stands, blackjack collects, the pair of queens sticks. Deuce-three takes a hit of three, and another of a nine, stopping with seventeen. Dealer turns up his hole card, a seven, for a dealt hand of 12. He takes a hit of four, giving him 16, mandating another hit. It's a six, and he busts with a 22.

Card-counters assign a plus value to low cards and a minus to the aces and ten-valued cards, divided by the approximate number of cards left to be dealt. It helps them predict what's likely to be dealt next, especially as the dealer's shoe of cards gets down to 150-200 cards remaining.

So far in this game, the Count is three.

* * *

We were sixteen that spring of 1953.

I had arranged to meet O'Riley at the 63d Street steel railroad bridge, to drop golf balls the 250 feet onto the road below, and watch from above as they nearly disappeared, then enlarged again as they bounced back, almost straight up, then to recede and rebound again and again. Each time, they cast a long shadow onto the pavement that got further away the higher they rebounded.

As I recall it was late on a Saturday afternoon, in early summer, so that it was still full daylight. We heard a distant train whistle from the north, so we started a leisurely walk toward the south end of the bridge. Three-quarters of the way there, we got another, extremely loud blast on the whistle as the train rumbled onto the north end. We ran for it, but we weren't going to make it off the bridge.

R.T. yelled to me: "Grab the rail!"

I did, and the Kansas City Southern roared by nine or ten inches from my puckered, forward-jammed, adolescent ass.

That's how I learned about sound islands and dead-sound spaces, and never to count on being able to hear a hazard in time to get clear of it.

We rarely meet these days without recalling that anecdote. And that train gets closer and closer as the years pass.

* * *

9.

1 June 1960

I lasted two tears (I meant to type "years" but always have trouble with the adjacent "Y" and "T" keys. Anyway, it certainly *expresses* events better, in this context) at MSU Med, or just over halfway through.

There's not much point in going into the details of the curriculum that ate my lunch. It was all incredibly difficult to grasp, there was too much of it, and I was not able to maintain quite a "C" average, although I do suspect a certain amount of faculty collusion in making *sure* I didn't. Toward the end of Second Year, ever-so-slowly, my test scores had gradually been *in*creasing . The sensations I recall are twofold: that there was no logic to any of the mountains of minute details thrown at us, and that there was just too goddamned much of it for me to absorb by rote memorization in the time available.

Before you are tempted to conclude that I was simply not physician material, I'd like to point out that as I write there are now *and were then* about 3,000 American students in second- or third-world medical schools who either were suspended as I was, were expelled, or who couldn't even get *into* American schools. The only difference between them and me was that their families could and would support them financially after they'd failed to measure up academically.

I seldom dream now. When I do, it's usually a nightmare about MSU Med, forty-plus years after the fact. Not Vietnam, not the Cuban Missile Crisis, not parachute malfunctions, not OCS, and not Desert Storm.

Dean Wilson's invitation to "pursue some other activity for the next year," had arrived by registered letter on 30 May 1960, and advised me, though only by implication, to perhaps re-apply in 1961. Unstated but also implied: or just get lost, boy, you bother us (with apologies to W.C. Fields).

Empirics aside, the question still haunts me, and influenced my every move as a faculty member thirty-three years later: *Who the hell elected* you *jokers to decide what America's medical care would be like for the next thirty years?*

No*body, that's who.*

* * *

At the time I was demolished; I hadn't understood that low grades only *might* be forgivable (as in the cases of The Dolt and The Giraffe whose GPAs were *lower* than mine) or not, and most importantly, that conformity was just short of godliness. And manifesting a phony humility was extremely helpful. It was equally true in medical school as in the old Chinese proverb, that the nail that stands out does indeed get hammered down.

One of the Smart Guys that I met again in 1971 told me: "Except for your appearance (relatively conformist; I always wore a clean shirt and a tie), Coe, you were a hippie before there *were* hippies."

I couldn't disagree. When the campus disturbances of 1964 began, I was sympathetic, especially when Mario Savio at Berkley and his ilk questioned the relevance of their course work.

I knew, firsthand, exactly what they meant.

* * *

2 January 2001

Today I saw a sneak preview of the movie Finding Forrester. *It co-starred F. Murray Abraham as one of those many professors who has never been published, and strokes his own...uh...his own...*ego *by not telling the students what he expects of them, and downgrading them* (degrading *them?) when they can't guess what it is.*

I remember them well.

* * *

Present Day

At the risk of being redundant, or self-serving, or both, and by now without self-pity, I'd like to say a few words for the edification of the psychology major who'd dumped me, of my psychology and pre-med advisors in undergrad school, and every one of the instructors at MSU with an MD, two of whom were psychiatrists, *not one of whom* recognized that I was clinically depressed and easily treatable with drugs then available, as follows: *You tried to put me out of the game (with unnecessary roughness, as Coach Basswood would have put it). You placed artificial obstacles in front of me, and I went over and around them.*

In the end I didn't fail.

But you did.

I made it, in spite of all of you.

And, parenthetically, I can buy or sell any four of you, now.

Especially you, Dean Wilson.

* * *

25 May 1961

After what I think of now as Debacle One, I went back and finished my bachelor's degree at Midwest's Undergraduate Division (I couldn't even afford to quit my job and to relocate, much as I'd like to have). And it would have been awfully easy to drop out of school, period, giving it up as a bad job, and accepting The Family's prior judgement that the appropriate route was to get a job, and stay with our own kind.

As it turned out, it was fortunate that I didn't.

On a blind date, I met Joan Ann Johnson, a friend of a friend. Our backgrounds were similar. She was from Washington, Missouri, an old steamboat landing on the Missouri River. We were both alone, lonely, and needed someone. And the chemistry (that means sex, to the slower readers) was good. Compared with the *alternative*, it was fantastic. We were engaged six weeks after we'd met. She had graduated from nurses' training in Kansas City, and liked the place.

Friends started to call us "Darby and Joan," from the English music-hall song.

Then, almost as an afterthought, at least as far as the timing of the event, I finally went to OCS.

I needed an achievement, a *win,* after the medical school bust, the girl I'll never forget, and the consolation-prize, almost-an-afterthought AB degree.

So, over less than five months time, I fell in love yet again, married Joan, graduated with that AB, bought a 45-by-ten-foot mobile home, and moved back to the city.

* * *

Camp Guernsey, Wyoming

11 August 1960

It had been sevent weeks since my dismissal from MSU Med.

I hadn't met Joan yet.

I was still pretty down, especially considering the bottom one-eighth or so of my classmates, whom they'd kept *in the class, none of whom I'd trust to treat a sick cat, then or now.*

Camp Guernsey was a World War II POW camp, a tent city on the north bank of the North Platte River. It was uncrowded, pleasant enough in summer, and gave us plenty of room to throw shells around.

Our battery Regular Army Advisor, a sergeant first class (three stripes up and two down), whom I hadn't known well, took me aside at our unit party, traditional on the last night of Annual Training.

"Sergeant Richards," he said, "I can look at a soldier for a few minutes, and tell how much of a problem he's likely to be to me in the future. It's a gift. Not everyone has it. I've been watching you for the past two weeks."

I waited, expecting the worst, again.

"You have it, too." he said. "Go to OCS next summer. You'd be a good officer."

I had just been dealt my first high card in two and a half years.

* * *

Binion's, Same Game, Hand Two:

The dealer has a ten showing. First Base has a pair of aces. Second man has a seven-four up. Third chair, the lady with blue hair, shows a pair of fives. Fourth-seat man catches a six and a three. Number Five gets a seven and a six.

First player splits his aces and hits one with a four and the other with a seven, giving him a fifteen and an eighteen, Second base doubles down, and catches a jack, for 21. The only lady playing, chair three, hits her five-five with an eight, and stands. Mister Four draws a ten; nineteen. Last seat draws a three and then a four, for twenty. The Dealer turns up a nine in the hole.

The Count is still "(plus) three."

* * *

My Midwest, 3.

My hometown has a problem. Or, perhaps I should say that because of my choice of a line of work, I *have a problem.*

There were (and are) too many doctors in and around Kansas City.

Hospital staff privileges, important in delivering the full spectrum of unrestricted patient care, are much sought-after, not always obtained, and tightly controlled. At the time that I was born and before, the hospitals were nearly all (except the charity General Hospital where *I was born) church-affiliated. If you were a doctor practicing the wrong religion, you were screwed. To be honest, that criterion no longer applies, but before 1955 or so, it did.*

Because of the fierce competition for patients, physicians' incomes were slow to plateau, though they did eventually equal those of the rest of the Midwest. It was not unusual for a new doctor to have to borrow money to cover his family's living expenses for the first six months, bounce around a breakeven point for two years, and then very slowly creep up, to plateau at about year eight.

As a comparison, in Dallas it was one month on credit, four months to breakeven, and two and one-third years to hit career maximum income. The difference was the price I would have to pay to stay in Kansas City.

Six years' income.

If I was lucky.

10.

That pretty much explains the how and why of OCS.

Let's get back to Zero Week, now, and to Class 1-A-61.

Our collective experience of Day One, 27 May 1961, was of being herded, always at the double, from place to place in the Oklahoma heat, leaving us gasping for air, as we waited in ranks in the summer sun in heavy, dark green new fatigue uniforms, stripped of our rank insignia, each wearing a four-by-six-inch white tag, suspended from our left shirt pocket buttons by a string.

Each tag had sixteen line items on it, such as "Personnel, "Medical & Immunizations," "Battery Supply Room," "Academic Supply Room," and so on. Our shepherds were middleclassmen, designated "babysitters," switched every few hours, spelling each other so that no one of them would miss any more classwork or study time than would any other.

The third-from-last stop was the Academics Supply Room. It was the source of some items of a unique nature. They included a two and-a-half-by-three-foot canvas gunnery bag, with sewn-on canvas strap handles at the mid-points of the long sides. It was not unlike an artist's supply bag. We got it first, and we needed to.

Then we were issued a gunnery plotting board, which just fit into the bag with half an inch to spare on all sides. Then came an excellent-quality pair of 6 X 35 binoculars, with a reminder of how much they would cost us if we lost them. Same for a lensatic compass, with the same warning. And a stereoscopic aerial photograph reader. And a stainless steel 90-degree plotting protractor foot on a side, with a protruding straightedge 22 inches long, looking like a cheap pork chop with a long bone. And five 5-H pencils, a red pencil, slide rule, a dozen push-pins, and on, and on and on.

At the *Battery* Supply Room, various more familiar small items were issued, along with the outgoing M-1 rifle, with the usual warning not to lose or abuse it (the M-14 rifle was being phased in, albeit slowly, because it cost more per copy than had been anticipated).

In retrospect, oddly enough, we were not issued ID cards, nor dog tags. No gas masks, either, in contrast with later years (1976-1996), when they were virtually inseparable from the student or trainee.

The army wasn't doing drug screens yet. The technology wasn't in place.

This sixteen-point check-off process took eighteen hours.

Dehydrated, we spent the short night waking up and padding barefoot to the fountain at the north end of the barracks (which in OCS were called “houses” for some goddam reason or other).

* * *

28 May 1961

"Who won the War? You know. The Artillery did."

GEN George S. Patton, 1945

At morning ("oh-five-dark") formation, we were told that our class had been designated Battery C, the Student Battalion, and then divided into three platoons.

We were loaded onto trucks driven by sleepy, School-support Permanent Party privates and PFCs, and taken to the field, dismounting on a high, bald hilltop, where, from large open bleachers we could see most of both the East Range and the West Range, with all the prominent landmarks of both. The country was rolling and semi-arid, what the ranchers of a hundred years before called "The Short Grass Country." The air, to my townie senses, smelled *clean.*

Artillery weapons have long ranges, measured in miles, and a lot of distance is needed to exercise them.

Europe is the same size as the United States, but has four times the number of people. Because of the high population density, there are whole *countries* in Western Europe where there is no place left to fire artillery. Their soldiers (NATO) come here to train. Even in my home state of Missouri, there is only one post that can support artillery range firing, and then only with use of reduced propellant charges.

The lesson to be learned today was that since 1915, the field artillery had caused more casualties than any other class of weapon, including a couple of nuclear-warhead bombs. That remains true at this writing.

Learning to place that fire accurately and in a timely manner was to be the lesson, the sole purpose, of the next three months' work.

Several cubical blockhouses several miles apart, located atop the three grassy, dominant mountains were carefully pointed out as cardinal base points. Originally, during the Indian wars, these were heliograph stations, to allow units in the field to signal the movements of the hostiles back to the cavalry at the main post. Now they were used to phone or radio our sensings and corrections back to the guns: "FROM the blockhouse, Signal Mountain, RIGHT 220 mils, DOWN 80 mils, Will Observe."

At exactly that point, what looked like a thousand shells exploded nearly simultaneously 500 yards in front of us, as if a volcano were erupting right there, as we watched, just to underline what we would be able to do before we left there.

* * *

Mils? What's a mil? Well, it was new to me, too, in 1961. A mil is an angle of 1/6400 of a circle. It's also the angle displaced by one unit *at a distance of 1000 of those* same *units. The Navy uses degrees and hundredths of a degree, and the*

Army uses mils in regulating gunfire. Mils allow more precise small corrections while using whole numbers *over ranges of five to twenty miles than do degrees. Oddly enough, the Marines who trained at Ft. Sill, and who would all go to the all-artillery Eleventh Marine Regiment, learned to use mils, though they would almost certainly have to call in naval gunfire.*

It's a derivation of the French mille, *a thousand.*

Down and dirty, a degree is 17.777 mils; call it eighteen.

One fingerbreadth, with the arm fully extended, is roughly 20 mils.

One handbreadth, at arm's-length, is roughly 125 mils.

A right angle is 1600 mils (remember that 90-degree protractor?).

* * *

There was no end of attempts to make us drop out of the School, fading ever-so-gradually, and at the time unnoticeably, to supportiveness over the 90 days.

I must be pretty dull, because I never saw the process itself, harassment (again, what does not kill us makes us stronger) morphing slowly into toughness, and finally to supportiveness *as a continuum* until this moment. I couldn't have designed it better, nor, I suspect could any expert in human behavior.

The Army had discovered it through trial and error over the preceding 26 years (quite old as Army schools go), i.e., that people who could and would withstand this much physical and mental discomfort tended not to fall apart in a setting of violence, wounding, and death, and would still be able to function as they'd been trained to do.

* * *

The whole platoon was doing 20 two-count pushups, yelling out the count in unison ("ONE, Sir! TWO, Sir!") as punishment for some trivial infraction seen by an upperclassman (a candidate in his last four weeks of school). Now, I see that it was all part of the breakdown process, repeated twenty times or more a day.

Early on the first day, we had packed away all our old uniforms, civilian clothes, or any item that wasn't part of the absolute minimum we'd require to complete this school. All of it was locked away for three months in the Luggage Room (again, of which more later). Any personal gear we had was kept in our unlocked (easier to inspect) footlockers in a shoebox, and nowhere else. No books, no radios, nor cameras were permitted.

We were then told about the Honor Code, violation of which was the one instantaneous way out of there, without quitting. Expulsion was certain and swift for honor violations. They consisted of lying, cheating, stealing, or quibbling about the definition of any of the three. Finally, knowing about a violation and not reporting it was as serious an offense as having committed it.

We were supervised by middle-classmen (the babysitters, again) who were four months ahead of us, sort of like fake corporals and sergeants. Then, over *them* were the upper-classmen, four months ahead of them, who wore bright red shoulder tabs (why they were called "Redbirds") and metal heel taps to warn of their approach. Supervising the uppers were the Tactical Officers, all Army second lieutenants (I make this distinction, because some of our academic instructors were Navy or Marine Corps officers). During the hellish Zero Week and the four weeks of lower-class, all of them came down hard on us. We were shorn to 1/8-inch hair length weekly. We were constantly dropped for pushups, and were not allowed to walk outdoors; every move was made at double-time.

I found out a few years ago (1994) that the USSR had a similar re-education school near Vladivostok, for wayward officers of the Red Army, which it, too, maintained for many years.

The small branch Post Exchange (PX) in the OCS area was the only non-duty place that we could go, and then only if sent there by a superior, usually to buy accessories to uniforms, and usually alone, to buy them for five or six other men. In short, every minute of every day was on-alert time.

* * *

Here, I've got to stop again, and describe the loser (there's no better term) that I was before the summer of 1961, of having intelligence only slightly above normal range, and of my erroneous conclusion that it was much higher. And I must speak, too, of the also-false belief that I somehow *deserved* what Tennessee Williams once described as "the kindness of strangers."

In retrospect, my personality had taken dead aim and shot itself in the foot.

I had an exaggerated sense of my own importance, but no coping skills to *maintain* it in the presence of even slight adversity.
I mean, it was *fragile*, and had been for as long as I could remember.

It's important that I spell it out, because at this juncture, over a period of a few weeks, that man ceased to exist. He *had* to, or would have had to leave OCS.

He could never have accomplished even the first four weeks of OCS, or faced up to Vietnam, Desert Shield, qualifying for a PhD program, another run at medical school, parachute school or internship without this reconstruction into a goal-directed, never-give-up, I-can-do-anything man, then just short of his 24th birthday.

Some Americans develop this approach to life in high school (like R.T. had), and frankly, I admire them for it, even now. Some literally never do, spending their lives as slackers.

Saddest, perhaps even most tragic, of all are the ones who discover too late that they could have and should have, but didn't.

* * *

These first four weeks' curriculum consisted of map reading, introductory survey, gunnery, division and lower organization, small unit tactics, and a lot of formal physical conditioning. It seemed to us as if we had been born running.

Radio and field telephone installation, operation, and basic repair procedures were included. We were required to use the phonetic alphabet at all times when speaking to middle- or upper-classmen, as a glorious combination of both instruction and harassment.

"What's your name, Candidate?"

"Sir, Candidate Richards, Sir!"

"Spell it!"

"Sir, I spell: Romeo, India, Charlie, Hotel, Alfa, Romeo, Delta, Sierra, Sir!"

"Too slow, Candidate. Drop and give me two-zero (pushups)."

"ONE, Sir! TWO, Sir!" And so on, twenty times.

Superimposed upon the stringent academic load was the Leadership Program. Every week each officer candidate was assigned to a different position within the battery, and was graded on his performance of how well he'd been able to function while still carrying his academic load. The slots (called "sweat positions" went all the way from staff sergeant to captain (the battery commander).

In Week One I was assigned as a staff sergeant, and had already failed it by the end of Day Two. Too disoriented by the new situation, exhausted, and never having been athletic, I didn't tolerate the physical training as well as most.

My TAC Officer gave me some good advice disguised as directive counseling: "It's too late to do anything about that 'fail,' but it's early in the course, and you may get a second chance at a leadership position. Meanwhile, keep your academic grades as high as possible and run till you drop, but never give up. As long as you are genuinely trying and don't fall behind academically, there's hope."

That could be expressed as, simply, "Never give up," and that's how I took it.

* * *

10 March 1968

Thua Thien Province, South Vietnam,
A Quarter-Mile East of the Laotian Border.

We were stalemated on opposite sides of a cleared field, each side sheltering in two facing tree lines about 200 yards apart. The occasional rifle-shot was fired back or forth, but neither unit, either side, was about to try an attack across that open area. Artillery fire would have been impractical; the terrain around the open area was so overgrown that it wouldn't have been possible to even see, much less correct, fall of shot. Our forward observer (F.O.) called Forward Air Control and asked for an air strike.

Two Air Force F-100s were diverted to the mission. When their sound became audible, the NVA ceased fire and took cover. They knew what was coming. We cautiously stood up to see the results of the bombing, which we expected would be eight 250-pound bombs from each plane, the standard load.

Instead, each plane simultaneously released a single 2000-pound bomb.

I was stunned by the double explosion, was knocked down, lost my helmet, and for the first time since 1954 (horrors!), dropped my rifle. Disoriented and dazed, I felt around on the ground for it. Where was my familiar wood-stocked M-1? And what was this peculiar dust-covered plastic-and-aluminum toy beside me? Then the current time began to come back. It was one of the new...no, it was my *M-16.*

The surviving NVA evacuated in plenty of time to escape. We were too dazed and shaken up to get organized for a good ten minutes, and that was all the time they needed to get away.

* * *

Grandfather Clair C. Richards

He was from Upstate New York, originally, where his family had lived and worked in lumber camps. He had described his forebears as "timber-working people."

They were the trailer-park population of their day, 110 years ago.

I can't say what brought the family to Paola, Kansas, or what led them to try to work a farm outside of town, in view of their prior experience in the North Woods, at least until the trees played out. In any event, his family decided to move west. Considering my own recent relocation to the timber country of Western Washington, I'm amazed that a family in the lumber trade *didn't*, a hundred-plus years ago. Of course, if they had, I wouldn't have *this* story to tell.

My father and uncles told me that they never saw Grandpa Clair in a coat and tie. He was always in work clothes, and, until the Great Depression, never missed a day's work. He also never had much to say about the year that he didn't work at all, from mid-1932 to mid-1933. He used the time to work in The Shop out back, working on the ever-present new boat, or doing Freddie's household repairs. Then, later in 1933 and on into 1934, he began to pick up small outside paying jobs again, and life began to improve for the family.

He was an enthusiastic hunter and fisherman, and had a cabin on the north bank of the Missouri River, near the town of Liberty, Missouri, opposite the mouth of the Big Blue River. It was his custom to take his rowboat out onto quieter parts of the Missouri, and fish there. One day in the early weeks of 1934, just short of his 54th birthday, he left the house with that avowed intention, and was never seen again by his family.

His rowboat was found drifting a few days later, but the body is still missing. That is not surprising; the Missouri was and remains a wild river, full of undercurrents, back-eddies, and underwater snags. It often does not give up its dead.

The insurance investigators concluded that he may have had a stroke or heart attack, and fallen over the side of the boat. Or, less likely, he may simply have fallen into the water.

He couldn't swim a stroke. He had left home so heavily dressed that his waterlogged clothes and boots would have pulled anyone under, swimmer or not. The life insurance paid without further discussion, except with the empathetic caveat that if he were to be found alive, Grandma Freddie would have to repay the full amount.

Since he died two years before I was born, I have only the history that I was given by his immediate family. That, and the odor of fresh wood shavings that persisted in The Shop until I was eight years old.

I still have his Remington Model 1905 semi-automatic twelve-gauge shotgun, a Browning design which works as well today as it did the day that he bought it.

Grandma Richards kept his favorite record, an instrumental rendition of "Listen to the Mocking-Bird" on top of the stack at all times.

And she left the telephone listing in his name until she died, nearly 28 years later as her way of showing due respect.

11.

5 July 1961

Suddenly, overnight, I was a middle-classman, was astonished to realize that a full five weeks of OCS had gone by, and that I was still there.

That's not to say that the way was downhill, but rather that the path to the top was visible and open, though still steeply *up*-hill. Guys could be, and were, dropped from the course through week eight with some frequency, usually for academics, since the coursework got progressively more difficult through-out the 90 days.

A new class came in, and they had to salute and call us "Sir," when they addressed us. We could harass them, as we had *been* harassed, but never did. There just wasn't time.

Ominously, Field Artillery Forward Observation was added to the curriculum. I say "ominously," because Medal-of-Honor-winner Robinson, of our Barracks of the same name, had been killed *while* forward observing.

The model toward which we were taught was a European war similar to World War II, even though 12,000 American advisors were then actively engaged in South Vietnam.

Unconventional warfare *like* Vietnam was never addressed by our faculty. Too bad, in light of later events.

Late on the night of August 13th, while I was the Charge of Quarters (CQ) for our battery, the whole post suddenly went onto wartime alert. Sensitive areas were closed off under armed guard. Military Police, sirens howling, fanned out through Lawton, the nearby Army town, and rounded up anyone who looked like he might be a serviceman, Army or otherwise, and if he were, ordered him back to Ft. Sill, ASAP.

All the Armed Forces had gone to Condition Yellow, Hostilities Imminent (Condition Red was open war).

The noise of heavy-lift transport aircraft landing and taking off never stopped, day or night. Large convoys of men, guns, and other materiel rolled out the South Gate, moving fast with full overseas loads of gear, (and didn't come back for several days) indicating that they were deploying to a combatzone, *now*.

With no access to radio, TV or newspapers, it took two-and-a-half days for us to find out what had happened: the Berlin Wall had gone up overnight, as a preliminary to who-knew-what.

We weren't afraid; we hadn't known enough to *be* afraid.

However, the Soviet tanks did not roll, and Ft. Sill stood down on the third day.

OCS classes and training had not been interrupted, probably on the assumption that this would probably blow over, and that if it didn't, artillery second lieutenants would be badly needed, and quickly.

* * *

A few days later, I volunteered for what was described to us as in advance a dirty job. One of the Tac officers had noticed a stink as he walked through the headquarters building. It appeared to be centered on the secured luggage room on the (July-hot) second floor. The first problem was to find the key to the room, which shouldn't have been needed until September 3.

Then, the footlocker, one of 200 stacked head-high, that was the source had to be identified and removed. That alone took 2 ½ hours in the heat of late afternoon. We found the locker that was giving off the worst odor (no easy task in a small room), pulled it out into the relatively-cooler 93-degree open air, and sent a man for tools to get the lock off.

How he turned up a bolt-cutter, or where, I'll never know, but he did. After getting the padlock cut off, and the footlocker open, the evil deed could easily be reconstructed.

A failed candidate named Bindle had been packing his gear to return to his unit, in Europe. During that time, instead of packing his footlocker, he'd stuffed all his clothes into a laundry bag, shit in the footlocker, re-locked it, and replaced it in the luggage room. A small act of combined rebellion and revenge.

No problem. A putty knife and Army-issue yellow soap will take anything off.

We were laughing so hard during the scraping and scrubbing that followed that it didn't seem to be such a dirty job, after all.

I believe that *that* was the moment it occurred simultaneously to all four of us volunteers that we were going to make it through OCS.

* * *

My Midwest, 4.
1956-1958

Sedalia then was a town of thirty thousand, on the north edge of the Missouri Ozarks. At that point, the land became flatter, had more topsoil, and fell away very gently down-slope to the south bank of the Missouri River, thirty miles to the north.

In the late 1950s it suffered from chronic unemployment, and from the resulting endemic migration of the younger adults to other parts of the state or country, where they could find work. That went double for the same age group who got any higher education. With nothing to keep them in town, they poured away, through the fourth-year recruiters, to both coasts or to the industrial cities of the Upper Midwest.

That left a class of young people who were underemployed, or who were willing (and many were) to commute the 83 miles to and back from Kansas City every day, until something turned up in Sedalia's Railroad Car Repair Facility or at the local (Corning) " Glass Factory."

A small upper-class of the sons of family businessmen and the professional stratum did return after college, to what can only be described as a sure thing; competition between businesses was relatively rare (see Anarene, Texas, The Last Picture Show, *Larry McMurtry, 1967).*

Sedalia was in the process of recovering from a heritage of a particularly ugly racism, even by the standards of 1956, and from several cycles of agricultural boom-and-bust.

The annual State Fair brought a sort of transient prosperity one week a year.

Physically, the town has not changed much in the past forty-five years. Along the main drag, Broadway, which is really U.S. Highway 50, the large two-and-three-story houses sit well back from the street on three-quarter or one-full-acre lots. They are surrounded by well-kept lawns and shrubbery, with hundred-year-old well-trimmed trees placed strategically around them. These mini- estares are rarely placed on the market, being still occupied by the fourth and fifth generations of the families who built them originally in the period 1890 through 1918.

When farm people talk of retiring, selling out, and "moving to town," this is the kind of place they mean.

He who dares to curse his parents will, himself, be cursed throughout eternity.
Ahmed Al' Haj
Seville
1192 A.D.

* * *

John Coe Richards, Senior

My father was *his* father's favorite, of the three boys.

He was literally the fair-haired boy. The other two, his older brothers, had brown hair and brown eyes.

He was the wild one, the undisciplined boy, the tennis player, the underachiever.

It is not just a male myth that women are attracted to guys like that; they *are*. Why, I don't know. Common sense would dictate that the relationship with such a boy for any girl in her right mind would be one of distance, and the more the better. That's not how it works out, though. Men and boys like that have to fight them off with a stick. We others wonder why, when we treat a woman respectfully and considerately, dress as well as we can, and keep clean and neat, our dance cards are usually empty, and our Saturday nights are often spent solo, at the corner pool hall.

Dad was a good, hard worker, *on his own terms.* Those last four words explain his notably undistinguished military career. Nobody in the Navy or War Departments worked on his own terms, from the Chairman of the Joint Chiefs of Staff down to Private Snuffy Tentpeg, USMCR.

He met and married my stepmother in mid-1945. As I said, *finding* women was never a problem for *him.* I've often reflected that it was a damned shame that it wasn't a hereditary trait.

He gave up carpentry at age 56 and opened a hardware store in a small, dying Ozark town. Again, the demographics were loaded against success, but he did it anyway. Why? Because *he damned well wanted to.* He was elected mayor of the town once, and was elected to be a sitting judge after that. I can't imagine him as a presiding court officer. Something out of Faulkner's fictional "Frenchman's Bend," perhaps.

At no time did he pay Social Security taxes on his income.

Like his own father, he had a Shop out back where he worked on various small jobs. Sometimes he did them for money, and sometimes just for the sake of doing them.

He kept my stepmother dependent on him; she never learned to drive, to write a check, balance the checkbook, or pay recurring bills. When he died in 1988 (leaving not a cent or one free-and-clear asset, not even a widow's Social Security), she had to self-instruct in all those areas.

He was an irresponsible man, and the concept of self-doubt was outside his frame of reference.

Make no mistake about this: first and foremost, *I loved him*, but I knew him for what he was, and so also knew that he would never change. I owed him nothing, but gave him a thousand dollars once, which he had felt quite free to ask of me.

In his own mind, he was simply always right.

And, of course, immortal.

* * *

12.

21 August 1961

I was a Redbird, an upperclassman at last!

It was Week Nine. I wore huge horseshoe-shaped metal heel-taps ("heel clickers"), red epaulet tabs, and as a second shot at a leadership position, was made a Candidate first lieutenant, second only to the battery commander of class 1-A-61. In fact, there were only seven Candidate officers in the three-battery Student Battalion of higher rank.

I passed Leadership with a 93%, not too shabby for having flunked a sergeant's position in Week One. Even though the courses were becoming more and more difficult, the only one that gave me any problem as far as comprehension was Field Artillery Survey, and I could pass an exam in that area by using dead reckoning as an approximation of the right solution. Empiricism, forever!!!.

There were 400 candidates junior to us in the School, now, and a high percentage of the pressure was off us, and on them.

As a sort of final exam on our training and cross-training, we took the entire class to the field, worked at firing and then moving the six-gun-battery several times under both night and day conditions, technically called reconnaissance, survey and occupation of position (RSOP). At our level of training, it all went off without a hitch. Every four hours, every man moved to a different randomly-chosen position in an artillery battalion, and performed it, usually well. You could be a simulated-PFC radioman for four hours, and then be a simulated-lieutenant-colonel battalion commander the next four, and be graded on each duty performed.

Then, it was graduation time. It was over, abruptly, just when we were getting comfortable with the School's murderous routine.

Graduation day came, and I MADE IT!

Half of Class 1A-61 *didn't* graduate. At long last, a success at something that *not* everyone could do.

Jesus, the exhilaration!

* * *

Joan had come down on the bus, and we returned to Kansas City the same way, Darby and Joan, on the afternoon of graduation day, a Friday.

I started job-hunting the following Monday.

* * *

In that dark, cold, early December of 1990 while I was at Ft. Sill again, waiting to ship out from my home station in Arizona to Arabia, I worked in a small dispensary, and tried to get used to below-zero temperatures again.

There was a historical display parked in front of my small outpatient clinic. It was an M-89 90mm self-propelled Scorpion anti-tank gun, on tracks, sort of like a small tank without a turret.

When I had last been there in OCS, in 1961, it had been the very latest weapons system being issued.

Now, it was nothing but a piece of junk, a falling-apart, worn-out, obsolete wreck. It was rusting where its paint had chipped away, and its rubber track shoes were hard and cracked through to the underlying steel links.

I felt like a fellow museum-piece, or perhaps some kind of living fossil.

* * *

21 January 1961

It was unusually cold in Washington that Inauguration Day.

A cutting, frigid wind drove a swirling light snow.

President-elect John F. Kennedy removed his silk top-hat and took the oath of office. Then he gave the traditional speech, which as I remember said, in paraphrase: "Let the word go forth...that a new generation, born in this century....will bear any burden, fight any foe....in the defense of freedom....everywhere. And so, my fellow Americans, ask not what your country can do for you. Ask what you can do for your country!"

Quite a few of us believed him.

That's how we got a Peace Corps, and an Army for Vietnam.

* * *

Fern Reidl Lawes

Aunt Fern was Mom's next-older sister, and is the next-to-last survivor of the six Reidl siblings.

She is 87, is alert, fully oriented, and lives alone in a small rented house in Cole Camp, Missouri. She is active in the lives of her children, and of her much-younger sister, JoAnn. She keeps the accounts for her church, and is active in a number of community projects.

She is a practicing Catholic, as are all the Reidls.

She has no health problems, dealing with several falls and probable diabetes with strong denial, a learned family behavior. And she still smokes.

Mom boarded with her for two years after my stepfather, Roy, died, in 1992. Then, for reasons still unclear to Fern or to me, she suddenly moved to a small town outside Chattanooga to live with my half-sister. She stayed there until her death, in late 1997.

Fern married Ralph Lawes in 1934. They were both in office work, he in management and she in accounting. He was from a poor family on the Kansas side of the Kansas City area. The two of them met on the job. They elected to defer having children, unlike all their brothers and sisters. With both of them working, even during the Great Depression, they did comparatively well financially.

Then came World War II. Ralph was called up, and with his clerical and managerial skills was promoted rapidly in the enlisted ranks. Fern worked at a high-paying job in a wartime economy chronically short of skilled personnel. More money, again.

They remained childless until the late Forties. That probably explains their collective warmth toward my cousins and me. We were always on good terms. I always looked forward to a visit to or from them. As I recall, that was not a sentiment that I felt toward all Mom's relatives.

Now, she is my surrogate mother. She seems happy to accept the role. And she gives me an unusually fortunate living link to my childhood, as well as a buffer against the absence of my own parents, Mom especially.

It can't last, of course.

But like Scarlett O'Hara, I'll worry about that tomorrow.

13.
January, 1962

I had no means of support after graduation (the CIA had interviewed me, and so had Burroughs, Wellcome (I had declined further processing by both). Following OCS, I got a job in September 1961 on the strength of my BA in Zoology, and in addition, at least the equivalent of half a master's in chemistry/physiology.

I was hired the same day that I applied, as a research assistant at MidContinent Research Institute (MCRI), in the Chemistry Department.

My first assignment was to assist in the organic chemistry lab, on a grant from the Iowa Department of Agriculture, to explore and find new uses for cornstarch.

Andwedidit.

In fact, the program produced four new practical applications, the most notable of which was a new, cheaper method of manufacturing slick paper, like that used in millions of magazine pages every week. The other three were a patent hypo-allergenic body powder, a non-lumping cooking thickener, and a bacteriologic gel medium.

At about this time, I also enrolled in the Army's five-year-long Medical Service Corps Company-Level Correspondence Course, E-24 (called for short the E-24 Course or, within the Medical Department, just "E-24"). If its phases weren't completed when your Reserve promotion date came up, you'd be passed over. Completion of the entire course was required for promotion to captain; 50% was required for promotion to first lieutenant. I worked on the subcourses for an hour every evening, and soon pulled far ahead of the mandated schedule.

As far as my day job in organic chemistry research at MCRI went, I'd say Iowa got more than its money's worth, and I felt I'd *accomplished* something using the OCS method of problem-solving, beyond OCS itself.

Still, seeing a sharply limited future with my current educational background, I applied to a five-year Ph.D. program in microbiology, with every expectation I'd be accepted. Most graduate programs will enroll a qualified applicant, so long as he's paying his own way, and doesn't require any financial assistance from the university, in this case Rockhill University at Kansas City. Graduation was *not* guaranteed, however.

Medicine had failed to work out, and was last year's newspaper. I was encouraged in my projected plan of career development by my boss, Kurt Sandall, Ph.D., whose area of expertise was bacteriology, and whose opinion of American medical education was as low as mine, if that had been possible.

Then, one day in the MCRI rat lab, an epiphany occurred. Our next project, basic research in the design of a planned (and first) American long-flight spacecraft, was proceeding on schedule. The Department of the Air Force financed the project. I was working on the toxicology (hence the lab rats) of beryllium metal and its breakdown salts. At the time, this seemed a distinct possibility as the material of choice for the craft's construction. Beryllium is a much lighter metal than aluminum, and is stronger than many steels. Certainly it was fascinating work, and promised to be a real cutting-edge area of concentration, a great service to mankind, and to science.

I'd even been sent on my first commercial flight to a beryllium mill, in Lorain, Ohio. to gather information and to negotiate prices of small amounts of beryllium and its most common naturally-occurring salts.

Being one of the researchers on the first real spaceship couldn't harm one's reputation or future, either, whether he was engaged in teaching or research. I was daydreaming along those lines while shoveling the rat litter, when it came to me that I was only kidding myself. I still wanted to be a doctor, still wanted to be a general practitioner, and still wanted to be of help to my fellow man. In particular it should be a role that was performed more *directly* than being a tiny cog in the machine that would send him into space.

Anyway, it turned out much later that beryllium, in addition to being brittle at low temperatures and hard to machine, was prone to break down into its oxide and hydroxide upon exposure to oxygen and to the unavoidable water vapor in the atmosphere. Those salts, in turn, produced some pretty ugly and untreatable disease states in mammals.

In space, there'd be no way to get away from the structure of the ship itself, for months at a time. An Earth-Mars-Earth mission, possible as early as 1986, would last 26 months, minimum.

Still, without enough money to bribe my way into another American medical school (aside: it *could* be done at a well-known half-dozen), or to support me in a foreign country's medical college system, it seemed plain that I'd better go to the osteopathic college in the old neighborhood, and talk to their dean, if he would even see me.

My usually-supportive spouse, a registered nurse, was scandalized. In her world, DOs (doctors of osteopathy) were a bunch of third-raters at very best, and probably were flat-out quacks.

To her credit, though, she went along with me on this venture, this time.

14.

Not only the Dean, but also the *President/C.E.O.* of the College wanted to talk to me.

In spite of my checkered history, and after stern warnings by Dean McDonald, with President Peerce nodding agreement in the background, that this would be my final shot, I took the three admissions tests required by the Kansas City College of Osteopathic Medicine (KCOM), and was accepted. One of the members of the Admissions Committee told me a few month later that my acceptance was partly due to my being a local. If the Board didn't take a few students from Kansas City area, he said, the classes would be filled by the flood of applicants from the other 48 states. There was no shortage of them.

First Year started the first Monday after Labor Day, 1962.

At last, finally (!), there was holistic teaching, patient-oriented instruction, and pressure from all sides to *BE* a GP. My rapid progress by comparison was vitally underpinned by a wife with the patience of a saint, who worked and supported us financially while we did without, and who never seriously questioned our deferred material gratification.

Again, our class was exposed to medical history, this time from more than one point of view. It showed us where we, as a minority profession, fit into the spectrum that extended from the conventional right wing of hard-science-based medicine (the MDI) past the middle (holistic medicine and osteopathy), to the far left (homeopathy, reflexology, chiropractic, and naturopathy to name but a few).

This was a second try, but it wasn't second-*best*; it was a *different* approach to medical education.

How much clearer it all seemed, and so easy to understand, if the presentation included something besides minutiae. And, this time, there was discussion of proportionality ("A and B are true, but A is more significant than B.") and of the *relative* importance of historical perspective as applied to everyday practice.

It's easier to grasp new material if the learner is happy, and not being purposely abused by the faculty entrusted with his or her education.

To top it off, we, The Class of 1966, most emphatically were *not* a cohort. There were a few students in their early forties, many in their thirties who'd trained for other careers and decided to make a change, and one boy of nineteen who'd graduated from an accelerated undergrad pre-med program. The class had four women and four black men, in a non-tax-supported college. We were from every state in the Union except Alaska and Hawaii.

Rather than bombard us with threats, this school threw a banquet for the whole class, with wives, husbands, and significant others invited, where the dean addressed us as "the best and most promising class yet admitted." I don't think that any of us even considered that this might be bullshit. Even now, I'd say that *if* it was, it still boosted morale in a group of kids smothered by classwork and a long way from home. As I said, it made quite a contrast.

In addition, all the Midwest State University (MSU) courses were repeated: gross anatomy, biochemistry, physiology, histology-embryology, basic physical diagnosis, and basic psychiatric theory. It would have taken talent *not* to ace them the second time through.

We also began to learn osteopathic principles, and by year's end could do spinal manipulation with reasonable skill. Repetition made mastering this year's basic science work less stressful for me than it had been four years before. Also, knowing the mistakes I'd made then, I did a complete 180 of everything not involving common courtesy.

Wore my hair too long in 1958? Crew cut, please. Too-casual dresser? Which way to Robert Hall (a really cheap mens' clothing chain store, but what the hell, its products only had to last for 3 ½ years)? Depressed? Whether you feel like it or not, smile, smile, SMILE, goddammit! Mustache? Gone. Hard to get to school? Move two blocks away, back into The Family's old neighborhood, to walking distance, in the face of wind, rain or snow, so Joan could take our venerable '51 Plymouth to work.

The Ph.D.-dominated basic science courses of Midwest State were gone, replaced by those same basic sciences taught *by clinicians* who were currently in active, hands-on practice. They would relate to us first-hand the relationships of the subjects being taught to skills that they used daily to cope with disease, wellness, life, and death.

And as if more were needed to make the whole thing perfect, we were on the trimester system, as we had been at Central Missouri State, and in which I'd always performed better.

To finance this venture at a relatively-expensive private school, I looked up an officer I'd known in the National Guard who was by then two years out of internship and practicing in Parkville, Missouri.

My intention was to get Dr. Mel Frank's advice on how and whom to approach to incur long-term debt (no Federal Student Loan Program in those days). Completely unexpectedly, he volunteered to make the tuition loans himself, one semester at a time. It appeared my luck was changing, to say the least. To cover the interest, he required only that I come to his office and work as one of his office girls (!) every Saturday. Hell, for that amount of help I'd have signed over my immortal soul. What was a lousy Saturday morning, even weekly? A mere 200 or so over four years? Piece of cake.

The E-24 Course? Easy to keep up with its middle phases, considering how far ahead of schedule I was.

My cup ran over even more: at the beginning of the second trimester of First Year I landed a part-time position in the laboratory of the College's Research Department, based on my MidContinent Research Institute experience.

So the first year passed, slowly. I was obsessed with one question; my head was filled with self-doubt and second-guessing: was this really where I belonged? *Should* I have grabbed for the brass ring a second time?

Or had they been right at MSU, and I was just on a temporary roll of good luck?

* * *

The Class of 1966, male *and* female, adjourned to Michael's, the School's traditional student watering hole, after the last exam on the last Friday of the year, where even our more religious members got royally plastered.

The pressure was off for the first time in nine months.

The next day, I staggered to the Top Secret Clinic in Parkville, took three Excedrin, and worked five hours as an office girl.

15.

Second Year began in September.

Now, basic science studies continued, but with a slightly higher *clinical* content. This last, patient-care oriented classwork also increased progressively from a little in the first trimester, to more the second, and even more in the third trimester.

We took the traditional courses: microbiology, basic obstetrics (hereafter abbreviated OB), clinical pathology, intermediate and advanced physical diagnosis, psychiatry all three trimesters, and basic oncology, to name only a few.

My classmate Frank Hawkins, who lived nearby, and I formed a two-man study group (it seemed to work better for us than the original three, including Johnny Moreland), to give each other the benefit of the other's approach to our subjects.

In October, for two ghastly weeks, the country very nearly went to war. To what might have been our *final* war, in fact.

The Soviet Union, to retaliate for our ringing their home territory with short-range ballistic missiles and with the Strategic Air Command (SAC), placed two battalions of intermediate-range ballistic missiles (IRBMs) in Cuba.

Their range with a heavy warhead was relatively short. They could, however render anything south and east of St. Louis toast, figuratively. And literally, too, now that I think about it.

The population of the United States, at least the ones of us with any concept of what a megaton-yield warhead would do, reacted with a sort of quiet dread. Or, like all the others, lived in denial of the all-too-possible.

Frank and I just kept meeting for our nightly study sessions.

Additionally, to add to the tension, at least a fourth of the Class of '66 were reservists, and, myself included, were under alert orders to be prepared to ship out, probably to invade Cuba.

Johnny Moreland actually received orders to report in, *now*, to Patrick Air Force Base, his last duty station, and the Dean had to intercede with Washington on his behalf, to obtain a deferment for him.

Since the fall of the USSR in 1989, we have learned something through Russian sources (circa 1994) that we *hadn't* known at the time. There was a *second*, smaller Soviet force on the island. It consisted of two separate and independently operating batteries of self-propelled battlefield rocket artillery, attached to the Cuban Army at widely separated locations. These short-range weapons too, had nuclear warheads, in the 20-kiloton- (or Hiroshima-) range of yield. Each battery had 27 of them. They were sited in several well-dispersed platoon locations, to defend specifically against an American or American-and-Latin-American Coalition invasion force. Had they been used they would have inflicted huge, if not universal casualties on the invading fleet and on the ground troops.

Then, as suddenly as it started, the incident ended over about a twelve-hour period on its fourteenth day.

It was as close a brush with nuclear war as humanity had or *has* ever come.

Classes at KCOM had gone on as if nothing were amiss. There was no other choice. After all, we could do nothing to change matters.

* * *

I was appointed as a lab instructor in gross anatomy to the Class of 1967, on the strength of my having gotten an "A" in it the year before, and the unspoken (but general) knowledge that I'd passed it the first time at MSU, too. It was fun, and
paid minimum wage, $2.65 an hour. I enjoyed it so much, I'd have done it for nothing.

An anonymous student posted a calligraphic card on the Anatomy Lab Bulletin Board, with a poem from the 1700s:

> Her body dissected by fiendish men,
> Her bones anatomized;
> Her soul, we trust, has ris'n to God,
> Where few physicians rise.

* * *

John F. Kennedy was assassinated during General Pathology. That's how I remember it, anyway. Same for Lee Harvey Oswald, except it was during a psychiatry make-up lecture. Rather appropriate timing, I thought.

The sophomore year flew past.

Johnny Moreland dropped out of our class and joined the Research Department full-time, with the proviso that he would enroll in the Class of 1967 (again, at the risk of overkill, this demonstrated a *flexibility* of the curriculum to a degree unknown at MSU).

As the end of Second Year approached, the usual Rumor Control/Jungle Telegraph word went around, truthfully this time: Some states required a candidate for licensure to have a valid Basic Science Certificate first, and that exam could be taken at the end of two years' schooling.

The best one of all those Certificates offered, because it reciprocated with the most states, was the South Dakota State Basic Science Certificate Examination, and it was given at Yankton, S.D., on a college campus. To save money, you could even stay overnight in one of the dorms. My circle of lab partners, a future radiologist, an anesthesiologist-in-the-making, and we three prospective G.P.s arranged to convoy the 426 miles dead north up I-29 on a beautiful spring Friday morning. Dave Mahler's Dodge (my ride) was air-conditioned.

I'd never been in an air-conditioned car before.

Oddly enough, I ran into two of my old classmates from MSU in Yankton, who'd deferred the exam till later in their careers. It felt good to see them, even better to let *them* see that though I had been humiliated and delayed in their sight, I had not been stopped. They seemed genuinely glad to see me, too.

Surprisingly to us at the time, there were chiropractors there. That Certificate was important to them, too, if they wanted licensure in some states.

* * *

Grandmother Freddie died in late April. She'd been 81. She'd had a classic left antero-lateral myocardial infarction, and vehemently refused hospital admission. A headstrong lady, to say the least. She lasted three days at home, but then decompensated and succumbed on the morning of day four. She died as she'd lived, dignified and in complete control.

Up till then, I hadn't been able to repay any part of what I owed her for financing me during Debacle One. I hope, truly, that she didn't think too badly of me. She hadn't been at all forgiving of people who don't satisfy their obligations.

* * *

At that point, in June, 1964, standing first in the Class of '66, I went with Joan to visit her parents in Washington, Missouri.

During that summer vacation journey, I made a two-hour solo side trip for back to MSU, to visit the anatomy associate professor and the chair of the microbiology department who, alone, had treated me and the rest of my former class like human beings. They had both engaged the students in Socratic dialogues, and tried to encourage them to *think*, rather than cutting them off at the knees.

They had not given me failing grades in their courses.

Two, out of two hundred on the faculty.

Their separate reactions were the same, chortling: "I knew you had it in you to be a doctor, and it looks like you will be, in spite of everything!"

For the first time, that day *I* began to believe it, too.

Camp Ripley, Minnesota
Annual Training, 35th Infantry Division
5 August 1964

I was working as a hospital registrar, a second lieutenant, Medical Service Corps (MSC).

R.T. O'Riley, MD, now out of his pathology residency, had recently been assigned to our unit as a General Medical Officer, which he hated.

It was 11 AM; sick call was nearly over.

Someone in the front office had a portable radio on, tuned to the one local Little Falls station that we could receive. The syndicated national news was on, and there had evidently been a naval engagement in the Gulf of Tonkin, a classic E-boat attack from North Vietnam intercepted by two American destroyers. It was 2 AM local time, air cover and recon would not be available till first light, and there was no report of damage or casualties.

I hustled over to the Officers' Mess, and announced what I'd heard. Most of my fellow-officers thought that I was pulling their legs; they weren't ready to believe that fighting could begin that suddenly, or spread rapidly from such a small incident,

But it could.

It did.

16.

6 September 1964

Third Year began in quiet chaos, a completely new experience.

From this point on, I was entering uncharted territory. It was as new and unfamiliar to me as it was to my classmates.

O'Riley advised me that the academic years, at least, sounded much like what he had experienced at the University of Tennessee.

Dr. Sandall had quit his job as MidContinent Research, and was now teaching Microbiology to second-year students at the College. He'd been given a full professorship based on his academic and published works.

Each member of the class registered with the Obstetrics Office to be referred the three patients he'd have to manage from presentation, through delivery, to the 6-week post-partum visit, write up the case studies and submit them, as a requirement for graduation. I, like most of the class, took six cases, to be sure of completing three. Ditto for ten autopsies, on-campus and off, the latter usually conducted in our hospital morgue, but sometimes they'd be done at a funeral home by one of the Pathology staff.

The morning half of each weekday was devoted to four one-hour lectures in clinical subjects.

The afternoons and two evenings a week were for the General Clinic service. Once a student reached the beginning of his or her third year, he was assigned, for want of a better term, a *deck* of cards. Each had an individual's name on it, plus a little demographic data (This, remember, was the pre-computer era.).

The third-year students, now called "Student Doctors", were expected to set up a patient's appointments, to accept that patient's *immediate family* as patients if they came in for care, to manage her pregnancies if she got pregnant (there's one OB out of your three!), and see her kids as patients if she had any. Naturally, you were required to furnish all your patients with your home phone number.

As the patient's point of first medical contact, you, the Student Doctor, had attending faculty and/or senior resident backup, which you'd need less and less as your experience grew.

And woe betide the chronic absentee Student Doctor, or the one who habitually refused to take new and/or walk-in patients. He'd be warned once, then again, sharply. I never heard of any third times.

This was medical education *by immersion*, unchanged for three and a half decades at the College, long before it was first described in the early 70s' mainstream medical literature as a family practice teaching tool.

Crazily enough, because the school wouldn't or couldn't find the funds for a medical librarian in the Clinic, we were required to ICD9-CM-code all our diagnoses. That involved assigning each final diagnosis the one (and *only* one) five-digit number that it most accurately matched. At the time, that had only the educational value of getting us into the habit of making exact diagnoses, because you can't assign an ICD-9-CM code to anything else. However, when diagnosis-related-group payment for hospitals and doctors became important in the late 1980s, I was one of the few doctors around who could code in a reasonable amount of time. A secretary can't do it. *She* didn't make the differential diagnosis mentally before choosing the final one, the diagnosis of record.

I was fortunate enough to have had my random clinical rotations fall so that I was in the Clinic continuously for 20 months. Frank, my study-group-mate, Paul Howard and I were together on most of our rotations, and the mutually-experienced stressors made us closer than just two random classmates. By treating and getting to know the same group of patients who were also getting to know and trust me, I couldn't *help* being a GP at the end of that time. No one could have. It was a classic case of *becoming* by *being,* almost like OCS had been.

And, of course, there was even more patient contact at Top Secret Clinic Number Two every Saturday morning, and most of the afternoon, in Parkville.

My Midwest, 5.

The National Guard armory in Sedalia that housed B/128 FA is still in use, but now hosts the headquarters of an artillery brigade, a larger unit by three orders of magnitude. Instead of the bare concrete exterior of 45 years ago, it's been contrast-painted with a black design that gives a much more modern appearance to its WPA-era construction.

It lies a block west of Broadway, and two and a half miles east of the famous Swine Pavilion at the State Fairgrounds.

The Portrait still hangs in the entry alcove. It is an unretouched photograph of the Missouri National Guard Artillery's most famous alumnus, Captain Harry S. Truman, taken in 1918, in his First World War uniform. He looks straight into the camera, and simultaneously out onto his beloved 35th Infantry Division, including the 128th, while it was an organization to be proud of, and before it, like almost all of our institutions, was gutted by the national nightmare of Vietnam and the seventeen lean years that followed.

* * *

October 5, 1964

My automatic promotion to first lieutenant came through on October fourth.

As quickly as I could, I transferred from the National Guard to the Army Reserve, where merit allegedly mattered more than connections in the State Capitol.

That premise turned out to be absolutely valid, for that time, though it was to be reversed nearly overnight five years later.

Over the next 32 years, I never once regretted making the decision to move.

* * *

Uncle Alf

Alfred was the middle son of the three, my father's older brother.

As I write, he is the only one who survives.

He is the recent recipient of a cardiac pacemaker, two new stainless-steel knee joints, and he is as alert and active as ever.

At the age of 92, he is still an accomplished woodcarver. He has an uncanny artistic ability to look at *and into* a block of wood or piece of lumber, and see a statue, plaque, or statuette in there, only needing to have the excess wood sawed away, then planed, carved, and finally sanded smooth. And as he does that, every stroke runs with the grain of the wood, along the long axis of the part he would eventually finish as a bird's wing, a human hand, or the curve of a woman's flank.

As a teen, he played the ukulele and sang along in a "pretty good" voice.

And, forever the Richards, he stoutly denies having any particular artistic ability.

Like his father and my father, he was a master carpenter. The difference between them was as simple as this: My father worked for as many different contractors as there were jobs in any given year. Alf worked for the same two builders for forty-two years.

According to my mother, he and his late wife surrounded us with solicitude when I was born, and Mom was eighteen. They'd had a baby boy who'd died of bronchopneumonia in 1934, when he was sixteen months old. This was in the depths of the Great Depression, while The Family, like most families during those years, was struggling to stay intact, perhaps by staying close together.

As I grew into childhood, he and his wife, Margaret, embodied everything that is implied by the word "kindness." Perhaps I was the son they had had taken from them, somehow come back.

Alf's been a widower now for 12 years. Marg (pronounced with a hard "G") died of breast cancer after a lifetime of little or no preventive care. Died of a disease that, even with the methods of 1989, could have been detected early, and probably treated successfully.

SHOULDER PATCH, CARRIER PIGEON DIVISION UNITED STATES ARMY SIGNAL CORPS, 1943

Alf has one daughter who's almost three years older than I am, and another a year younger.

Because he'd been a pigeon-fancier and a racing-pigeon breeder (We ate the losers. They're good.), when he was drafted in 1942 he was assigned to the Carrier Pigeon Division of the Army Signal Corps.

Coincidentally, the Manhattan Project was underway and going full bore by that time. I've often wondered if the scientists at Los Alamos *suspected* the existence of electromagnetic pulse (EMP), which we now know accompanies nuclear detonations. Besides heat, blast and ionizing radiation, the net effect of EMP on the battlefield is destruction of all electronic equipment, which in World War II was radio, radar, and telephonic devices. That would have left human messengers *and carrier pigeons* as the only feasible methods of communicating, say, during a nuclear/conventional invasion of the home islands of Japan.

When I heard Tom Brokaw use the words "The Greatest Generation," Uncle Alf sprang to mind immediately. He was the wrong age, caught up as a young married man by the Depression, and a few years later by World War II. Quiet, strong, talented, self-effacing, generous, kind and steadfast, he will leave big shoes for us to try to fill.

And he did break character once, in 1980.

"We are all, all The Family, proud of you," he'd said, giving my right knee a squeeze.

It meant a lot to me. It still does.

* * *

17.

Hospital rotations made up the overwhelming bulk of the fourth and final undergraduate year. Frank Hawkins and I stayed together for the first half of the year; then the Master Schedule split us up. The rotations usually involved a twelve-hour day, with one noon lecture per day.

Except for that, the usual day started with Morning Report, we (the Student Doctors) accompanying the resident and the head nurse (it was unusual to include her in those days; again we were running ahead of the MD world) at 6:45 AM, which covered a discussion of each patient. This included his or her current condition, as well as any change that might have occurred over the past twelve hours. Then we made rounds again with the residents and the *attending* physicians. We observed their management techniques, and answered their questions, between patients, with respect to what we'd do if things turned bad in some way, or how we would avoid a common complication of the disease or patient in question. It was done with us as *learners*, not as objects for criticism.

Then, it was on to the next patient, until we'd seen the 30 or so who were on the Teaching Service.

About the time that rounds were over, the elective admissions to our assigned service were beginning to come in, and it was our job to work them up with a history, physical, lab and X-ray studies, and report our findings to each patient's attending physician. By then, it was 7:00 PM, and time to go home, sleep, and do it all again the next day.

On the Medicine Service, there were no days off. That month, you were *on duty*, period.

If you were on a surgical rotation, you were off from Saturday noon to Sunday noon. Monday morning was hell on wheels, with more surgical procedures being performed then than on any other day of the week. Those patients had to be admitted and worked up Sunday afternoon and night.

On OB, we rotated a day off a week, but worked twelve-hour shifts, day and night, and could not leave if we had a patient in the delivery room, even if our shift was over. That's how a teaching service works best, with the same doctor following the same patient from beginning to end of what, in this case, we were taught was a natural process.

Some of our specialty rotations were at sites distant from the campus.

The main hospital was about two miles from the undergraduate campus with its General Practice Student Clinic. The maternity hospital was on the main campus. Psychiatry was taken at State Hospital Number Eight at Perryville, 54 miles from the college. Some of the students took part of their Medicine and/or surgical rotations at Lake Grandview Osteopathic Hospital, eleven miles to the south across Kansas City.

Internal medicine was the make-or-break subject, a third of the whole year, and OB *hospital* duty (not to be confused with following of our own three patients) one-sixth. Surgery was another one-sixth, other subjects another one-twelfth each, and the General Student Clinic continued as a secondary but vital component, as did the ten autopsies and the 3 OB patients. These last were followed from conception (nearly) to the 6-week post- partum visit for mother and child.

As I stand back and look at the course of study in written form, I know that it *sounds* chaotic and disorganized. It looks like it, too. It did to us at the time. However, that's what a GP's life is *like*, and that's what they were training us to be. Somehow, it seems to have worked.

Our immediate superiors were the interns who had graduated the year before, the so-called "extern-grinders."

At the end of the year, I took the Missouri State Board's licensing exam, passing it with no difficulty. Again, one of my Midwest State classmates was present to take it, too. He'd taken a residency out-of-state, and waited to take the board until he decided where he planned to practice. We had a good forty minutes of lunch, gossip and catching up the past four years, "whatever happened to...?"

Tommy Kirk, he said, was in a place called APO 96347. I found a little later what that meant: Vietnam.

As far as my Saturday Morning Secret Preceptor Routine went, I continued working at Mel's office religiously throughout the Fourth Year. By this time, many of his patients had known me for over three years, and had learned to respect my honest (though some might call it tactless) approach and conservative judgement. Dorrie, the older office aide, told me at about this time: "You came to us in the old office in 1962 as a college student with a little hospital nursing experience. Now, you're a second doctor in a new office."

* * *

The psychiatric rotation at the local state hospital in Perryville was a new experience for their staff and patients *and* for us. We needed the broader exposure to a wide spectrum of psychopathology that one can only get at a large (1000 or so patients) hospital. *They* needed someone to satisfy the new (and badly-needed) State requirement that each patient would receive a reasonably-complete yearly physical examination, because at their staffing levels, their physicians couldn't do their jobs of psychiatric care and the new task also. And there we were, fourth-year students, 100 strong, close-by, and would cost the hospital only three meals a day apiece, plus dorm rooms already present, sitting vacant on the hospital grounds.

I'd say we were a bargain. And we *got* a bargain in return.

My supervising staff physician was an elderly refugee German Jew who had been in the Kaiser's Army Medical Corps in the First World War. He had served for over three years in the chalky mud, dugouts, and trenches of the Western Front, in Artois (the French part of Flanders).

With the arrival of Hitler in 1933, he'd emigrated to China, of all places, been interned but correctly treated by the Japanese when they overran his new home, and then had finally come to the United States after the Second World War. In his German practice, 1918-1933, he'd been an ophthalmologist. He taught me a great deal of basic clinical psychiatry, with a fair amount of outpatient ophthalmology, and, incidentally, the medical history of the Great War, from the German side.

With respect to the last subject, two years later I was astounded at how little of it had changed by 1967.

* * *

I finished my third OB case in February 1966.

I had completed and submitted the ten required autopsies the month before. Bored with simply sitting or standing and watching the procedure, I'd asked permission and, under supervision, *performed* the last three. R.T. O'Riley had given me some pointers on the actual procedure, making it much easier to do it before an audience, which was made up of students from the Classes of '66 and (by now) of '67.

Now the pace was speeding up, at least in our minds; graduation was approaching us like a rocket, head-on.

* * *

Sniper Course, 3d Battalion, 14th Infantry, USAR
Camp McCoy, Wisconsin, 1 June 1965

It was my first AT in the Army Reserve, after transferring out of the National Guard. It had also been several years since I'd been associated with infantry.

When the quota of students for the Brigade Sniper School came up one short, I signed up, as a sort of cram course in fieldcraft.

We were equipped with M-1D sniper rifles, and learned to work in two-man teams, a spotter and a sniper. Wait, wait, wait, identify, shoot, and move away after one *shot was the school sequence.*

Try for a second shot, and die, *was the rule. A few Match Grade Winchester Model 70s with the same scope were available for familiarization fire, to show how much more accurate a bolt-action sniper rifle is, inherently.*

A good sniper can make a head shot ten times out of ten shots at 800 yards, nearly half a mile. At 1200 yards, he will have to settle for a truncal center-of-mass target, but it's still going to be ten hits out of ten shots.

18.

1 August 1965

As I and the rest of the KCCOM Class of 1966 had approached our fourth and final year, we each noticed with varying degrees of interest that a war was going on in the Republic of Vietnam (RVN), and was getting ever-larger as we watched.

At that time osteopathic physicians were not commissioned in the Medical Corps of any service, thanks to a cozy agreement between the AMA and the various Surgeons General, dating from early in World War II. For that reason, DOs were not drafted, either.

Glen "Pops" Macabee and I met, talked, and decided to volunteer for Vietnam, through command channels at first at least, and try to break the monopoly.

Pops was older than most of our classmates. He had fought in Korea as an enlisted man in the Seventh Division, and had then taken Army ROTC in GI-bill-financed pharmacy school. Like me, he was now a Medical Service Corps (MSC) first lieutenant in the Army Reserve. Neither of us had made any definite post-internship plans.

We both felt that our prior service had paid our dues, and we wanted *in.* "Prince Henry," a former Air Force navigator (hence the nickname) in the class, intended to finish his radiology residency, so as to present himself to the USAF Medical Corps as a finished product.

One more thing was beginning to bother me. As far as I could see this war was passing beyond the phase of being fought by the Regular Army, and was being taken over by young men of color and poor whites. College students (today's gutless-wonder academic, political, and business leaders) were deferred (Look at them! Count the ones who were in combat in Vietnam, these 52-to-62-year-old WASP men who are public figures. Can you come up with ten? I doubt it.).

I wanted to do what I could to change that, and at my age, with my background, the only way to actually adjust the numbers was to volunteer myself. I did, and still do, have only contempt for protestors who don't put anything on the line except words, while they're "quartered safe out here," as Kipling phrased it. That's also why I rather admire *sincere* conscientious objectors who are willing to go to prison rather than report in; they are acting on the strength of their convictions, and are anteing up two years in Leavenworth to show that they mean it.

My Reserve unit didn't want to hear about my volunteering. They couldn't see why anyone who didn't *have* to go to a war would want to. And they weren't about to process paperwork challenging the well-known aforementioned AMA/MD monopoly of the Army Medical Corps. Especially not for a first lieutenant who'd *found a seven-year-old amendment* to the regulation, *permitting* DOs to enter the Medical Corps, which, tucked away in the paper jungle since 1957, had never been invoked until this time.

I'd been too clever by half.

Still, there *is* another way to do almost *any*thing, in my experience.

The Army Medical Corps Procurement Officer in Topeka, Kansas (I had approached him to get out of my Corps home area) advised me, deadpan, to enlist fraudulently.

I couldn't believe I'd heard him correctly, and said so.

"Sure," he said, "the Army will catch up with you; it always *does* with enlistments made under false conditions, but the fingerprint match that they use to do it will take a few months, and what are they going to do then, make you a battalion surgeon in Vietnam? That's the job you're volunteering *for.*"

They *did* finally pick up on my (our?) duplicity, too, while I *was* surgeon of the 2d Battalion, 502d Airborne Infantry on the Cambodian border. All that they did was to take away my new serial number, and to direct me in a formal letter to change all my records to reflect the old number.

My long-suffering spouse wasn't charmed by the idea of my being gone for a year, but finally agreed. She understood that this was something I had to do. That *men* have to do.

As I said at the beginning of this account about The Family, men are attracted to wars. Always have been, probably always will be. And, later, usually regret that they were.

Graduation Day came at last.

Made it, *made it*, MADE IT, *again*!!!

And the Class of Sixty-Six dissolved.

Frank Hawkins and Prince Henry were off to take radiology residencies. Johnny Moreland, who wouldn't graduate until the next year, was there as a guest and former classmate. Rudy and Dallas split for their rotating internships around the country. Paul Howard had married a local girl, so he stayed in Kansas City, and we interned together.

* * *

The Family met at our apartment after graduation.

True to form, my father had not attended the graduation of his only (legal) child from medical school.

I was talking to my Uncle Alf that night, and, without warning broke down and wept, on what should have been a happy occasion, for the first time since my childhood. I'd been calmly saying that my only regret was that Grandma Freddie, that grand lady of the late Victorian era who had formed me, at least as much as my own divorced parents, had not lived another two years, to see this night.

I could *not* hold it back.

Joan told me: "Never mind. She knows."
I'd like to think that she was right.

* * *

Binion's, Hand Three:

First chair is taking a break.

Second chair gets a pair of eights. Chair Three is dealt a six-ace, soft seventeen. Number Four is dealt a seven and an eight. Chair five is empty, the player having withdrawn after the last hand and a run of five straight losses. The dealer, a lady now, has a four showing. Second base splits his eights, catches a ten on one and a nine on the other. Third player, the little old lady from Pasadena, hits for a three and a hand of twenty. Number four gets a five and stays on twenty. The dealer has a nine down and a four up. She draws another four and has to stay on seventeen.

The Count is now six.

19.

Internship was much like the fourth year of school had been, with marginally longer hours and with added supervisory responsibilities. There were six rotating interns in the class that would end on 30 June 1967.

We were all now licensed to practice medicine in Missouri.

We oversaw the externs who rotated through our assigned services, evaluated their performance and even recommended grades to the department heads, who generally at least considered our input. Our day-to-day supervisors were the residents in our serial departmental rotations.

The clandestine (and never-discovered) Saturday Morning Secret Clinics at the Parkville office were over. There just wasn't time for them.

This was to be the first year that interns were paid more than forty dollars a month. To compete with the rest of the country's programs, the stipend at Osteopathic Hospital had been raised to $480 a month, the most money that I'd ever made in my life. And Dr. Mel Frank, Junior, wouldn't hear of my starting to pay back what I owed him.

He'd said: "You and Joan have a baby due, and you'll need the money for that."

So, we moved out to the north, to the suburb of Platte Woods, in Platte County, Missouri, four miles north of the Parkville office. I rented a three-bedroom split-level house with a one-car garage. It, too, was a new high for me, after a lifetime of furnished rooms, share-the-bath apartments, cockroaches, mice, parking on the street, dead batteries, nine-tenths-empty gas tanks, dead ends and hopelessness.

The first eight months of internship sped past.

Our first child, a wonderful blonde-haired, blue-eyed boy, was born in early March, 1967.

I bought two one-quarter-ton window air conditioners, an undreamed-of extravagance as little as six months before.

Had the internship been less time-consuming, I might remember more about that time, but I can't. It's all a blur of long days, and of moving our furniture, baby boy, and our adopted stray tortoise-shell cat.

* * *

Mel Frank called me at 4:30 AM, April 12, 1967. His father, whom we called Dr. Frank, Senior, had had a heart attack and died suddenly a few hours before. His very active practice on the Kansas side was now without a doctor.

I owed Doc Junior big-time, for $6000 in loans for tuition (equivalent to

$25,000 in 2001 dollars) and for a world of illegally-acquired Saturday morning experience. Like a scene from *The Godfather*, he now called in an also-illegal favor: to work as many afternoons as I could, without a Kansas license, in his father's office, to keep it open.

Those patients had supported him while he was growing up. Now, he felt obligated not to leave them high and dry. The risk I was taking seemed to him acceptable. If word got out about what I was doing, I'd be dismissed from internship and possibly prosecuted. But, I reasoned, if I were to play it close to the vest, be absolutely paranoid, and practice very conservatively, what were the chances I'd foul up and get caught in the 3 ½ months till the internship was over? I estimated that they were minimal. In any event, I had no choice.

As the Family would say, collectively: Obligations must be met.

* * *

30 June 1967, Midnight

Made it again!
Internship was over!

* * *

1 July 1967

The Ann Street office, in Kansas City, Kansas, was located in the front one-third of Mel Frank's childhood home. The house had been purposely-built (in 1934) by Doc, Senior to include a doctor's office.

I started right in, the morning after graduation, seeing patients in the Kansas Side office, as agreed, full-time, for a salary of one-third of my collections, while I waited for my orders to report in, if the Army Medical Corps decided to accept my application. It was by no means certain that they would.

I must confess that I breathed easier, though, when I had a Kansas license in hand, after July 9th.

As each patient of Doctor Senior would come in, I would introduce myself. Some of them had not known that he'd died. They'd occasionally seen Mel in the past, and were not surprised initially that Senior was out of the office. Usually, they stayed on to see me as patients, at least until, and especially if, they needed the care of a specialist.

More often than I'd expected, patients were reluctant to see better-qualified physicians or to be hospitalized, insisting that I just go ahead and do what I could, or what I thought best there, in the office. It took a lot of persuading to convince them that this often wasn't the best treatment plan.

My first patient was a cheery little old lady of 83 with a dark spot on her left cheek, which her daughter had insisted needed medical attention. A biopsy showed that it was a malignant squamous cell carcinoma (my bet had been on a benign seborrheic keratosis). I advised her that she needed a rather extensive surgical procedure, and would need to see an ENT surgeon or a plastic surgeon. "No," she said, "go ahead and remove it here, in the office." I demurred, since the possibility of having to extend the procedure into a radical neck dissection was very real.

"Forget it," she said. "I'm old. I won't live much longer anyway." And, though she didn't know it, a complex radical neck operation *would* very likely kill her, from either the procedure or the prolonged anesthetic, in 1967. She also had the belief, common in those of her age, that she would not survive hospitalization. So I did a wide excision, and closed the cheek with a three-inch long Z-plasty, one day out of internship.

It healed beautifully. The biopsy showed the margins to be free of tumor cells. She lived another six years, and died of heart disease.

I remember one man with bilateral leg pain that I was never able to diagnose or treat. I felt guilty charging him for his office visits, considering my lack of results.

And then, a fat nine-by-twelve-inch brown envelope from the Army was delivered in the mail.

* * *

HEADQUARTERS FIFTH UNITED STATES ARMY
Fort Sheridan, Illinois 60037

24 August 1967

LO ALVAG-ZD 08-416
SUBJECT: Active Duty

TO: 1LT JOHN COE RICHARDS, JR, MC, USAR
7106 N.W. Montrose Drive Kansas City, MO 64151

TC 133. Under the provisions of Title 10, U.S. Code, subsection 672(d), following individual having been determined medically qualified, is ordered to ACTIVE DUTY, with his consent, in the grade currently held as a reserve officer of the Army, and assigned as indicated.
Permanent change of station.
You will proceed to TDY station in sufficient time to report on the date specified. Travel directed is necessary in the military service. Travel by privately owned conveyance, commercial aircraft, commercial rail and or bus authorized. Officers are relieved from present Reserve assignment on EDCSA.
By direction of the President, announcement is made of the advancement and commissioning of 1LT JOHN COE RICHARDS, JR as captain in the Army of the United States under provisions
of Title 10, USC, sections 3443 and 3447, effective on date of entry on active duty and with rank and promotion eligibility date as of entry.

RICHARDS, JOHN COE, JR, 1LT 05 547 684. MOS 3100 Ready Reserve.
Social Security Number: 479-63-8552.
TDY ENROUTE TO: Student Detachment, Medical Field service School, Brooke Army Medical Center, (MD 3410-01), Fort Sam Houston, Texas.
Reporting date (TDY) Not later than 1600 hours, 11 Sep 67
Period (TDY): Approximately four (4) weeks.
Course: AMEDS Officer orientation (6-8-C20A)
Class Number: 3
Account Classification: 2182030 06-P2450-21 S9999

Further TDY Enroute to: USA Infantry School (3A-3151) Ft Benning, Georgia.
Reporting Date (TDY): Not later than 15Oct 67
Period (TDY): Approximately 3 weeks
Course: Airborne (2E-F1) SQN: QS-32B

Class Number: N/A
Account classification: 2182020 06-29
P2450-21 S99999
ASSIGNED TO: Active Duty Accession Detachment Hq Fifth US Army and reassigned as directed below. Initial assignment to Active Duty Accession Detachment Hq Fifth U S Army is for purpose of strength accountability only, travel of individual and dependents and shipment of household goods to station of initial assignment is not authorized. DO NOT REPORT TO THIS UNIT
Permanent Change of Station (MDC) N/A
Effective date of change of strength accountability: 08 Sep 67
REASSIGNED TO: USARV Transient Detachment APO San Francisco 96307 for further assignment.
Allocation: Nov 1486 (IDC-2)Reporting date (POE): Prior to 1200 hours. Not later than 16 Nov 67.
Home of Record: 419 Brooklyn, Kansas City, Missouri
Leave date: N/A
Permanent Change of Station (MDC):4BZXZZm
Accounting Classification: 2182010 01 1112-1113-1114-1115-1116-1117 P1411 S9999
EDCSA: 13 Sep 67
Security Clearance: Top Secret 16 Dec 66
Basic pay entry date: 10 Jun 54
Active Duty Commitment: OBV 2 years

FOR THE COMMANDER
BARBARA S. TEMPLE
MAJ AG ; ADJUTANT

Camp McCoy, Wisconsin,
1 June 1954

The road was made of starkly white gravel running across grassy flats. Low, rounded-off, sparsely-forested hills flanked the road, a few hundred yards away on both sides.

Thirty-eight boys between the ages of seventeen and nineteen moved along the verges in two files, keeping a ten-yard open-terrain interval. We were wearing gloss-painted olive drab M-1 helmet liners and carrying M-1 rifles. The shiny brown boots, brown leather equipment and the solid green fatigue uniforms were mostly left over from World War II, plus a few items not as subject to wear and tear that were dated "1917" (my canteen and field pack to name only a couple).

Bill Anderson, the company-supply-clerk-enlistee, was the next man ahead of me in my march file. "Man-Mountain" Bob Knight, destined to carry a 23-pound Browning automatic rifle for the next 7 ½ years, was behind me. In any stationary formation, just as soldiers had been doing since the 16th century, they had assigned permanent posts that were to my right and left, respectively.

Photographed, we would have been indistinguishable from a similar training scene of ten or twelve years before. When you're 17, that's ancient history.

During the two weeks to follow, we'd learn to fire for qualification with our M-1 rifles, and for familiarization with the .45-caliber pistol, the Browning automatic rifle (BAR), the M1919A6 30-caliber machine gun, and the 3.5-inch rocket launcher ("Bazooka."). We'd also learn to attack as part of a tank-infantry team. And how to use the ten-inch bayonet.

It was far enough north that the heat was not unpleasant to these young soldiers-to-be, even carrying their field gear in full sunlight.

We were the Recruit Platoon of the 137th Infantry Regiment, on our first active duty tour. Our sole teacher and leader was Second Lieutenant Al Bukaty, a paratrooper fresh-back from the fighting in Korea as a member of the 187th Regimental Combat Team (ABN). He was thin, serious and deeply committed to this duty, which, after I'd *become an officer, I couldn't have done without at least one enlisted assistant. Unlike us, he was wearing tropical worsted tailored khakis, at least partly so that he would stand out and be easy to locate. He, working alone, was to teach us more in 17 days than I've ever learned since in twice that time.*

* * *

Now, whenever I hear arguments against a military draft, I think of Lieutenant Bukaty. He was the epitome of the citizen-soldier, and performed in that order of priority. He also taught us to behave as soldiers in the same way. When a country's government borrows its citizens and its civilians' sons and daughters, its armed forces become part of its society, as they are now in Israel, and its Army reflects the behavior and values of its societal structure.

Conversely, and to our shame, the all-volunteer army of today is made up of the sons of no one special, and thus no one important really cares much what happens to a few of them, someplace far away, now and then.

* * *

There was a time when the last few paragraphs would have been superfluous. At any time before 1975, eighty-plus per cent of the men in the United States would have lived it, themselves, to the point of universal mind-numbing boredom. Now, it's probably eight per cent or less, which, at least partly, is the point of iterating it here. You can spot them pretty easily, though; they'll be the ones whose hair isn't styled, and never has been.

* * *

Amy

Amy is my cousin.

She is three years older than I am, and Uncle Alf's eldest daughter.

We grew up together, were *children* together. Whenever I hear the word "cousin," I think first of her, seldom of her younger sister, though *she* is nearly the same age as I am. As children, all three of us resembled archetypal Campbell's Kids, all dimples and chubby cheeks.

Amy's been widowed for thirty years.

When I was nineteen, she had married a dreamer, a romantic with impossibly high personal goals and standards. Those were (and are) only marginally compatible with earning a living. Parenthetically, some of the older members of The Family were shocked by her marriage to a Roman Catholic.

So, Amy worked, too, as a high school PE teacher in the city's school system, taking time off to have three children. After fathering their three daughters, her husband had a massive heart attack, and quite literally dropped dead at work one day. He left Amy with an insurance-paid-up house, and a small amount of cash.

She elected not to remarry, and instead threw herself into her teaching (and I suspect also into mentoring of selected students) and the rearing of her daughters.

I've been in love with her as long as I can remember. However, when you're under thirty, three-plus years might as well be a full generation. And by the time you are thirty, you're both married to someone else.

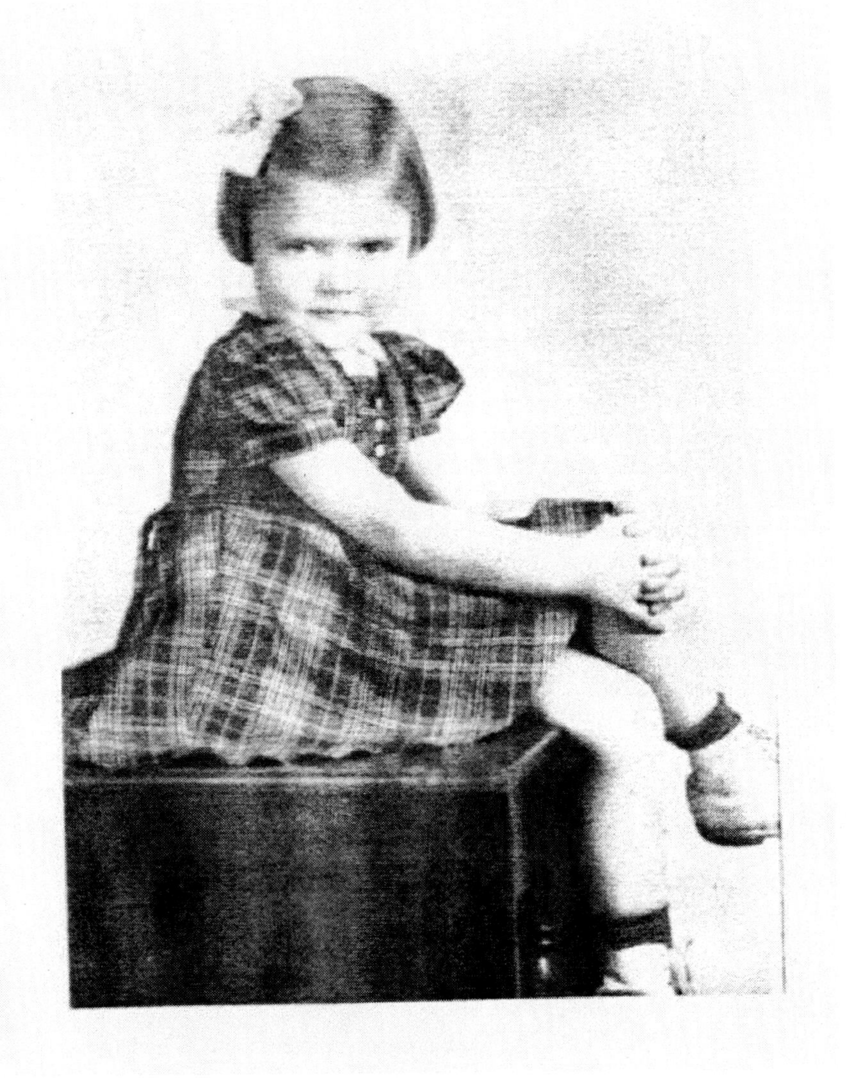

AMY

Anyway, cousins cannot legally marry in Missouri; I'm not sure that it's legal anywhere, except perhaps among the nobility of Europe. And look at how *they* turned out. And worse, at their offspring.

So I never told her how I felt.

What would have been the point?

20.

09 September 1967

Medical Officer Basic Training at The Medical Field Service School, Fort Sam Houston, San Antonio, Texas, consisted of two parts: One, military subjects, so that the historically- and notoriously-unmilitary docs would at least look and act like company-grade officers, and Two, military medicine, as distinct from what they already knew from their medical schools and internships.

Pops and I were in the same class; captains, Medical Corps, at last, reporting in on September 9, 1967, along with about an eighth of the former KCOM Class of '66. Interestingly, they were the eighth with the highest grades.

Now, that's what I call *selective* service.

Either Pops and I had broken down the wall for all of us, or, more likely, the decision to call up DOs was coincidental, and kept secret until about March of 1967. That's when the first one-eighth of the class of 1966's draftees had received greetings from their neighbors and President Johnson. Another approximately one-eighth was called every three months until about the lowest-graded one-third of the class was reached. After that point, *no* further members were selected or drafted. Meta-selective service? *Mega*-selective service, perhaps?

We were in-processed by a group of three MSC first lieutenants who were seated inside three identical Dutch doors. The doors' upper sections were open. The three officers' desks were pushed flush against the inward-swinging lower halves of the doors, so that they couldn't be opened from the hallway where the incoming student officers were standing. The three lieutenants sat with their backs to a single huge office. We were supposed to hand over a three copies of our orders and fill out a basic personnel data form while the reception officer skimmed our orders to be sure that we were the right person, in the right place at the right time.

Everything went well until I handed in my completed form. It had asked for my security clearance. I had checked the box marked "Top Secret" instead of "None," or "Don't know," as expected.

The lieutenant looked up at me.

"You marked 'Top Secret' on your form," he said.

"Yes," I answered.

He showed an ever-so-slight sneer.

"I very much *doubt* that you have a 'Top Secret Clearance,'" he said.

Might as well try it out, I thought.

"Are you sure," I asked, "that you don't mean: 'I VERY MUCH DOUBT IT, *SIR?*'" My not-quite shout quieted the murmur behind me. I didn't hear any pins drop, but easily could have.

He choked on it and turned a lovely shade of medium red. "*Sir.*"

"You will find, over your career," I advised him further, "that nuclear-capable units require that level of clearance of all their officers. My last unit *was* nuclear-capable. So I *do* have it. Any further comment?"

He did better this time: "Nossir."

"Questions?" I asked.

"Nossir."

I took my introductory literature packet and left; our orientation session was the next morning and we were free till then.

I really *was* a captain, after six years as a lieutenant.

It was most gratifying.

I checked into the Rodeway Inn nearby; there weren't enough quarters to accommodate even 10% of the class.

* * *

The class consisted of 690 physicians, 60 dentists and 12 veterinarians. If there were any optometrists, pharmacists or podiatrists, I didn't meet them. Later in my military career, they would all be prominently represented at every advanced training course I ever attended.

We had a formal assembly formation every day at 7 AM and again at 1 PM. Perhaps the band needed the practice, or the administration felt it would instill the proper spirit in the troops, to have them playing at both.

I couldn't help reflecting at the time upon the similarity to the inmates' orchestra at Auschwitz.

Until this experience, I'd never been forcibly amalgamated with this many heterogeneous characters, and except for a few prior-servicemen, I suspect that this was a universal and mutual experience and exposure. For example, I'd never realized how much of the population lay in the Northeast. Our Basic class was roughly representative of the citizenry's geographic distribution. Nearly half our doctors came from that part of the country. With some exceptions, that fraction of the group was bright, and *knew* a lot, but didn't know how to actually *do* much. These guys (there were no women in the Medical Corps in those years) had a much harder time adjusting to the Army than those from, say, the Midwest or Southwest. The dentists (dubbed "tooth fairies") and the vets (or "doggie doctors") generally handled adversity better than either group of MDs, as did most of the DOs.

I suspect that this was true because, like Avis, we in the minority schools of practice were used to trying harder (and expecting less, by inference). This fraction of our class, with a few exceptions, knew less minutiae but had more hands-on skills.

I was really unable, initially, to understand the dissonance of the Yankees (which I'd previously thought I was) and the Army. After all, they were pretty much the same age I was, and there'd been a draft since 1940. Their fathers, like mine, had almost certainly served in the Second World War. Why were they so unready and unwilling? Had they *all* thought that they'd never be called up?

One day, a section of us was walking back from the rifle range, where we'd fired the M-14, and I was talking to a Jewish kid from New York, whom I'd coached a little, based on my prior marksmanship training, and I asked him about it.

He told me that boys destined for a medical career back east were started early in the way they were treated as special by their families ("and for your bar mitzvah, here's a nice fountain pen for you to write prescriptions with, when you're a doctor."). That goes on for twenty years. Then, one day, someone hands him a rifle and tells him "Go out to Asia and (maybe) die. How would *you* feel?" I never asked again, and was a better officer for knowing it, I think.

Even at that, any place with Pearl beer at 15 cents a bottle couldn't be all bad.

Never having been outside the USA, and being less than 150 miles from Mexico, a bunch of us went down, for our first exposure to the Third World. It was a pleasant place, with funny money, friendly, hardworking people, no shortage of dirt, dozens of shops with trashy tourist junk for sale, rotisserie-roasting whole goats outside cafes, each with nimble-footed flies moving to the up-side out of the heat, and strong tequila sours available for fifteen cents.

Any description of the infamous walled-off compound of sixty bars and whorehouses, called "Boys' Town," outside Nuevo Laredo, would be just too sordid for the tender ears of the gentle reader. Think of it as a series of dance halls with loud mariachi music and lots of working girls and women in attendance. You entered the walled complex through a checkpoint manned by three Mexican cops; they searched everyone. Weapons, alcohol, and women don't mix. The cleanest establishment, with the most refined ambience, was La Diamante Azul (The Blue Diamond). Let me give you one tip, based on my experience: anyplace that sells beer in seven-ounce bottles (and they all did) is a tourist trap, and you are going to get stung. I won't go into it further, except to deny that I was anything except a spectator at the scene.

* * *

Paul Howard had set up a solo family practice in San Antonio, his hometown. We were able to get together four times during the first three weeks of Basic.

Most evenings, I ground away at the last and longest phase of the E-24 MSC course. Even though I wasn't an MSC any longer, and never would be again, it went against the grain to abandon a course of study that was over 80% completed.

21.

There was one slightly older doctor in Class 6-8-C20A who'd been drafted as a major, who was thus the senior officer in the class. I was assigned as his second-most-senior (why they didn't pick Pops is still a mystery to me. He had at least 4 years seniority on me). I would walk the ranks and correct appearance ("Get a haircut. Shine your shoes. Your insignia are backward.") and the wearing of the uniform (Thank you, thank you, Robinson Barracks!) at the morning and noon formations.

Half the class, myself included, was slated for Vietnam upon completion of this training. The other half would, if they couldn't avoid it, go the next year. Surprisingly, there was a significant number of the holdovers who were, in some way, able to evade Vietnam service.

As a personal plus, the half of us with orders for Vietnam weren't required to buy dress blues. Over the following thirty years, *I* never did.

* * *

Joan flew down (we of the Greyhound stratum of society were beginning to get accustomed to flying in jets to save time) to spend the weekend, and we, along with Paul and his wife, Connalee, went to Nuevo Laredo. I showed Joan all the sights, less Boy's Town, of course.

The four of us had lunch at the Cadillac Bar, the unofficial meeting place of medics on pass, known for carrying a less-than-average risk of gastrointestinal disease, la turista. By 2 PM, we were ready to return home, having seen as much of Mexico as we could handle, loaded down with tooled leather goods, Mexican silver doo-dads, and souvenir coins.

This time I was struck intensely by the foreignness of the place, the different money (obtained as souvenirs), and the serious lack of First-World sanitation.

* * *

Early in the fourth week, the class was bused to Camp Bullis, 20 miles north of San Antonio for field training, and were put up in tin-roofed, screen-walled huts.

The first class was devoted to the care, cleaning, and wearing of the gas mask. Then we went into a gas chamber to see how well they worked. Then we took them off, so we could really appreciate how tear gas, Type CS, feels without a mask (note to rioters: you can get a perfectly good Israeli surplus mask for eleven bucks, mail-order. And I'd recommend it, after that experience.).

That night, after a late-afternoon preparatory briefing, we crawled under live M-60 machine gun fire, 30 inches off the ground, while explosive charges were detonated at random around the training area. There was barbed wire strung across the field, to get through without, obviously, raising a body part 30.0001 inches above the ground. The trick is to roll onto your back and lift the wire upward just enough to work your way under it. The nurses' basic classes, usually held separately, were with us that night.

Next day, we had half a day of classwork in map reading, and that afternoon was spent in a field exercise involving land navigation, using a map and compass, across open country.

The following night was devoted to the infamous compass course, where teams of four students walked a 2 ½ -mile unmarked overland course in full, moonless dark, crossing low hills, wadis, and mostly open arid country. The only guide to the finish point was a list of six compass headings, with the distance in yards between each, and a description of a prominent landmark that would indicate the place to change headings. Each group was given different directions and checkpoints, so that they ran roughly parallel to each other but was out of sight of any other group. My team used the stars for a check, and came up 40 yards off, acceptable for that long a course. About 700 yards into the problem, my team nearly fell into an arroyo, laughing, at the sound of a nearby group of New Yorkers stumbling around after one tripped over a live, naturally-nocturnal armadillo.

Sometimes, I fantasize some of those guys, *still* out there, stumbling around in the dark, lost, trying to finish the Night Compass Course.

The nurses' class accompanied us on that exercise, too, and easily performed as well as the men.

At the end of the fourth week, the DOs in the class volunteered almost to a man for paratroop training, flight school, Special Forces and various other optional programs, as did enough of the MDs to fill the Army's quotas.

22.

The medical half of Basic Training was largely oriented toward the difference between civilian (called low-velocity) wounds, and the very different characteristics of wounds caused by high-velocity projectiles, and toward resuscitative surgical procedures.

We trained to debride devitalized tissue, perform tracheotomies, insert and tie down large-bore intravenous and central access lines, and place chest tubes, all in an animal lab using live, anesthetized goats, who'd been shot with .308 rifle bullets while they were under the anesthetic.

Tropical and cold weather (we weren't *all* going to Vietnam) medicine with emphasis on infectious diseases unique to those theaters of operations were covered. Likewise, treatment of chemical casualties and of burns were described in detail. And preventive medicine. And aeromedical evacuation. And organization of the Army Medical Department. And on, and on, and on. It was a busy five weeks. And I have to say here, 33 years of family practice later, that I've never once practiced for 24 hours straight without using something, however small, that I was taught during Basic.

* * *

Graduation was perfunctory; if anyone *didn't* complete the course satisfactorily, I don't know it.

* * *

Pops, Mrs. Pops (her proper name was Maria), and I paired up and formed a two-car convoy to parachute training at Ft. Benning, Georgia. We had from 3PM Friday to noon Sunday to make it to Fort Benning, though in those days of the 70-mile-per-hour speed limit, it was possible. I couldn't help noticing that there was no time for even a weekend off for those of us going to a limited war. And no time for anything else for those who weren't. So we hauled it: Houston, Baton Rouge and Mobile (my first sight of salt water) on I-10, then diagonally northeast across rural Alabama to Columbus, Georgia.

My first contact with the civilian world while I was a soldier took place at one AM, in a Faulknerian hamlet in southeastern Alabama. I'd stopped at a closed gas station to look at my map, and a local cop was on me within sixty seconds.

I showed my ID card and orders, Smokey started calling me "Sir," and I was on my way in less than ten minutes. Not everyone in the country looked down on us potential baby-killers, evidently.

23.

7 October 1967

The U.S. Army's Airborne School has been in the same part of the post at Benning since 1941, and except for progressive enlargement during the war years, I suspect it hadn't changed much in the fall of 1967.

Platoons double-timed past, singing:

"I wanna be an Airborne Ranger,
Live on blood and guts and danger,
I wanna go to Viet-nammm,
Gonna wax them Viet Cong!"

The barracks were old and tumbledown, which is typical of any military school, in my experience. The students come and go quickly and often, and they give little attention to maintaining their temporary housing.

There was an assembly area with orange-painted 1 ½-inch cables, half-imbedded in the ground, and stretching from side to side of the field, six feet apart. These were used to align our ranks quickly. We were inspected there every morning and noon for proper rigging of equipment, for jump boots being shined, haircut status, canteens full, with plenty of pushups if any all-too-frequent deficiencies were found. The field (the Marines call it a "grinder") was about sixty by thirty yards, with the cables running parallel along the long axis.

In the grassed areas around the grinder were eight drinking fountains and four open-air showers, designed to be entered and used fully clothed, against heat exhaustion and heat stroke.

The only break in the routine was a one-hour lunch period.

The officers' mess was Deep South. I was offered pre-sweetened tea for the first time (a kind of tea syrup), and fried entrees with okra, black-eyed peas and fried corn offered on the side at every meal.

The first week of the three-week course was called Ground Week, where we learned to exit mockups of C-130s, at ground level, then at 4½ feet off the ground to incorporate parachute landing falls (PLFs) with aircraft-exiting technique. Finally, the mockups were hiked to 34 feet off the ground. At that height, the pupils hooked themselves to a trolley, stood in the door, executed a vigorous exit on the command "GO!" from the ground, jumped, and slid down a 300-foot cable to an embankment, where they did a PLF. Why 34 feet? That's the high limit of human depth perception. Each exit's form, jump posture and PLF was graded by an instructor jumpmaster on the ground, and was repeated till it was perfect. Anything less was and still is unacceptable; things go wrong fast at 200 miles an hour, and tend to crescendo into a hopeless situation with fatal results.

Attention to detail saves lives. The faculty believed it, and they were right.

Most of what I remember is a blur of running to exhaustion, sweat, aching muscles, and absolute craziness.

I was 30 at the time, was five-eleven, and weighed 170 pounds. And this was as agonizing as OCS had ever been.

We learned to count: "ONE one-thousand, TWO one-thousand, THREE one-thousand, CHECK canopy." At the top of our lungs, being sure to throw our heads back all the way, on the word "check," as if looking upward for a parachute malfunction. And lots of running, calisthenics, and bullshit harassment. Officers and EM trained together. There are no ranks among the students at service schools. There were a few marines in the class, who pretty much kept together and only talked among themselves. There were also two SEALs who didn't even talk to *each other*. They were solitary, lean, and silent, dressed in solid black, head to toe. I never even saw them *breathe* hard during the entire course.

An interesting statistic: more than three times as many men refused the 34-foot tower as refused to jump from an aircraft. No one has ever explained that phenomenon, to my knowledge.

Tower Week consisted of more of the same, plus dropping from a 250-foot amusement-park-style tower with an already-deployed ring-mounted canopy. Later subjects included learning to control and collapse the T-10 parachute on the ground, with or without a wind, and how not to get dragged by an inflated canopy. A jumper lands at about 25 miles per hour, which can be approximated by a tower jump. Or by free-jumping from a 4 ½-foot elevation. One lands with his hips and knees slightly flexed, feet and knees together, fists together and arms tight against the chest, and, *keeping* them that way, rolls into a fall, ending with the head facing 180 degrees away from its position when the feet initially contact the ground.

Jump Week, weather permitting, could be as short as three days, involving only four daytime jumps and one made at night, hopefully compressing two into one day, or four into two days.

Then, it would be off to your unit. If you were injured, and couldn't finish on time, the school would hold you over till you could. That's how I got to Vietnam ahead of Pops.

Jumping, as you leave the plane through the side doors, you swi-i-i-ng back under the tail, all the time that your static line is uncoiling. When your full weight pulls on it, you break away from the 80-pound test line attaching the apex of the canopy to the plane. Meanwhile, you've been counting, while a little voice inside your head, in response to the swing-back says: "Are you shitting ME?" And I still think that your heart stops for a good 15 seconds. Then you just ride it down, do a PLF, and that's one jump done, and down for the record.

For officers (suddenly, the ranks were back), graduation was cursory, involving an entry in the 201 File.

I've heard it said that Marine Corps recruits, having completed the grinding madness and severe discipline of Boot Camp, were Marines, not just then, but would be until the day they died. I suspect that the same thing occurs with paratroopers.

Once you exit a C-130 in flight, you are marked as different. Not better, just *apart,* from those who cannot or will not do it.

* * *

Following jump school, all of us slated for Vietnam went to a mandatory Preparation for Overseas Rotation (POR) course, which took four days. It included a full records check, to be sure everything was in order. Malaria prophylactic pills were issued, to be started three weeks prior to departure for Asia.

A lot of the time was spent on the M-16 rifle, which was entering general issue about then. I fired expert with it; compared with the M-1 and M-14, it was a snap.

On the last day of the POR course, a big second lieutenant instructor with a German accent faced the class and said: "Last four rows, stand up. The rest of you, look at them. That's the twenty per cent who won't be coming back."

Inspiring and uplifting to say the least.

* * *

All my life, I've been afraid to fly. And any sane person, myself included, is afraid to jump. I did, and still do both, as a personal Mount Everest: Because it is there.

In high school, one October night, I had climbed a 200-foot-high city water tower, just to demonstrate to myself that I would do it. Anyone could. *Lots of kids wouldn't. Some* would. *I* had *to know which group I was in.*

* * *

HEADQUARTERS THE STUDENT BRIGADE
UNITED STATES ARMY INFANTRY SCHOOL
Fort Benning, Georgia 30190

SPECIAL ORDERS
NUMBER 261

23 October 1967

EXTRACT

TC 241 Folrsg dir. Indiv WP in mil unif to the place assigned and will report at the hour on the date specified in PC. TDN.2182101 01-1111-1112-1113-1114-1115-1116-1117 P1411 S99999.
RICHARDS, JOHN COE, JR 05542684 CPT MC USAR (3100) USARV Trans Det APO SF 96507 for fur assignment to be detm.
Aloc: Nov-1486 (IDC-2)
PC Data: Rept on 13 Nov 67 NLT 1200 hrs to the
SFOA Trans Det
OARB APO 94626
Lv Data: 10 DDALVAH
Arr MO NLT :13 Nov 67
PCS(MDC): 4B
Auth: TC 133 LO ALFAG-ZD 08-416 Hq Fifth USA 24 Aug 67
PPSC: A
ADC: OBV
EDCSA: 13 Nov 67
Sp instr: Off ordered to AD and pres TDY theat str per auth indic w/EDCSA: **13 Sep 67**. Bag all 62 lbs. An ex bag alw of 134 lbs personal eff auth to accomp off while tvl by acft. Cncr tvl of depn and shpmnt of POV not auth. The introduction pur and poss of pvt owned wpn is prohibited in the RVN.

FOR THE COMMANDER:

ANDREW J. DiNARDO
Captain, Infantry
Adjutant

R.C. BROWNARD
CW-3, USA
Asst. Adj

24.

I drove home from Georgia to spend a few days before my port call, via Birmingham, Tupelo, Memphis, New Madrid, Columbia and on into Kansas City, to our rented house in Platte Woods.

Joan and I decided to take the train to San Francisco. I thought I should see the country while I had the chance.

I was expecting the worst, at that point, and saw no reason to deny myself the experience. A few days alone with Joan would at least be something for us both to remember, live or die.

I'd never been to the West Coast. Joan had been to L.A., but never to San Francisco. So we booked a room on the San Francisco Chief, an express, that made only one stop at a place called Belen, New Mexico.

I expected a desert, with mountains and rock formations out of a John Ford western. Instead, the West was an unending grassland, like Western Kansas, extending all the way from Kansas City to Richmond, California.

We stayed at the Travelodge on Fishermans Wharf, two up-to-now-poor over-age twenty-nine year-old kids from the Midwest who, for the first time, had a few dollars to spend. I tasted lobster for the first time in a second-floor seafood restaurant on the Wharf. We took the obligatory Gray Line tour, visited the Haight-Ashbury, and Chinatown. I was awe-struck by the Wharf, the fog, and the cable cars of the city that I'd heard called Baghdad-by-the-Bay.

That description wasn't exaggerated.

Walking through Chinatown, and along the Embarcadero, listening to the foghorns, each with its own characteristic sound, was like being in another world. Whenever I visit San Francisco, even now, I still feel the same way.

On the third day, I put Joan on the train to go back to Kansas City. She put on a cheerful face. By not crying or showing her feelings at that time, she showed as much bravery as I was ever to see in Vietnam. For that matter, she had more guts than many of the Regular Army wives I was to treat in later years, when their husbands got orders *back* to Vietnam.

Then, as if I'd just gotten off the train, I walked to the ever-present military personnel desk and asked for transportation to Oakland.

25.

I had a three-day wait for my estimated departure date, so I asked Billeting for temporary housing.

I checked in to the Oakland Army Depot guesthouse on a quiet Wednesday morning. The place was uncrowded, and was only a short walk from the Officers' Club. That walk never changed. The fog was always there, so thick that it was like walking along, always in the center of a bubble-like sixty-foot-diameter hemisphere with solid white walls.

It was a peaceful quiet place. It smelled of the sea and the mud of low tide. The only noise was the occasional cry of a far-off gull, invisible in the fog.

Friday afternoon, I came out of the Officers' Club, and walked back, inside my hemisphere, to the guesthouse .

The place was in pandemonium.

At least four sergeants' wives with three or four kids apiece were sitting and *living* in the lobby, one or two in tears at any given time. They'd assumed that a guesthouse would have rooms available, and hadn't made reservations.

Just one of the many casualties of limited war, never to return; a certain graciousness and redundancy.

When it became obvious that space for them wasn't going to become available, I moved into the lobby and let a mother with four kids have my single room.

I sat up in the lobby for 24 hours, and then reported in, more than ready to be gone.

Raydene Hale Richards

She married my father in 1945, when I was nine.

I liked her from the first, I think because she began by treating me like a valued relative, and has continued to do so until this day.

I never think of her as a stepmother. She's more like a dear mega-aunt. As I write, she is 82, and still going strong, twelve years after she was widowed in 1988. She has a.....friendship with a widower from two towns over. God bless them both, I say. I imagine that my father would say so, too.

She has a lovely daughter my age, who resembles Raydene to a remarkable degree. She is also one very smart lady.

Talk about your missed opportunities, since she and I are unrelated by blood.

Water over the dam.

The daughter, in turn had another daughter, who can only be described as beautiful, with her first husband.

That side of The Family is doing just fine.

DEPARTMENT OF THE ARMY
HEADQUARTERS UNITED STATES ARMY PERSONNEL CENTER
OAKLAND CALIFORNIA 94626

SPECIAL ORDERS

14 NOVEMBER 1967

NUMBER 318
EXTRACT
58. TC 999 FOL RSG DIR. TDN. 2182010 P1442
599999, 218204413 p1444 599999, cic 281A0100.
TBMAA.
REL FR ASG-USA OS:
REPL STA 6020-01 THIS STA. ASG TO-USARV TRANSIENT
DET APO SF 96307 FOR FURTHER ASG TO ORG/UNIT INDIC.
WP-OA 15 NOV 67 DESTINATION DSG- VIETNAM. AMD-SUU-HOA-
3PU-AZ. PCS/MDC/- CA TVL DATA- TO OAB WILL
FURN NEC MTA & TRANS TO TAFB
CALIF FOR TRIP NR CKA B239/15/319 ETD TAFB
CALIF 1600 HRS 15 NOV 67 FISCAL DATA- PER DIEM
AUTH UP PART f CHAPTER 4 JTR. ECSDA- 18 NOV 67.
SP. INSTR- INDIV WILL ARR VIETNAM WEARING
KHAKI TROUSERS AND SHORT SLEEVE SHIRT & WILL HAVE
IN POSSESSION BASI REQ SUMMER UNIF WORK UNIF &
CBT BOOTS. BAG ALW SIXTY-SIX /66/LBS ONE
HUNDRED THIRTY-FOUR /134/ LBS EXC BAG
AUTH.

199 INF BDE HHC FBDA APO SF 96279
ROGET, CHARLES C O-5249215 2LT IN 74512 NOV
1687 J 13A02 10
2500 VN TRANS DET O OBRC APO SF 96307
RICHARDS, JOHN C O-5542684 CPT MC 03100Y NOV
1486 J 13A01 27
And 28 other men.

26.

The Oakland Army Depot was a place that housed troops for one to four days while they were processed for overseas duty throughout the Pacific. There was a huge open space within its walls. I'm not sure how big the actual building was because I couldn't see all the walls in the indoor darkness, outside the bright pools of light cast by ancient overhead bulbs.

The Depot had been subdivided into more manageable areas marked by three-digit numbers and wire-caging walls into supply rooms, dispensaries, immunization stations for missed-but-required shots and malaria preventive pills (in case they'd been missed before), mess halls, bunk-bed barracks areas for the lowest four enlisted grades, military police desks, personnel records offices, and at least one chaplain's section with a chapel.

For all I know, it could have been a thousand feet square. Or more.

I could see that one long side of the building opened onto deep-water piers, holdovers from the pre-jet, pre-limited-war days, when men were moved to the Pacific *en masse* by surface ships.

All replacements for Vietnam went through this system from point A (arrival) to point B (aboard an airliner bound for the Western Pacific) (WESPAC) via Honolulu, Guam, and the Philippines.

I found out during the next year that troops arriving back from Vietnam went through the same Depot from point B to point A, departing for their next duty stations with new orders, or, for the time-expired, through a separation center with a discharge, carrying a forced issue of all earned decorations.

At no point did returning traffic cross or mix with outgoing troops.

* * *

The buses to Travis Air Force Base (AFB) left at 1030 AM.

We were assembled at the Depot building in khakis, with a single small carry-on ditty-bag apiece, most weighing much less than the 66 pounds cabin luggage authorized for the 25-hour flight ahead. Our hold baggage was weighed to be sure it met the 134-pound weight limit. We loaded our duffel bags into the compartment under the bus, much as we would have on the Greyhound back home.

We were then driven to Travis, up Interstate 5 from San Francisco. There was an unreal feeling about it, and strangeness not just due to this being California, nor the scenery new to me, nor even to it not being Missouri. It was as if these sights would have to last, *because it would be a long time until we saw anything like them again.*

* * *

We were dismounted, checked off a list by rank, and marched single-file through a large staging terminal building, and then straight *out* again, through huge open doors in the opposite side, under an overcast Northern California winter sky, to board a blue-and-white PanAm Boeing 707. Before getting aboard we were briefed by the plane's First Officer who advised us that we'd be refueling at Honolulu, Guam, and at Clark AFB in the Philippines before landing at Bien Hoa, Vietnam (No long-range non-stop jumbo jets, yet). The stops would be long enough for us to disembark the aircraft and stretch our legs, but we'd not be allowed to leave the departure lounge areas.

An Air Force ground crew transferred our luggage to the plane's cargo hold as the briefing was in progress.

Takeoff was at one P.M.

Six and a half hours later, it had gotten dark, and we landed in Honolulu, another first-time visit for me, in the early evening if November 16th. This was still the U.S., and I don't recall much being obviously different except the sight of lighted palm trees around the terminal building.

The plane's cargo was loud, boisterous, and laughed too much, and too loudly. Some of it was a little or a lot drunk. The humor was sort of reminiscent of whistling as one walks past a graveyard at midnight.

The men even sang, to the tune of "Camptown Races:"

"*You're* coming home in a body bag,
Doo-dah, doo-dah;
You're coming home in a body bag,
Ooooh, do dah day."

With apologies to the memory of Stephen Foster.

The next leg of the flight seemed to be the longest of the three. Compared with Hawaii, though, Guam's darkness was a different story. It was still dark, since we were sort of chasing the night around the world, just above the equator.

Unlike Honolulu, the field on Guam was an air base at war.

The heavy-laden B-52s never stopped taking off, nor did the empty ones stop landing.

Our transport plane was just one more jet out of dozens, landing, filling up with JP-4 and us, and taking off again. *We* were *its* bomb load, I thought.

Throughout the flight, the cabin crew was uncommonly kind to all of us, even the passengers who promptly got drunk and stayed that way as far as the Philippines, 1000 miles short of Vietnam. I later read that the planes were leased to the government for the amount of the airline's expenses plus one dollar per flight. The solicitous treatment, then, certainly wasn't motivated by the profit motive.

Clark Field, north of Manila, *smelled* funny. It was a combination of 99% humidity, turned earth, shit, and jet fuel fumes. No odor I've ever smelled in Europe or North America matches it, exactly.

Approaching Vietnam from the east at midnight local time, even at 20,000 feet or so, you could see tracer fire first at one place, then another, along the shoreline and further inland.

Then we rapidly lost altitude approaching Bien Hoa, dipping more steeply than a normal civilian flight, then flaring onto the end of the runway, rather than just touching down.

Once we'd rolled to a stop, the stewardesses sprayed insecticide throughout the cabin before opening the passenger doors. The pilot came on the PA speaker, thanked us for flying with him, and said, matter-of-factly, that he'd be seeing us in 365 days.

We walked down a metal stair (this was before jetways) and were on the ground in Vietnam. We had also stepped straight into the middle of what was later determined to have been the most active year of the war, with more men involved, more casualties, and more fighting than in any year before or after, until the Americans left in 1973.

The smell was vaguely similar to the one in the Philippines, and the one in Mexico, with the addition of insecticide, probably sprayed on and around the field to control mosquitoes. So, it smelled of what we later learned was called smit; smoke, shit, mud, water vapor, and malathion bug spray, all intermingled, inseparably.

27.

17 Nov 1967

I recall having multiple impressions, visual, auditory and olfactory, surrounding my arrival on the flight line at Bien Hoa Air Force Base, at 1 A.M. local time.

The terminal was big, and had a high, arched ceiling. It was made of rough wood on a concrete slab, and smelled of soap and raw lumber, giving an impression of temporariness. During the three-hour wait for transportation, you could watch the dimly-lit (evidently) candle- or oil-lamp lit absolutely *foreign*-looking hovels lined up along the Vietnamese Air Force (VNAF) side of the field. The backsacatter from the streetlights showed shacks made of what looked like unpainted boards with sloped lean-to roofs of the omnipresent corrugated galvanized-iron sheeting. The walls were made of tin sheets imprinted with American beer-can labels. I later found that these panels of tin had been rejected by the brewing companies, and sold cheaply on whatever market would buy them.

I remember having a long talk in the dark with a faceless Air Force SFC, over the background roars and spooling-up and -down of jet engines. He told me that the government of Vietnam didn't take any responsibility for looking after the families of its servicemen. I found out in graduate school many years later that the French in 1914 had done the same thing, i.e. made the same mistake, during the first year of the Great War. It had the effect of lowering morale of the soldiers and airmen who had left their relatives behind, in both cases.

People never learn.

We were wearing new, or at least minimally-wrinkled khakis. Across the terminal, there was a single file of thin, darkly-tanned men wearing grungy, fold-wrinkled khakis with shiny new decorations pinned to them. They were waiting to load onto our plane, and ride it home.

One of them was wearing Medical Corps collar insignia, a Silver Star ribbon, and the Combat Medical Badge. I broke away from our huddled mob and walked over to him, a distance of perhaps sixty feet. He watched me approach, saying nothing. I found that when I got there, I had so many questions that when I tried to talk, I made no sense. He put his hands on my shoulders and shook me gently two or three times.

"Relax!" he said. "It isn't going to be nearly as bad as you're afraid it will be."

I mumbled a heartfelt "Thanks," and rejoined my group, which was forming up to be counted off by bus-loads.

* * *

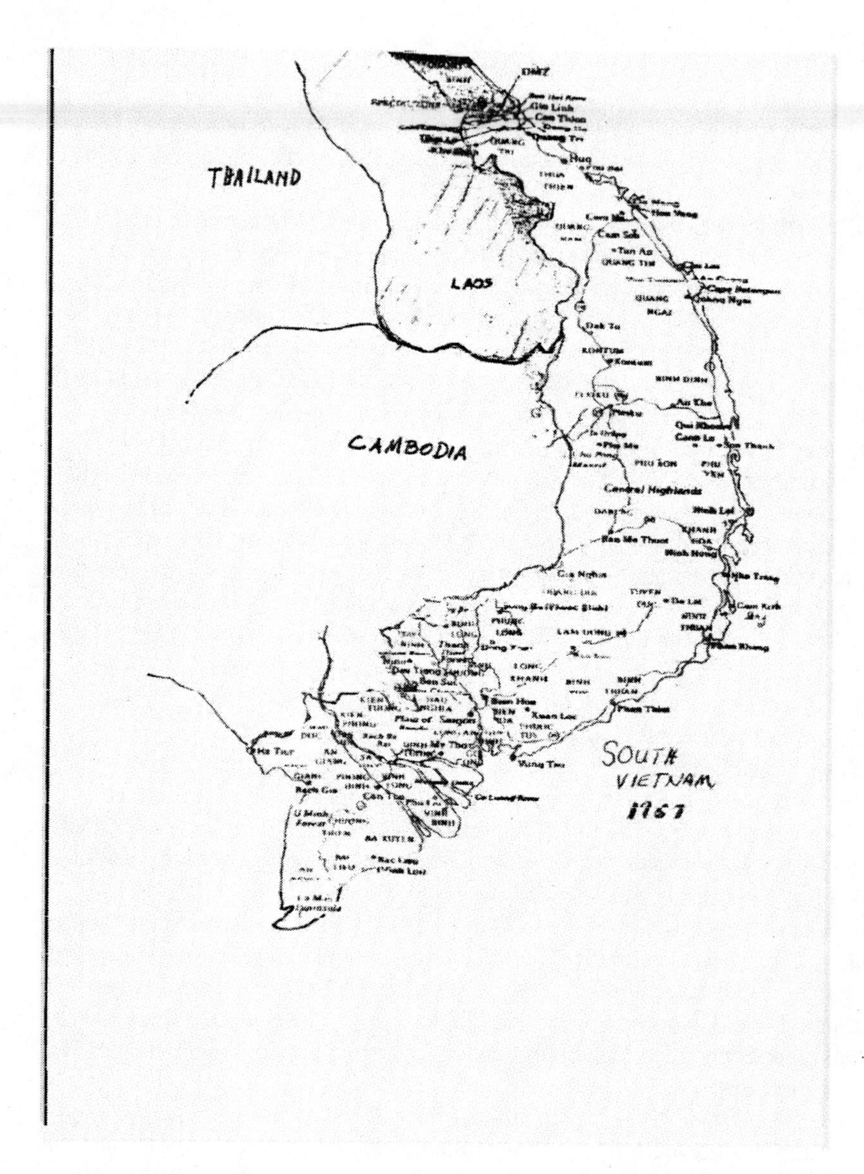

Southeastern Indochina, 1967

We were driven, subdued, through the night and the deserted streets of its curfew, skirting Saigon from north to east, through Bien Hoa town proper, to

Long Binh Junction, inevitably shortened to "Camp LBJ." Our olive-drab busses

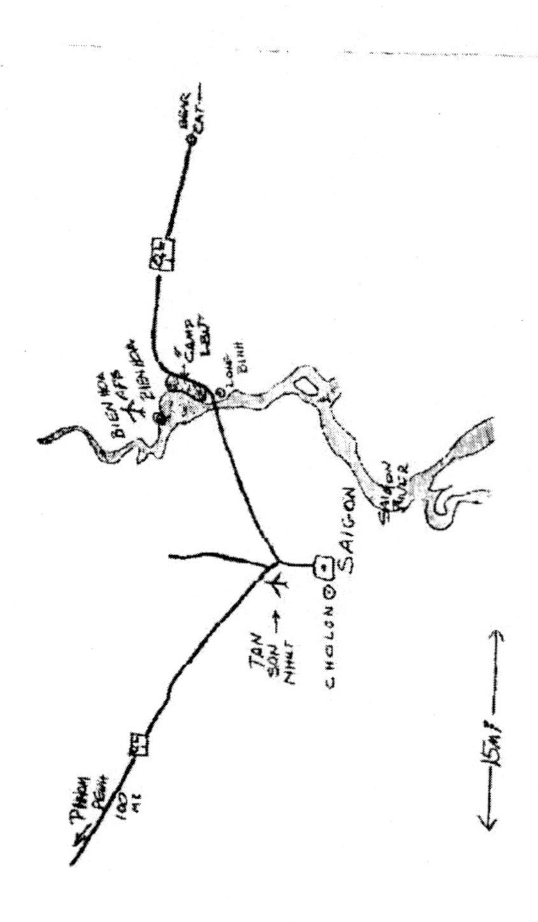

were fitted with grenade screen covering all the open windows. There was no air conditioning. We were all quiet and inwardly scared, faced as we were with the reality of being foreigners and fair game in a country at war with itself.

I had to keep reminding myself that I was an active reservist, and that I'd *asked* for this.

It took about forty minutes for the buses to get to the 90th Replacement Battalion.

There was a subtle difference about these replacements that I couldn't define until several months later: Talking to them at random, they were almost all recent high-school graduates, had never been steadily employed, were nearly all single, and most had lived in their parents' homes until they had been called up. Most of them, too, were just short of 19 years old.

By contrast, my father's generation of soldiers and Marines averaged 27 years of age upon reporting in for initial training. They came into the Service with a wide range of employment experience (Alf was often used as a carpenter, Kenny was a master electrician. Even Dad, because he held a civilian chauffeurs' license was assigned as a full-time driver) in addition to their principal combat duties. And the reservists with whom I'd been serving for the past 13 years *all* had (honest, mostly) jobs outside, thus bringing along every imaginable skill from auto mechanic to dispensing optician to chiropractor, to their rifle companies or artillery batteries where there were no slots for those skills. Nonetheless, it was amazing how often that, like Mighty Mouse, here they came to save the day, with those same unauthorized civilian skills.

The lack of that diversity was to cost the country dearly, but it wasn't suspected at the time.

* * *

On arrival at LBJ we were unloaded and herded into a classroom of about two bus-loads' capacity, where we were welcomed to Vietnam, and given short list of dos and don'ts to follow till we got to our units.

First and foremost, the advice went, was that no matter what we'd been told or even promised Stateside, *this* headquarters had the authority to cancel stateside orders and send us wherever it deemed we were most needed at the time. Second, in a few minutes we'd be asked to turn in all our U.S. money in exchange for Military Payment Certificates (MPC) to be used in cash dealings within the Army. It was a court-martial offense to be caught with green dollars after this time. These would have to be further exchanged for Vietnamese piasters (worth 118 P to the dollar) from an army source, in order to have any dealings in the Vietnamese civilian sector. The Vietnamese would not be able to trade MPC to or from anyone. These measures were quite rightly designed to stabilize the Republic of Vietnam (RVN)'s economy, its currency value, and to control inflation.

Then came the issuing of our foldout in-country ration cards, with spaces to punch them for each item. We were limited to a case of beer 60 times in the next year, 48 bottles of hard liquor, 100 cartons of cigarettes, ten minor appliances and five major appliances, to discourage any more than a little black-marketeering. Oddly enough, there was no limitation (no doubt an oversight) on the plentiful PX supply of gold or pearl jewelry, which could then have theoretically been sold on the black market for a huge amount of piasters. Damn. *Why* didn't I think of that at the time?

We were then issued five suits of tropical-weight green jungle fatigues, a few basic items of web equipment and a canteen each. Then we were herded to our quarters, which deserve some description because of their universality throughout the Republic of Vietnam.

At the time, they seemed pretty primitive to us, less than 36 hours away from the United States. There were signs advising occupants to roll under their beds and to pull heavy items, such as their mattresses over them, in the event of incoming mortar or small arms fire.

Another shock to our peaceful, civilized backgrounds.

What I call the "Hut, Tropical, Mark I" deserves some detailed description.

The floor was a 22-by-36-foot concrete slab.

The huts were made of raw, rough lumber and had corrugated galvanized sheet-iron roofs. They were boxed in hip-high with one-by-ten pine boards, and then screened up to the eaves, to allow any breeze to blow through for cooling. The screening was overlaid with the eaves at the top, having a twenty-inch overlap. The lower parts of the huge screens were covered by down-slanted jalousie-style one-by-sixes to turn away rain, even the monsoon, but still allow free air circulation. There was a single lengthwise line of four overhead light bulbs hanging at what would have been the level of a ceiling, if there had *been* a ceiling.

These structures had been built by either Pacific Architects and Engineers, or by the Bechtel Corporation as contractors, using native labor (They were pretty stoutly built. I hope the North Vietnamese Army (NVA) finds them comfortable). No interior finishing was needed, so there was none.

Showers and latrines were in similar buildings nearby, posted with signs warning us that the running water was not potable, in no case to drink it, and to use water from our canteens to brush our teeth.

Bare-bones as they were, from my point of view they would soon be a luxury to be fondly remembered.

Being jet-lagged, we were ordered to get some sleep, since we'd soon be levied to our units. We did so, and turned in at about 6 AM to the strains of Johnny Cash's album "*Ride This Train*" over the PA system. Two hours later I was awakened with the cheery news that I had 45 minutes to be ready to report to the Surgeon of the U.S. Army, Vietnam (USARV). I headed for our latrine to clean up and change to the proper uniform.

28.

Forty-five minutes later I was waiting at the orderly room for my ride to USARV Headquarters. I was royally jet-lagged; even shaved and washed up, my eyes looked (and certainly *felt*) like two piss-holes in the snow.

I found out later that, unlike other soldiers, all physicians came into Vietnam through Long Binh, specifically so that the USARV Surgeon *could* allocate them country-wide on an as-needed basis. Officers and men of other branches of the Army could, and did, come in through Pleiku, Cam Ranh, or Da Nang as well as LBJ.

A jeep pulled up, and off I went through the cool of my first morning in Vietnam. It was the first of many visually beautiful experiences in that country. The trees that shaded the hamlets resembled the ones you can see in Chinese paintings hundreds of years old. They even seemed to bend in one direction, suggesting a wind that didn't blow. The brilliant greens, blacks, long shadows cast by trees and huts and gold reflections off the ponds and paddies were so striking that they are still fresh in my mind. I can see them clearly now, thirty-three years later, and they'll be part of me until I die.

We drove over two-lane blacktop roads, proceeding a little south of west, unescorted, through tiny crossroads hamlets and open rural stretches of road with a Viet Cong (VC) behind every bush, I had no doubt, about to shoot us up, if not about to pull a neck-high wire across the road, and decapitate the driver and me. I was advised subsequently that this close to the Capital may have been the only area in the country that was secure day and night. There had been no danger.

Francis W. Benjamin was a full colonel, Medical Service Corps (MSC). I never did find out if he *was* the USARV surgeon or just the officer in charge of Medical Corps replacements. I say that because, for the most part, a theater surgeon's functions are administrative, and could easily *be* done by an MSC (remember, I *was* one for six years). The assignment of a physician, though traditional, was a waste of patient-care expertise. COL Franklin met me politely, and strongly suggested I volunteer for the First Brigade of the 101st Airborne Division (the other two brigades were still at Ft. Campbell, Kentucky), now in-country 2 ½ years, with its Regular Army cadre, less a few casualties, intact. In retrospect, I wonder if he was considering my military experience and schooling against an upcoming command vacancy in six months within the First Brigade? If he was, he didn't mention either.

I volunteered forthwith, and his driver took me back to the 90th Replacement Battalion to pack and wait for a flight north to the Brigade's base camp at Phan Rang, in southern II Corps.

My jet-lag must have been pretty severe at the time; *memory* tells me that the terrain of LBJ itself was hilly, but review of photos taken at the time shows low, rolling bare ground.

One plane was going up the next morning, and I was scheduled and manifested to be on it.

I used the time till departure to catch up on sleep.

* * *

Several truckloads of replacements were hauled to the airfield, to a waiting C-130. My previous five Air Force flights had been at jump school. They had been very short, not at all crowded, with four longitudinal rows of nylon-web seating. Each hop had consisted of takeoff, level-off, and jump. I hadn't even experienced one landing in the airplane. This flight would be very different.

The plane was crammed full of troops. There were no seats, just an empty cargo bay with 2 ½-inch web strapping running from side to side across the cargo bay, stretched about 2 feet high off the floor plates, about 3 feet apart from front to rear. The passengers sat on the bare deck surrounded by their duffels and other gear, steadying themselves by holding the strapping material. This was, the pilot called it, a "combat loaded" configuration. The plane's cabin soon reeked of sweaty new clothes, from yesterday's issue.

Older heads had warned me to beware of Air Force-induced airsickness, but I have never had a smoother flight. It was noisier than a commercial plane, but tolerable. Of course, just like the landing at Bien Hoa, we expected to land in the face of heavy fire across the runway, with mortar shells dropping around us, at the very least.

As the ramp dropped, my first sight was of a half-asleep road- grader driver, sitting bare to the waist, waiting for us to pass so
that he could drive his machine across the runway. It was a beautiful day, with only a few clouds in a bluer-than-stateside-blue sky. Once our four turboprop engines stopped, it was very quiet.

In about thirty minutes, trucks arrived to take us to the Phan Rang Army base camp.

2d Squadron, 17th Cavalry with borrowed M113 APCs

* * *

29.

18 November 1967

The First Brigade of the 101st Airborne Division should have had a platoon-sized replacement section, since a whole division only rates a full company. Still, we reported to the whole Replacement Company, which was in Vietnam as all of this division's one-of-a-kind assets. This was probably necessary because a peacetime or stateside division doesn't *need* a replacement company, any more than it needs enough military police (MPs) to man a 500-prisoner POW cage. Secondly, the First Brigade needed the capacity; it had, not the usual three infantry battalions, but four, a five-battery artillery element and a support battalion, for a total of 6500 men.

If 1/365th of them rotated out on any one day(and on average, they did), then that same number had to come in as replacements.

In a typically efficient Army maneuver, just as was done at Oakland, the Replacement Company was also used for temporary housing for those men leaving for home in a day or two, so that the traffic went both ways.

Interestingly enough, though, *this* mixture of veterans and newbies was, intentional or not, the first part of our on-the-job training for Vietnam duty. Unlike the traffic lines in Oakland, we were not kept apart. We buttonholed the veterans, asked them about whatever concerns we had (like living through the next 12 months). And they answered. Their information was brief, to the point, and solid. The principal Viet Cong (VC) in this area, they said, were in small, lightly armed units, who seldom bothered or annoyed the Americans, lest we respond by deploying a larger force in the area, or worse, that the South Korean (ROK) troops also in the area might do the same. The ROKs were known for their fearlessness, and were absolutely ruthless in suppressing the VC. And if they accidentally shot an innocent bystander or two, unlike the American army, they didn't let it bother them.

"Keep alert," the cadre said, "and stay alive."

* * *

We replacements took the next day in Personnel, to go over our paperwork, medical forms, the inevitable shots-if-needed, and issue of all field equipment except weapons. In short, final in-processing. . This was the end-point of all the quartermaster, medical and personnel services the Army offered. We were at the end of the line. There was no level left, below this one, to do any of it.

It was up to us, individually, now, to become part of the unit, and to survive the next twelve months.

PRISONERS

The captain who gave us our initial briefing told us that the First Brigade was GEN Westmoreland's reaction force for the whole country. That meant it was sent here and there on short notice, as conditions demanded, taking advantage of its ultra-light makeup and organization and its air-mobility. It also boasted a kill ratio of enemy to friendlies of ten-and-a half to one, to be confirmed by touching an enemy corpse, and *only* by that method. The point was this: plan to be moving often with no real base.

Another caveat was pointed out: in 2 ½ years we had only one man missing in action, and we were still looking for *him*, even posting a reward for him, if found alive. No one was to be left behind, or unaccounted for, wounded or dead. Not ever. I was relieved to hear *that*, at least.

And also, as mentioned before, we were admonished not even to bother estimating enemy casualties. You were either standing over his body, or you couldn't count him.

Among the many Brigade Standing Operating Procedures (SOPs) applicable to all personnel, at all times were the following caveats:

- The mosquitoes bite at night. So we roll our sleeves down and start using insect repellent half an hour before sunset and continue the behavior until half an hour after sunrise. There is no proof that the V.C. can smell insect repellent.
- Take your chloroquine-primaquine tablet every Monday, and your Dapsone tablet every day.
- Push salt tablets and water *before* you get heat exhaustion, not during its onset. You can't abort an attack, once it begins.
- Don't drink from native water sources, nor use native ice.
- Re: native foods, if you don't boil it or peel it, forget it.
- When on patrol, avoid trails and roads; they will certainly be booby-trapped at best, and be a prepared ambush site at worst.

* * *

The third day, as in-processing ended, I was advised I'd be assigned to the Second Battalion of the 502d Infantry (abbreviated 2/502), which had, like the rest of the First Brigade, been in-country two and a half years. Many of the officers and men serving in the more senior or middle ranks had been in their units, or at least Vietnam the whole time, especially the unmarried men among them. Their sentiment was that they had all served together at Ft. Campbell before the war, that they were professional soldiers, that soldiers fight wars, and that if the war was here, then *here* was where they belonged.

They got a thirty-day leave in the United States between 12-month tours. They could re-enlist for their old jobs, or for a new one, either in their old or in new units, anywhere in Vietnam.

They were, oddly enough, not the only ones who stayed past their year's tour.

A lot of foot-soldier privates for example, though not Regulars, would re-enlist as helicopter door gunners. That occupation was probably equally as dangerous as being assigned as the riflemen that they had been, but they would live on an airbase under better conditions, and that assignment usually promoted them one grade, plus which they'd draw added flight pay to the higher salary received due to the promotion. That nearly doubled a private's pay. And it sure as hell beat Stateside service as a Private, E-2.

Other ratings that were popular as in-country re-enlistment options were supply clerk and military police patrolman.

* * *

Early on the third day we began in-country training, which would take either nine or ten days depending on the weather. It was hot, but the dry winter was approaching, and rainfall was unpredictable more than a couple of days in advance (no satellite communications yet, remember). Classwork was held in bleachers, under a 50-foot cargo parachute canopy to keep the sun off, and let breezes through.

Training films and recreational movies were held at night in an outdoor bench-seated theater.

We were further taught how to call in air strikes, adjust artillery and mortar fire (thanks again, Artillery OCS), and how to radio for aeromedical evacuation, using live ammunition and real helicopters. We also learned to throw live grenades, and how to use explosives to clear away trees for landing zones, or to blow houses, forts, and anything else to smithereens with C-4 plastic explosive or blocks of TNT. We learned how to move silently at night, and to rappel down a sheer sixty-foot-high face. On the next-to-last night, we learned to fire enemy weapons and at the same time to recognize them by their distinctive sounds. The overwhelming "COUGH!" of an American Claymore mine is truly unforgettable. Finally, we were taken out on a night patrol inside the base, but were by no means isolated from infiltrating VC recon patrols. At briefing, we were told that if anyone shot at us, to shoot back.

With exertion, it was *hot.* And I had never handled heat well.

There were twelve men, officer replacements who came into the First Brigade with me. Four were to be killed, four more wounded severely enough to be sent home immediately, and the four left, myself included, emerged in one piece twelve months later, having at worst sustained minor injuries during the year-long tour of duty. The one officer *best*-trained to survive in this environment, Ranger First Lieutenant David Myers, was the first one to be killed, three weeks into our first operation. Only an artillery captain and I were destined to be unharmed throughout the twelve-month tour.

During the eighth day of in-country orientation, the rest of the Brigade, which had been operating in the northern part of the central coast near Duc Pho, returned by ship to the base camp at Phan Rang. The first sign I saw of their re-deployment was my being awakened in the officers' hut at 2300 by a Medical Corps major whom I didn't know. He introduced himself as Stan Raible, the brigade surgeon, and advised me that the MD I'd be replacing would be along the next evening to fill me in on the unit in which I'd be serving. He was due to rotate home in three weeks. As it turned out, I never saw MAJ Raible again. He, too, was due to leave soon, his year in Vietnam nearly over.

Most of the replacements couldn't wait to get to a MARS (Military Audio Relay System) station, get on the phone, and make calls to their homes in the United States. It was a multi-step, cumbersome project that could take half a day to complete, because it involved patching a phone at the Vietnam end through the Army's radio relay system, to a volunteer civilian amateur short-wave operator in the States, then to *another* ham operator located in the area code of the recipient (who had to be present to answer the phone), who again patched into the local telephone system at home. And the caller and call-ee had to use radio procedure, saying "over" at the end of their sentences. This allowed for the several-second delay inherent in a system with that many patches, relays, and the speed of light all functioning serially in it.

When it worked.

I never used the system.

Perhaps selfishly, I thought that I could handle the loneliness and the isolation if I knew that they were irrevocable, with no halfway measures at contacting home. And probably, that the same held true for Joan.

So, for a year, daily letters would have to suffice, sometimes written, and sometimes recorded on reel-to-reel (no cassettes yet) audio tape.

30.

"Doc Harry" Kohl, a budding neurosurgeon, came by on schedule. He briefed me on the duties of a battalion surgeon (formally called "Medical Platoon Leader"), and promised to return in three days, when my in-country orientation was finished. He also said that he'd bring a vehicle to carry my gear down to the battalion.

Sure enough, that morning, three days later, he brought one of his two frontline ¼-ton ambulances (FLA) by; I threw my bags in back, and we departed for Headquarters and Headquarters Company (HHC), Second Battalion, 502d Infantry, Airborne, (abbreviated 2/502 Inf (ABN)). I met the company commander, 1LT Mike Keane, who much later would become a three-star general, and the battalion sergeant-major who asked me to let him know when I wanted my R&R (already!), and he'd set it up. I was shown to my aid station, where I'd be expected to sleep. My impression was that they couldn't do enough for me.

They took good care of their doctors at battalion level. That was most assuredly *not* the case the further one got from the actual fighting line, as I would learn some months in the future.

I was told by the Headquarters Company First Sergeant that my platoon was 28 men strong, and that it now was up to full strength.

"At last count," he told me "it's the most decorated platoon in Vietnam."

He advised me that ten of the 28 platoon members were black. It had six Latins, one Algerian Arab (!) and eleven whites, if you counted the two officers.

As one of my senior aidmen, Sp4 Ralston, walked me to my quarters, I was shocked to see piles of equipment, including live grenades, loose explosives, dirty belts and clips of live ammunition, and clothing, *lying in ranks* in the company street, where they'd been dropped and discarded *on orders.*

I waas shocked. In my previous (peacetime) service, every cartridge was counted and accounted *for.*

The uniforms were too worn and torn to be laundered. A detail would pick this stuff up later, recycle what they could, and burn the rest as trash.

* * *

A medical platoon leader has a fine line to walk. He provides a direct personal service to the battalion's personnel. He answers to a brigade surgeon in professional medical matters. He also leads a platoon of twenty-eight medics with the help of a Medical Field Operations assistant (MOS 67H), a lieutenant, MSC, just as I had been three months before. His immediate *command* superior is the battalion commander.

My progression along this line may be a unique phenomenon; it was almost surely a speed record, from MSC lieutenant in a peacetime artillery battalion to captain, Medical Corps, in combat, in 61 days.

* * *

On the theory that underwear was just another layer of cloth to foul a bullet wound, and that it would be cooler without it, like many of the men, I stopped wearing it.

* * *

Sanitation was somewhat challenging in a Third-World country. The water table is so high in most of Indochina that conventional latrine digging would have (even further) contaminated it. Country-wide, when we could tap into existing drains and sewerage, we did, in the rear areas. Outside the cities, we used burn-out latrines for solid human excreta, and piss tubes that fed into buried soakage pits. Both had to be screened, and located fifty yards, minimum, from any food preparation area. Pacing it off was one of my jobs.

The burn-outs were oil drums cut in half along the short axis. These were grabbed with a 3-foot iron rod with a handle bent into one end, and a hook into the other. The hook was used to drag them away from the screened latrine buildings to a distance of fifteen or twenty feet. There, two parts kerosene or a diesel-kerosene mix was added to one part feces, and the two were mixed with the hook. Then, the resulting mix was lighted and allowed to burn away. The process took two hours.

* * *

20 November 1955

All my National Guard service had been in segregated units. Then, the order came down: Integrate and like it. *I was a corporal-armorer then, checking weapons in and out, and inspecting them to be sure they'd been cleaned. The first two black guys came in, a private and a PFC. They were visibly uncomfortable, surrounded by 198 white men. I issued them rifles, and two hours later, they turned them in, spotless. I grinned, told them "Good job," and stowed their weapons away.*

I felt lighter on my feet, as if I'd lost 20 pounds.

* * *

November 20, 1970

What can I say about race and its problems in the Vietnam-era Army? One certain thing is that the closer you get to the shooting, the less it matters. Most of the race-based problems that were reported in the States originating in the Army in Vietnam had their origin in rear areas where men had time to think about things other than survival.

I was brought up in a former slave state, in a segregated educational and recreational system, both of which, however, did their damnedest to be separate *but equal.*

When I was growing up, the term "nigger" was used freely in my home. When I see a black person, it's *still* the noun that pops into my mind first. I know that it's wrong, but childhood imprinting is permanent.

Don't believe me? Then, try *not* thinking of a zebra.

You did, didn't you?

* * *

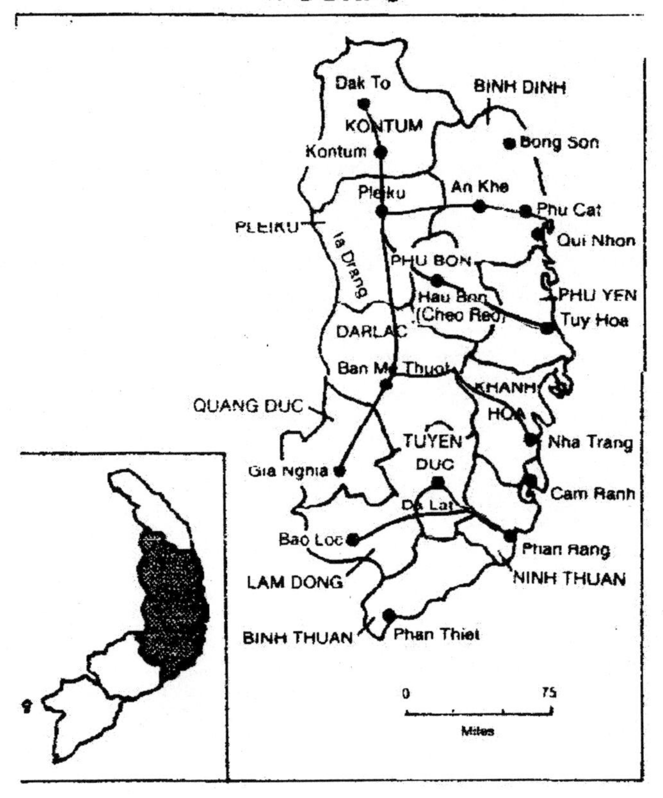

II CORPS AREA

25 November 1967

The Medical Platoon Leader was supposed to be armed with a 45-caliber Colt M1911A1 automatic pistol, but I asked the supply sergeant if he had a rifle to spare, because I felt more secure carrying something I could hit a target with at more than fifteen yards. He was surprised, but was happy to comply. What the hell, anyway. I'd been carrying a rifle since 1954, and even now don't feel like a real soldier without one.

Also, with a rifle, at a distance you look like any other soldier, and are less likely to draw fire.

The aid station and all the other buildings at Phan Rang Base Camp were built to the same specifications as the huts at LBJ, though this one was knee-to-shoulder-high partitioned and caged inside for patient privacy and for security of the medical platoon's equipment. I settled in, expecting to be coming in and out of it for the next twelve months.

After this week, I'd never see it again.

Again, things change. Life is uncertain. Eat dessert first.

31.

At this point in my part-tourist, part-soldier life, something happened to me that I can't explain. I realized that, intentionally or not, assignment to this unit, surrounded by a hard core of dedicated and experienced professionals had, in a sense, made me one of them, though a very junior member, at best. Their behavior and logic *became mine* almost overnight.

I still believe that no newly-organized unit like the 9th Division, the Americal, or the 3d Marine Division could have matched that degree of unit solidarity with an officer that new and that junior.

Only a month later did I realize that while I would be going in harm's way some of the time, I doubt I could have had better life insurance than being surrounded by 800 paratroopers, led by the cadre I've described in the last chapter.

The next day, Thanksgiving Eve, I received a call from our Brigade's Supply and Transportation Quartermaster (QM) Company to come and certify a body dead, and write it up. I was the newest medical officer and had the fewest duties, so I had drawn the short straw.

I walked the quarter-mile to S & T.

When I arrived at the company, the section sergeant of two-man attached Graves Registration (GR) Section showed me to the mortuary, a building like all the rest, where the deceased was lying on a litter.

He was a major, just a little overweight, with a single bullet wound to the left chest. He'd started to gray around the temples, and I estimated his age at forty-two. He was brought in by the MPs alone, had no wallet, dog tags, or ID card. He wasn't in the Brigade, and no one in the Graves Registration section knew anything else about him. He was wearing Stateside fatigues, a Military Assistance Command, Vietnam (MACV) patch and a sew-on name tag. My guess was that he had been an advisor to the ARVN, and had, after being wounded, been stripped of anything of military or monetary value. Since there was no other information to put on his death certificate (a GI form just like Missouri's), I signed the summary, asked the GR team to fingerprint the body as soon as possible for a double-check on his identification, and left, depressed, wondering when his wife and family would be told, and how they would take the news of his death. At his age, he must, surely, have at least talked about the possibility with his wife, if he had one (as expected, no wedding ring). Had he written The Letter that we all had, sealed and stored in the very bottom of our gear, to be found and mailed home if we were killed?

That way lay madness; better to consciously think about something else.

* * *

Thanksgiving dinner was luxurious for a war zone. It consisted of the usual turkey, ham, mashed potatoes, bread dressing, gravy, cranberry sauce, soft rolls, mixed nuts, and three kinds of pie with ice cream. When the Army could make things more tolerable, it spared no effort to do so. They'd recently opened a second dairy-processing plant in Vietnam, so whole milk and more ice cream had become available.

* * *

The Pacific PX-BX System had a bus/store which followed troop movements from base to base, catching up with the Brigade Rear on the third or fourth day after the departure of the main body of troops. The vehicle traveled in whatever convoys it could join that might be going its way. It was showing some signs of two-and-a-half years' wear and tear, exterior dents and scratches, hesitant engine start-up, and a visible blue exhaust. Its small interior space made it possible for it to stock only small items like razor blades and shoe polish, Brasso, Coca-Cola, nail clippers, and limited amounts of cold beer and soft drinks. You would enter the bus at the front, and move through it in single file front-to-rear, shopping from the shelves along both sides as you went. Check-out was at the rear exit door.

The Air Force Exchange on the Phan Rang Base was another story, however. It was air-conditioned and could have been transplanted as it stood from any small air base in the United States. It stocked or could get about anything a soldier or his Vietnamese girlfriend could reasonably want.

I bought a Canon 35-mm automatic-focus-automatic-f-stop camera and a Seiko self-winding watch, for ridiculously low prices. Neither was then sold in the States.

The Brigade officers gave a party featuring a Filipino rock band and a three-girl Filipina vocal group who had learned American popular songs phonetically. I think of it as a *pseudo*-USO show, because in the outlying (or forward) areas where I was, I never saw the genuine article. It had, as most parties did, a Hail-and-Farewell motif, for those coming into the brigade, and those going out, respectively. As a whole, it was pretty tame.

Two nights later, a smaller, more intimate group, of the 2/502's officers met for the same purpose. I was formally introduced by the battalion operations officer (another future three-star general) with a chorus of: "Let's hear it for the new doc! Hi, there, asshole! Say hello to the new asshole: Hi, there, doc!"

And I was *in.*

It was an evening not memorable for its restraint, in sharp contrast to the Brigade affair. The first and last toasts of the evening were identical: "To Joe Tentpeg. Hip, hip HOORAY!" Joe was (and still is) the typical private or PFC that makes American infantry a force to be reckoned with; we all knew that without him, we counted for very little. And we never forgot it.

The following morning we were alerted to move within 72 hours. We weren't told till the last few hours before takeoff where we'd be going.

Then, at a special evening formation after chow, the base went into lockdown. This was a sure sign that something was up, but to the VC intelligence officers outside, it was uncertain just what.

If it was an upcoming move (and it was), they had no way of knowing our destination. Then, and only then, we were told that we were going to be based out of Bao Lac, a quiet area in the Central Highlands. The nearest town of any size was Dalat.

There were a few small bands of VC making nuisances of themselves in that province. We were going there to hunt them down or drive them away.

Each of us was assigned to a "chalk," which was a number written (usually *in* chalk) on both sides of an airplane's nose. When we would arrive at the airfield at dawn the next day, we'd thus know just where to go, and expedite the loading.

The whole Brigade then went to their billets and packed for a trip of indefinite duration, which, the veteran troops told us, could be as little as two weeks or, though less likely, as much as twelve months.

At 9PM I heard a faint gunshot. Then a sergeant came in at a run, and told me to come with him. Double-timing the way back to the scene, he told me that one of the men had gotten fighting drunk and broken into the Mail Room. The CQ (another sergeant) had warned him that he was in a secured area, and to get out o it, now. The victim, evidently, wasn't in any mood to listen.

The CQ had then drawn a forty-five and shot him in the upper abdomen. He was dead when I arrived. All that I can remember thinking was: "What a waste of somebody's son or brother."

There was no other discernable motive traceable to the sergeant involved or to the deceased. The dead man was awarded a posthumous Purple Heart, and listed as "Killed In Action," or KIA. Let him be a remembered as a dead hero, and not a drunk who ran into a fatal obstacle.

* * *

32.

1 December 1967

The rank of eight clearly-numbered C-130s was waiting. The guides and passengers were well-practiced in the drill. I doubt it took more than ten minutes to load everyone aboard.

This time "combat-loaded" meant that we'd share space with vehicles and equipment already on board and strapped down by the USAF loadmasters. I found a seat at the bottom of the big under-tail ramp. We taxied to the far end of the runway. The pilot gunned the engines, standing on the brakes, then releasing them.

We almost *blasted off* rather than the expected gentle takeoff. We felt actual G-forces as we accelerated toward the upwind end of the field, and then even more as we left the ground, moving (what felt like very nearly) straight up.

The straight-and-level part of the flight to the southwest took a mere 22 minutes. You should remember that when you see a 130 taking off or landing that it is flying at a low speed, and looks fat and clumsy, almost wallowing.

They remind me, aerodynamically, of a horsefly or a bumblebee.

What you usually *don't* see is that when they get to altitude and retract their flaps and landing gear, those four jet engines can use their energy to go *forward.* They can and do move along horizontally at around 400 miles an hour. Commercial civilian turbojets only do about 525.

And at its widest point, South Vietnam is only 130 miles across, from east to west. Hence, the short ride.

The pilot banked, descended and leveled off. The plane lost altitude rapidly. When we touched down, the hard contact made such a bang that I thought we must have crashed. We hadn't. That's just the way a C-130 hits the end of a short runway. The plane stopped at the end of the 2800-foot runway, the ramp was dropped, and we unloaded. The empty planes taxied to the end of the runway, took off again, and went back to Phan Rang for another load.

Over half my platoon was farmed out in five-man sections to our four maneuver (rifle) companies. The remaining twelve of us bivouacked just off the berm of the airfield that night, while the rest of 2/502 closed from the base camp. We ate cold C-rations out of individual cans that night, and continued to do so for the next few days.

* * *

2 December 1967

The next day we were shuttled in Hueys to a bald hilltop covered with brown grass about a foot high, 15 miles from the airfield. The medical platoon took three of these reliable light jet helicopters to move to what was rapidly becoming a fire support base (FSB), or firebase, especially so once the 5-howitzer 105-mm battery was flown in as sling-loads under CH-47 Chinook medium cargo helicopters.

* * *

105mm firing batteries usually have six guns, not five. When the Brigade had been authorized a fourth infantry battalion, each of the other three batteries had had to contribute one gun, and one was found as a Corps float asset, to give the new battalion a four-gun supporting battery. This is what's meant by "taking an asset out of your own hide."

It is a typical expedient of a limited war.

* * *

The men knew their jobs better than I did, so I watched as they dug in around the perimeter, pitched small sleeping tents, and stacked filled sandbags hip-high around them. Trip wires were laid just outside the perimeter, and concertina barbed wire strung between the trip wires and the outermost perimeter fighting positions. Claymore mines festooned the wire. Machine guns were sited for the best fields of fire they could cover. All our mortars were placed at the FSB, and could *really* throw a barrage. There were eight 81mm tubes, and four more of 4.2-inch caliber.

By the second day on our bald hilltop, the rear echelon was preparing and sending hot meals to the firebase once or twice a day by helicopter. The army had been transferring "hots" from
the rear for fifty years by that time. Only for the past twenty years, however, had it been made realistic and practical by the use of the Mermite can, an insulated chest of about five gallons' capacity. It had snap locks holding the insulated, hinged, slightly inset lid in place. Its design allowed it to keep hot food hot or cold food cold for several hours. A 25-minute resupply hop presented no problem to the mess section in keeping us supplied. Part of my job was to keep an eye on the food service at both ends to forestall outbreaks of foodborne illness.

The hilltop firebase was surrounded by a tree line 250 yards away.

At dusk that first day, a family of wild Asian elephants, curious creatures that they are, walked out of the trees and looked us over. There was a bull, the biggest one, two cows, and two juveniles. Satisfied, they withdrew, though they came back several times that night and the next morning. Then, the artillery started registration fire, and scared them away for as long as we were there.

33.

4 December 1967

Here comes the most dangerous thing known to man; on officer with a map.

Robert McGowan and Jeremy Hands,
Don't Cry for Me, Sergeant-Major,
Futura, 1983.

The patrolling started the second day. The men, as was the routine, spent most of their time cutting their way through the wait-a-minute vines, elephant grass and bamboo, scrupulously avoiding the beaten tracks and pathways.

Our typical battalion operations scheme, as shown on the map, always reminded me of a giant four-leafed clover, with the FSB at the center, and the four maneuver companies each covering a circular area corresponding to one of the leaves. The whole clover was about 9 miles across. It was called an area of operations, abbreviated "AO."

No patrolling unit was ever out of range of the centrally-located supporting guns and the 4.2-inch mortars.

The VC would shadow our companies at a distance for a day or two, but would, if not seen and shot up, lose track of them by day five or six of a patrol. That was when *we* became dangerous, because if they couldn't pin-point our positions, they couldn't do much to hurt us, while we could and often did attack *them*, if we saw them first. At best, under those conditions, they had but two choices: fight or run. They usually ran, if they could. The only times they preferred to fight was on ground of their choosing, at the time they also chose, to maximize their chance of winning an engagement at low cost to themselves. It made sense, in a guerrilla war.

We had an additional advantage: the 42d Scout Dog Platoon, a group of handsome, well-cared-for mature Alsatians, each with a dog handler. They were allocated one section to each of the four maneuver rifle companies. The VC might see us first, but we were more likely to sniff them out before they did.

We moved the FSB every fourth day, sometimes every third, to keep the VC from concentrating (which takes a few days) enough to mount a successful attack on it.

I should say a few words here about the very bare-bones nature of life in the field, especially until it becomes an accustomed routine. And remember, I wasn't an inexperienced soldier. I'd spent at least a few days, sometimes as many as 14, per year in peacetime field training exercises (FTX) for 13 years, and had thought that I was well-prepared. But there, for example, you could shave in a vehicle's mirror. Airborne units have very few vehicles. And we could usually get hot water to shave in the States.

Not in Vietnam.

Keeping clean is important in the tropics, but hard to arrange. I bought a tin garden sprinkler in the native market, and sprinkled myself holding it over my head, as an alternative to having no showers. Then, as platoons, we rigged a nozzle as a showerhead that screwed into the end of a 55-gallon drum. That, filled with water in the morning, heated by the sun all day, atop a platform, made for a fine evening ablution.

At the same time that I bought my sprinkler, I also bought a bottle of Vietnamese orange pop, a gross error. Diarrhea, massive, bloody and painful.

Until I could buy a small mirror (the Viet-marketed ones were too big), I simply shaved by touch. If we weren't in active contact with the enemy, paratroopers, especially officers, were expected to shave daily.

PATROL MOVING OUT

* * *

34.

After an obligatorily-restless first-night-out, I slept like a baby the second and third nights near Bao Lac, with the three of my medics who weren't on perimeter guard, in a bagged-up hootch with ponchos pitched over it to keep rain out. We were about 4000 feet above sea level, this was November, and it got pretty cool at night. It was the same the next three nights. Days, sick call was light. I attended Officers Call at 8 AM and 6 PM daily, which were remarkably informative. As my work cycle became more routine, I got more comfortable with it.

I have a snapshot of myself made at this, my first FSB, with the chow line in the background, and with stainless steel 10-gallon coffee dispensers, insulated like the Mermites, to handle either hot or cold beverages. The background is just one green hill after another. I carry an M-16 rifle, and am wearing the M-1 steel helmet issued at that time. I was 31. Can it have been 33 years ago?

We weren't hitting much in the way of resistance. Our consensus was that the few VC in the area were trying to stay out of our way, stay alive, and wait till we left.

I had settled on a basic load that I carried everywhere, more than 25 feet from my tent where I kept my gear:

My rifle, cleaned every third day, more often if fired to
check its serviceability.

8 magazines with 18 cartridges in each, number 16 being a tracer.

One magazine in the rifle.

Pistol belt, and pack straps.

Two canteens filled with water at every opportunity.

USMC K-Bar fighting knife (after a March, 1968 visit to a Navy Supply Warehouse).

First-aid dressing.

Four M-26 fragmentation hand grenades.

The load weighed about 20 pounds.

If I needed more than that, I reasoned, I probably needed more than *anyone* could carry. If I didn't carry that much, even a small action involving only one or two VC, could catch me short. I also continued going to bed in my boots, but started taking them off if I woke at 2 AM or later, and went back to sleep, in relative comfort. By then, if we hadn't been hit, we weren't going to be.

The 2/502 was deployed in what was called the Central Highlands of South Vietnam. The Highlands were spectacular in their appearance.

From a hilltop, they looked like a progression of high hills, one after the other, going on forever, almost uniformly covered with trees. The greens were lighter than the leaf colors at home, and seemed much more brilliant. The sunlight contained a little more blue than is seen in more temperate countries. Certainly, the sky was a more intense shade of blue than I had ever seen before.

Twenty years later, I noticed these same color phenomena in Panama, 600 miles above the Equator (only 100 miles closer than in Vietnam).

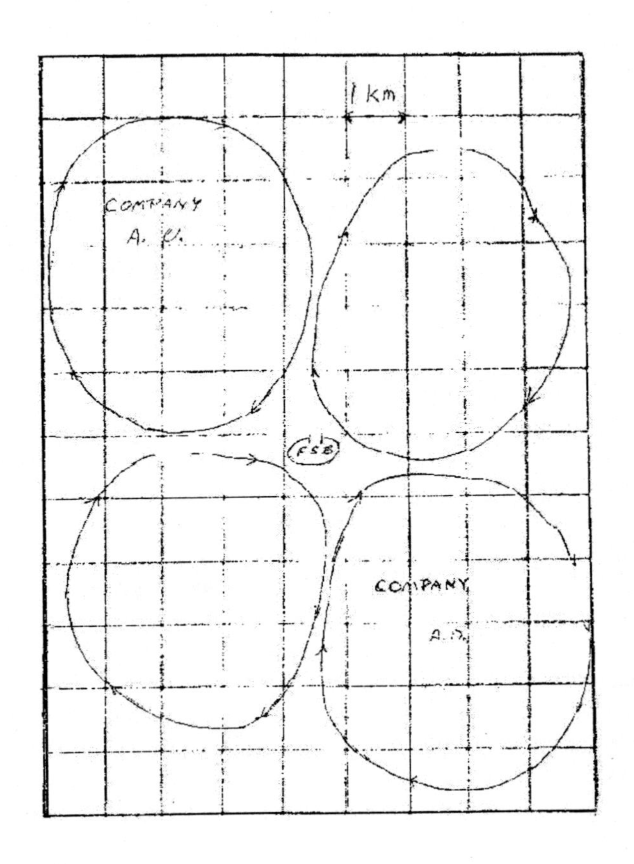

TYPICAL BATTALION AREA OF OPERATIONS (AO)

* * *

Flying over the Highlands at high altitude was like being slowly drawn along over a bright green carpet, seemingly uniform. The rubber, tea, and other commercial plantations abandoned by the French in 1954 were so overgrown that there was no distinguishing them from the jungle that had grown up and reclaimed them.

Lower down, however, there were many discernible breaks in the virgin forest, where men had cleared and tried to farm, or had erected hamlets, occupied or abandoned. Here and there would be a gigantic old
tree, standing out only because it was especially large-trunked, or was denuded until one reached the very top, in the edge of a wooded area, or was of such extraordinary height that it protruded to an unusual level above the upper canopy.

But it was from *within* the forest, standing at ground level, that the appearance of the terrain was the most unique and dramatic. There, under the triple-canopy, there were coexistent areas of black shadow, dark green lower canopy, medium green foliage of the middle canopy, and tiny bright gold laser-like beams of direct sunlight that had somehow missed all three canopies.

I'd never been able to think of a simile for this, until the day in 1984 that I visited Rheims Cathedral and watched direct parallel beams of sunlight filter through the tall, narrow multi-paned stained glass windows. Unlike Rheims, however, no matter how far or how fast you walked into *this* cathedral, there was no relative movement. The blacks, greens and golden lasers ran ahead of you, and *stayed* ahead, into what looked like infinity.

The smell of the triple-canopy jungle floor was a seemingly- contradictory mixture of wet leaves *and* dust. It was certainly unique; the forested mountains of the Mexican Sierra Madre should have the same odor, but don't.

In other locations in the mountainous center of the country, a platoon patrol might stumble into a stand of bamboo, which grows like gigantic grass blades, close together, and be completely frustrated by efforts to cut through all but the smallest stalks.

I have stood in a bamboo grove packed so tightly that I literally could not see another soldier five feet away.

Another patrol had two men step forward, and fall through vines and shrubs into an empty Olympic-sized pool, all that was left of the good life on a mountain plantation in pre-war Indochina. The place was too overgrown to even see what crop had been grown there.

One day, I went out on a resupply mission to one of the rifle companies, to see if there was anything my medics there might need. On my way back, I was asked to carry a few captured weapons out, and turn them in to battalion headquarters. They were a captured French MAS-36 rifle, a Soviet-made Moisin carbine, and a US 30-caliber carbine, all three rusty and in poor repair. All three also used different calibers of ammunition. These characteristics showed our opposition to be a bush-league team. I also carried back some captured papers, and turned the lot over to CPT "Bronco" Nagorski, our S-2 (intelligence) officer.

On another resupply mission, I was standing just outside a tree line, in one of the V-shaped gaps between two high hills that have to be flown through, rather than over. Company “A” was in a perimeter inside the trees, and hadn’t seen a VC for weeks. It had been really quiet in the District for some time.

As I stood there, in a green American uniform, U.S. rifle over one shoulder, and G.I. helmet on, a Huey flew past 400 yards away, and level with me. I waved to him. His portside door gunner fired a burst of six shots at me, and then another. He missed me by 20 yards at least. My only thought at the time was “Whaaa?” The gunner’s motivation remains an open question to the present day.

Another similar mission is considerably more memorable. The supply transport bird that I rode in had to evacuate three dead Americans, to the GR detachment at Phan Thiet. They had been casualties of friendly fire, probably due to one platoon or the other not reading its map correctly, and blundering blindly into the other.

Since they were ours, and since I was there, I did their death certificates, too. They all had multiple-wounds in the trunk and proximal extremeties, and weren’t facially disfigured. They were so youthful. The three of them looked like sleeping children, even younger than their eighteen years.

I vomited after I’d finished the write-ups.

I stayed out with the FSB for four more nights, and did practically nothing else useful. The fifth day I went to the rear and didn’t recognize it compared with the day that we’d arrived.

* * *

Jingle Bells, Vietnam

Splashing through the mud, in a truck that should be junk,
O'er the roads we go, half of us are drunk.
Wheels in mud ruts bounce, making asses sore,
Lord, I'd sooner go to hell than finish out this
war. Ohhhhhhh:

Jingle Bells, mortar shells, Charlie in the grass;
We'll get no Merry Christmas cheer until this year is past.
Jingle Bells, mortar shells, Charlie in the grass.
Take your Merry Christmas cheer, and shove it up your ass.
Christmas season's here, and everybody ducks.
Homefolks think it's dear, G.I.s think it sucks.
All at home are gay, children all at play,
While we are all stuck way out here, so God-damned far away.
Whoaaaaa:
Jingle Bells, mortar shells, Charlie in the grass.
We'll get no Merry Christmas cheer, until this year is past.
Jingle Bells, mortar shells, Charlie in the grass,
Take your Merry Christmas cheer and shove it up your ass.
The moral of our song is one that's plain to see:
Please, no more Christmas carols sing, and fuck your Christmas tree.
There's one last thing to say, before we have to leave:
Vietnam is not the place to be on Christmas Eve. Ohhhhhh:
Jingle Bells, mortar shells, Charlie in the grass;
We'll get no merry Christmas cheer until this year is past.
Jingle Bells, mortar shells, Charlie in the grass,
Take your Merry Christmas cheer, and shove it up your ass.

Song Parody, Christmas, 1967

* * *

I began to lose my awe of helicopters and to get used to riding in them as a matter of routine. At first, they seemed really high-tech, and for 1968 I guess they were.

The crew was dressed in flame-resistant gray-green one-piece flight suits and spheroidal bubble-face-mask flight helmets, with dark-shaded visors and attached radio mini-microphones, all these giving them a space-age appearance.

I still wasn't used to the two futuristic-looking M-60 machine guns mounted on each slick. To me, a machine gun was still the Browning thirty-caliber I'd grown up with. And the way infantry moved was by truck or on foot.

From the vantage point of thirty-plus years, and the advances in power plants, armament, and especially in avionics helicopters of that time weren't much more than platforms to carry cargo.

* * *

Like everything else that 2/502 did repeatedly, there was a standard layout of battalion rear, usually at right angles to the road that was our main supply route (MSR). That same long-serving professional cadre I spoke about at Phan Rang didn't have to be told what to do. They just got off their trucks, paced off intervals, and began to set up, in the same location relative to each other, the same way, every time. By this time, eight days after arrival, it looked like they'd been there for months.

Doing a left face in the MSR, you faced down the dirt street. On the right, in this order, were the motor pool and maintenance shop, and four (later five) company orderly rooms, arranged A, B, C, and Recon/ Headquarters. On the left were Supply and Transport(S-4), Operations and Intelligence (S-3 and S-2), Personnel (S-1), Medical, and Mess. On the far left, closer to supply and mess was the helipad, terrain permitting. The last distinction is important because supplies, wounded evacuees, and prepared food should be hand-carried the shortest distance possible to the transport slicks that would take them direct to their destinations.

At that time, Company "A" 's Orderly Room aimed its 106mm recoilless rifle straight up and decorated it like a Christmas tree, tinsel, lights, and all, placing it next to its Lyster drinking water bag.

Every battalion in the Brigade had a similar rear-echelon arrangement, with about a 300-yard interval between them.

I was treated to my first mass-casualty situation the next night. A disgruntled Vietnamese soldier had thrown an M-26 grenade into one of the many combination bars and whorehouses that follow soldiers everywhere. Our medical company got all 31 of the wounded. The mama-san owner was beyond help, and died about the time that I arrived. The rest of the wounds were relatively minor and just took time to find the fragments and remove them. Two of the survivors were transferred to the local civilian hospital for inpatient observation. The rest were referred there for outpatient followup. After all, it hadn't been an American who threw the grenade.

On the second night I spent there, I was in the S-4 tent when someone from the direction of the road fired a burst of small-arms fire at us. As I ducked out of the light, a Chinese stick-grenade bounced down the slope toward us, and exploded in the air about ten yards away. Knowing what I did about the U.S. M-26 grenade, I figured that I was dead. Fortunately, Chinese metallurgy (or it could have been North Vietnamese) wasn't good. Those grenades tended to break up into three or four big pieces, with a good chance that they would miss a given target.

Then the firing stopped.

Next morning, I dug one of the bullets out of a tree; it looked like a thirty-two special or 30-caliber carbine bullet to me, or possibly one from a Soviet PPSh-41 submachine gun.

Several times a day, a USAF light plane flew over at 3000 feet and played Christmas music over a loudspeaker.

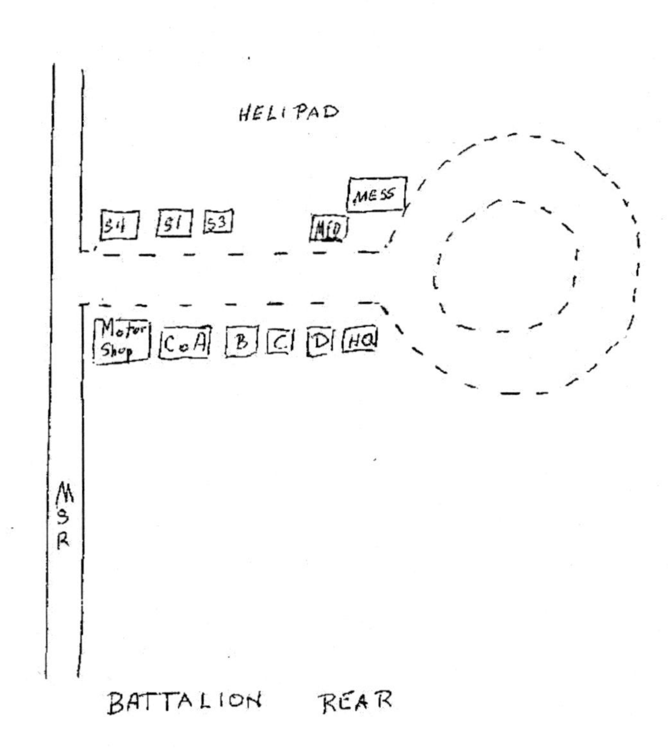

The town of Bao Lac had reliable electricity. I don't know about central water or telephones. I doubt that sewerage existed, unless septic tanks were used by the affluent.

There were many small shops, usually operated by overseas Chinese, often called "the Jews of Asia." Same for small, family banks. The huge cross-country power lines were never sabotaged, I suspect because the VC didn't want to have to repair them when they won the war.

* * *

I made it a point to visit the central market area to buy half a kilogram of rice, a head of garlic and two or three small, hard onions (which don't go bad as quickly as large juicy ones) to carry in the field. They didn't weigh much, and I was getting tired of straight C-rations. If some of the canned entrees were mixed with boiled rice, they weren't bad at all. I replenished this "basic load" as it was used up.

The ARVN Military Academy was located at Dalat, 30 miles away. Early in the 20th century, Theodore Roosevelt had frequently visited there to hunt tigers. The Emperor Bao Dai, too, had kept a hunting lodge in the area.

Three other officers and I found a native lakeside restaurant on the edge of town. It had an awesomely beautiful view of the lake and the sun setting into it.

I *still* think that my steak was water buffalo. At least it was fresh meat, served on china, and was welcome.

* * *

20 December 1967

On a routine resupply mission to our Recon Platoon, every man that I saw had a pumpkin-yellow cast to his skin and sclera. They all had hepatitis A. They had all, officers included, drunk from a clear, clean-looking, cold mountain stream.

Afterward, a mile upstream, they found a dead VC wearing black pajamas, with an empty ammunition belt, in the water. I'd imagine that he had been the source of their hepatitis A.

* * *

BALD EAGLE

Lieutenant Colonel Howard Danford (radio call sign:"Strike-Six" or "Bald Eagle") ideally deserves his own chapter. If I had the material, I'd do a whole book about him. I think it is fair to say of him, as someone once did of General Creighton Abrams, that he deserved a better war than Vietnam. The clear implication is that he was much too valuable to waste on such a fiasco.

I met him the same day that I reported in to HHC, 2/502. He was, I'd estimate, six feet tall, and probably weighed about 170 pounds. He was, as his radio call sign (Bald Eagle) indicated, bald, with only a minimum of fair hair in a wide, U-shaped fringe area extending around the back of his head. He had bushy eyebrows and hairy ears. The eyes were blue, and they never lost contact with yours. There wasn't an ounce of fat to spare visible anywhere on his frame. His uniforms fit well without being ostentatiously tailored. He was in splendid physical condition, which was expressed as an unflagging stamina. He never seemed to finish overseeing the dozens of details involved in operating and managing a light infantry battalion.

I never saw the man asleep once in the six months I knew him.

Being one of the Army's first osteopathic physicians, I had a rough script in mind when I was summoned to meet the colonel. Rather than having to explain what a DO was, I was surprised to find that he already knew. His father, he said, had been a doctor. So he was, I found, well-versed in the general pattern of the world of medicine.

Of all the problems affecting the Officer Corps in 1968, this West Point graduate, Class of 1954, manifested none of them.

There was never a suspicion that he might be withholding part of the truth, or even be flat-out lying. He seemed to care nothing for his own advancement; completely unselfish, he invariably saw to the welfare of his men and his officers (in that order) before considering his own. He shared the danger and discomfort of combat with his men, rarely leaving his forward firebase or maneuver companies to visit his battalion's rear echelon, even when his duties there were pressing.

He believed in strict, fairly-administered discipline. When he had no choice, courts-martial were held. Some of his men got six months in the Stockade at Camp LBJ. In every instance, this convening of the legal system was invoked only in cases of repeated offenses, of self-inflicted wounds, of refusal to obey orders, or other infractions that simply cannot be allowed to pass in a combat zone. Discipline, goes the old saw, is the glue that holds a unit of individuals together. Lose it, and the unit disintegrates.

He is one of the brightest men I've ever met, and one of the most professionally capable, overall. The myth of the Army as the employer of last resort certainly didn't apply to him.

My experience in associating with him antedated the current practice of so-called "mentoring." Nonetheless, I modeled the remainder of my military and professional career on him. In a tight spot, after weighing the variables, I'd ask myself: "What would Bald Eagle do? How would *he* handle this?"

And, acting on what I determined would be his advice, I would do what I thought he would have. I always slept well afterward. I still do.

When I last saw him, in 1996, he didn't seem to have aged a day.

And he *did* deserve a better war.

* * *

27 December 1967

When 2/502 been at Bao Lac a few weeks, I was invited by the Vietnamese District Chief to accompany him on a routine visit to a leper colony that lay within his district. My impression at the time was that it was Church-supported. It was a peaceful, quiet place. The second impression you got after a few minutes speaking French with the staff and the inmates was that this leprosarium had been there a long time, and would continue to be there, operating outside the dimensions of politics and war.

The nursing personnel were all Vietnamese nuns, members of a French nursing order, with their broad, white headgear and long white aprons worn over a light blue uniform. The Hospital Director was a French priest who was also a surgeon. Amputative surgery was his principal method of treating Hansen's disease (the politically correct name for leprosy). He habitually wore a soutane in the French style and a pith helmet.

His institution had not yet received supplies of the new drugs that were only then being initially released in the U.S. for leprosy, that could cure it, and which would close America's two National Hospitals for HD, in Louisiana and on Molokai, within a very few years.

Like most of Vietnam's institutional structures, the hospital was a group of one-story stucco, in this case white, buildings, connected by roofed-over but otherwise open-air paved walkways. The buildings were almost always low-set, with wide porticoes and porches on three or four sides, with the work areas well-ventilated by the prevailing mountain breezes.

There was a small central market square, with small quiet groups of patients and their families bartering handicrafts for fresh fish or vegetables.

The acute-care four-bed wards were furnished with large glass windows. They each had a fireplace and a red-tiled floor. The windows could be closed against the occasional cold snap. Each hospital bed had mosquito-net suspension bars for night use. It was easy to forget that leprosy does not render one immune to the falciparum malaria endemic to the mountains. For that matter, most occupants of the acute-care areas were not there for their Hansen's disease, but for the usual common disorders affecting the inhabitants of any small town.

The grounds were beautifully landscaped, with well-manicured grass lawns and flowering bushes surrounding the leprosarium on all four sides. The mountains acted as a blue backdrop. The same bushes were planted as matching internal hedges. Their bright-red sweet-smelling winter flowers brought an air of cheerfulness to what must have been a grim lifestyle, at best.

The grounds even had a rudimentary street-lighting system.

The patients lived in family units. Not all members of each family were (at least visibly) infected. Their housing was in wall-less villas. Up in the central Highlands it gets cold enough so that you need a blanket at night. But, with a good, stout roof to turn away rain, walls are superfluous 16 hours a day at most, and in summer, twenty-four.

The patients themselves could be almost unmarked, or could have hideous facial or extremity deformities, with absence of a body part being so common as to be unremarkable in the population. Both lepromatous and leonine forms of Hansen's disease were everywhere.

I have no pictures of the patients, though I took many slides of the facility and of its personnel. It struck me as bad form to even ask or try to photograph any of the patients, out of respect for their privacy.

The VC never came near the place. If there were any tuberculosis sanitariums in-country, I'll bet that they stayed away from *them*, too.

* * *

I hitched a helicopter ride down to the Brigade support area and visited the medical company of our support battalion, Company D, 326th Medical Battalion, (ABN). It was located on the south, or seaward, side of an airfield, in a sort of semi-permanent *micro*-Army-post called "Landing Zone (LZ) English," on the south side of Phan Thiet.

I was able to start a routine of visiting the four companies where I had medics on the resupply days for that company, to the FSB for two days, two more in the rear to do administrative work, and restart the eight-day cycle. I was usually able to get to Phan Thiet for a change of scene one of those days. I would check on any of our wounded who had passed through the medical company there, stretch the trip into an overnight, and return to the mountains early the next day.

Our AO abutted that of part of the 1st Air Cavalry Division, so one of *their* medical companies was also located there.

There was also an attached team from outside the 101st (what we'd now call "cellular") to reinforce either unit, should the need arise. It was called a Team KA, or general surgical team, comprised of one surgeon, one anesthesiologist, and two enlisted technicians. The team traveled in a jeep (part of its equipment), towing a small trailer full of surgical equipment. They moved by road or air in an effort to have the team's capability in place *before* an anticipated increase in wounded.

Though I spent relatively few overnights at LZ English, the images that remain are vivid to this day. I was quartered in a stucco villa, on a clifftop overlooking the South China Sea. It had once been a place of great beauty, formerly landscaped, belonging to persons now unknown, at least to us. Now there was no electrical power, and there had *never* been indoor plumbing. There was a hole in the red-tiled roof about three feet in diameter, probably caused by a falling mortar shell during some nuisance shelling. The twenty yards or so from the dooryard to the cliff edge was wired, and the barbed wire was hung every twenty feet or so with the yellow signs with red letters that mean "mines" to every army in the world, whatever language it spoke.

There was a half-mile of gravel road leading down to the beach at the foot of the cliff. I walked down, and for the very first time, waded in salt water. The road was lined with stalls selling junk and stolen American goods. For eighty cents I bought an Army-issue stainless steel jackknife which I still have. After 33 years, it shows no wear whatever. I think it will last forever.

One memorable night, I woke at 3 AM and went out to piss into the minefield. I noticed that the odor of the sea was stronger than was noticeable during the daylight or early evening hours. Across the entire silent vista, as far as I could see, the ocean was covered with tiny dim lights. For a few seconds I thought that these were stars reflected in the inshore waters. I knew it was too late in the year for fireflies, if there *were* fireflies in Asia. It took me a few minutes to figure out that it was the Phan Thiet fishing fleet, going out at that hour to catch the outgoing tide.

The town of Phan Thiet was the hometown of the president of South Vietnam, Mr. (formerly General) Thieu. It was on absolutely flat ground, perhaps eight feet above sea level at high tide. The town was crisscrossed with sixty-yard-wide canals that really gave off a stench. They may have been the town's sewage-disposal system. When the fishing fleet was in, that was where its boats were moored. The typical fishing boat was a sampan with turned-up bow and tail posts, twenty-five feet or so in length.

The town's water tower, dating from the French days, was made entirely of masonry from the ground up. I had never seen one like it before. It looked *permanent,* and probably was. The streets swarmed with the ubiquitous civilians, most wearing faded-black two-piece loose-fitting pajama-like outfits topped with flattened-conical straw paddy hats.

There were even a few cyclos (short for cyclo-taxis or cyclo-cabs), a two-passenger rickshaw-like seat powered from behind with a bicycle frame and pedals. Later, I found that there were many more of them to be found in the larger cities. Like any taxi, they depended upon the presence of a large, fairly-affluent population in a hurry, which was not much in evidence in Phan Thiet.

Small businesses flourished, usually on the ground floor of a building with a French-style roll-up metal multi-hinged cover that, when rolled up, opened the shop to the street. At night, the owner just rolled his storefront down and he was closed. As I later found to be the case in rural France, there were no general stores; every shop dealt in a specialized type of goods, and they expected the shopper to bring his own shopping bag. The more affluent customers had bicycles with baskets for transporting their purchases.

There were also more humble, hovel-like farmers' markets and fish stalls, operated by the producers themselves, consisting of a four-pole-supported tin roof, period. No walls, and a dirt floor.

The seafood was excellent there. I only hoped that it had been caught far out to sea, away from the canals. The sea salt was served, not in shakers, but small salt cellars at each plate meant to be used by the pinch. While I was in a restaurant on the main drag, a middle-aged Vietnamese civilian came by my table and offered to sell me some locally-grown pot. I told him no, thanks. Well, then, how about a nickel bag of brown heroin? Again, no. Then he tried to sell me a locally-printed copy of the porn novel, "Fanny Hill" with French punctuation and English text.

Verily, verily, this man was a true retail entrepreneur; he had something for everyone.

* * *

The young soldier with the left chest wound was more comfortable after we had reduced his pneumothorax. There was no sign of serious bleeding. I volunteered to fly up to Nha Trang with him, to safeguard the canteen-water-seal-chest tube rig that we had made up. I think I pissed him off; all through the flight, I kept waking him up to see if he was all right. He was probably starved for sleep, wanting nothing more than to be left alone to rest.

* * *

Most of the casualties I treated when I was at LZ English were Vietnamese civilians. I saw the only case of bubonic plague I've *ever* seen there, a six-year-old boy. He came to us late, unconscious, marked with acupuncture pinpricks over his anterior chest wall. And he died, his plague too advanced for antibiotics to help.

After three weeks of relative quiet, we were alerted to move again.

As per our routine, the companies withdrew to the FSB. Everyone there then withdrew to the rear echelon at Bao Lac. Then, the entire battalion was helicoptered to the airfield at Phan Thiet, where it bivouacked for three days. This delay was due to an error by either the Army or Air Force, and planes could not be allocated to move us to Phuoc Binh, near the Cambodian border, until then.

On the way to Phan Thiet we flew along the flat coastal plain for a few dozen miles.

There, standing out and visible for miles, within sight of the sea, was a large, ornately-carved rusty reddish-brown stone temple, now disused. It had been completed in the year 1121 by the Cham culture, which had been based in what is now Cambodia. At that time, and for several centuries before and after it, its territory extended into central Vietnam. The temple resembled the pictures I'd seen of Angkor Wat, the lost city of the Cambodian empire. The two were roughly contemporary.

On the first night that 2/502 spent on the edge of the Phan Thiet airfield, I was awakened about two A.M. by a series of explosions, and was startled and frozen immobile by the sight of red fireballs the size of grapefruit flying past my upturned face. They could have been twelve inches or six feet off the ground, but as long as they were missing me, I felt no urge to move. Then, as quickly as it had begun, the racket stopped and the field was dark again. It turned out that the leader of the air defense artillery section assigned there had fired a Harassment and Interdiction mission (commonly known as H&I), and no one had warned us to expect it. What I had seen had been 40mm tracers, outgoing. No harm done, I went back to sleep.

I took advantage of the break to give a few refresher training classes to my whole platoon; it was one of those unusual times when they were all in the same place. I learned a lot from them, particularly with respect to field-expedient resuscitation during the training classes, perhaps more than I taught them. After the first few minutes, the classes turned into seminars, with an informal sharing of experience among equals.

As it turned out, where we were going, I'd need it all, and more.

* * *

Before we moved on to our next mission, Colonel Danford asked me to accompany him to the Eighth Field Hospital, at Nha Trang, to see some of 2/502's wounded from the Bao Lac operation. It would involve a rather long helicopter flight of an hour and forty-five minutes each way.

We flew high for the helicopters of that time, at about 5,000 feet. I got a splendid view of the coastal lowlands, cut through by numerous slow, shallow, relatively short estuarine rivers. Each one I saw had fishing weirs near its mouth. I think they were so placed as to fill up with fish during the outgoing tide, for harvesting at low tide. And they had probably been there for 6,000 years, long before there *was* a West and its civilization. On that time-scale, we were transients in a land that had seen many other outlanders come and go.

As we circled to land, I was able to see the airfield, as always divided into a Vietnamese Air Force (in this case their Air Force Academy) and United States Air Force sides.

I was impressed by the number of various aircraft *in revetments*, indicating that they were based there permanently, and not withdrawn at night, as they were further forward.

Nha Trang was a modern city, like any in the United States. We broke up for lunch and to shop a little at a small PX branch (a mirror at last! And a sponge!). I remember getting a vanilla shake at the snack bar. It was my first luxurious dairy product for what seemed like years. Actually, it had only been five weeks. Field duty *really* messes up your perception of time.

Then, after lunch, we re-formed and headed for the hospital. All that I recall at the time was astonishment that the First Brigade had an administrative full-time sergeant first class present there. His only job was to look after the interests of the men from the brigade who passed through the hospital as patients, and to keep track of where they went when they physically left it.

* * *

35.

06 January 1968

The planes finally came at daybreak on the fourth day and ferried us west to Phuoc Binh, a district headquarters in northern III Corps, analogous to a county seat. It was also a social center of the surrounding area. It was the town where farmers from the surrounding countryside brought their produce to market. It lay about twelve miles south of the Cambodian border. Even during this, the most active year of the war, the country's agricultural activities, with the help of American civilian aid such as the Peace Corps and AID, were booming.

Montagnards (abbreviated "'yards,") who physically resemble Navajo Indians, and are thus racially distinct from the Vietnamese, mostly inhabited that area, on both sides of the Cambodian border. The two racial groups detested each other.

A group of the 'yards were gambling in the Government market building with its open sides, playing some game I didn't recognize. They invited me to play. I pled no money, all in sign language. They pointed to my watch. I smiled all round, nodded to all four of them, and took my leave. Walking away through the tin-roofs-on-poles surrounding the market, my column bore northeast through the town, past the ever-present militiamen and white-uniformed National Police (the "White Mice").

The main drag of the town was lined with shops like those in Phan Thiet, except that they were in one-and-a-half storied buildings. I suspect that the proprietors lived over and, after hours *in* those stores. There were food and drink-selling pushcarts much like the ones I would see years later in Juarez, Mexico. The more enterprising operators provided a few stools and a canvas shade for their customers' comfort. Here, for the first time, I ran into Orientals who didn't want to be photographed. There is a superstition that the camera steals their souls. Not to put too fine a point on it: *This was hillbilly Vietnam.*

We marched from the flight line to the site of 2/502 (Rear), and set up. Everyone started to dig in. I keeled over with heat exhaustion while digging a sleeping position that afternoon. That was the first of the four times that it would happen in Vietnam. The enemy here had access to greater numbers and heavier weapons than he did in the Bao Lac area, so bunkering-up was necessary. In fact, at that time Cambodia was a protected sanctuary for the North Vietnamese Army (NVA), and we were 12 miles from the border, and from whatever they might care to throw at us.

The next day, we were able to recruit some Montagnard day laborers, who were glad of the work in a farming off-season, to help prepare the rear area position. They even went so far as to dig out stumps, to allow for a less cluttered campsite. We were not pressed for time, so we were able to build so-called "clean" bunkers, lined with plywood.

The roof and walls were thus layered, from inside out, plywood, stamped steel engineer stakes three inches wide by 96 inches long, more plywood, and sandbags.

110-volt power lines were laid on the ground, connecting the bunkers in series, like a cheap set of Christmas-tree lights.

Telephone lines were strung on overhead poles from orderly room to orderly room throughout the rear echelon area.

During this slack time, I visited a rice mill. I was surprised to see even in these modern times, the women still used sieves made of woven dried palm leaf, rather than the manufactured variety that would be made of screen wire. Once the straw and other debris were removed, the brown rice was poured into a hopper atop the mill, and the hulls were expelled from a chute at one side.

The polished white rice fell through, to be caught beneath it in palm-leaf storage baskets with a very tight weave.

The soil of this area, which runs all the way to Cambodia, is a bright red dense clay-like stuff called laterite. It makes a good base for buildings and roads, as long as a waterproof cover, like asphalt or concrete, overlies it. Without it, the lightest rain will wash it away.

Its dust gets into everything, including cloth. It took four launderings to get a uniform clean after leaving the area.

We had a move scheduled for the next day, though, per routine, the destination was not announced.

* * *

The first wave of the move air-assaulted into the area we had chosen for our latest FSB. They were unopposed. The site was about six miles from Phuoc Binh by air. Our new firebase lay in the westernmost of two 20-acre cow pastures, the only meadow I ever saw in Indochina. The one to the east was our helipad. Between them ran a north-south dirt road of the omnipresent laterite, which ran straight into Cambodia, four-and-a-half miles away.

We had a 106mm recoilless antitank rifle from "E" Company mounted on the west shoulder of the road, pointed north along it. The gun was mounted on a tripod, and could easily have been manhandled through 360 degrees if the need arose. Its ready ammunition was eight antipersonnel rounds, but there were a few antitank shells as backup nearby; you never know *what* might come down an open road.

I usually hung around the S-3 (Operations) post so that I could monitor the action on the Command radio net, and get the aid station ready to receive casualties, if any came our way.

At about 0900 on 15 January 1968 a Huey landed and shut down. The passengers dismounted and went about their business. At 10 AM I heard the familiar whop-whop-whop of the bird starting up again, and thought no more about it, right up until the first bullet went "Whack!" past the right side of my head. It hadn't been a helicopter starting at all. We were under fire from two or three guys, probably local Viet Cong (VC) with AK-47s, firing from somewhere on the north (or Cambodian) side of the helipad. We all flattened out, taking cover, and waited for them to stop shooting. We didn't return fire right away, because the men firing couldn't be seen, we'd likely shoot up the parked helicopter, and because they ran away after 5 or 6 minutes, before we could start working around their flanks. One man got a cut lip diving for cover. No one else was hurt. That's how I got shot at the first time, and experienced what the historian S.L.A. Marshall called "the six-inch horizon" (of the prone infantryman under fire) for the first time, as the V.C. swung their arcs of fire back and forth, back and forth, five or six times.

The sound a bullet makes as it passes close-by was not the "whannnng" of the movies, nor the "whizzzz" denoting a bullet passing at a distance I'd estimate at ten yards or more. I'd heard that sharp, ominous slapping sound before, in 1954, pulling and marking targets on the rifle range at Fort Leavenworth. I believe that the characteristic loud "SNAP!" sound of a near-miss is caused by air rushing *back into* the partial vacuum that the supersonic projectile leaves immediately behind it.

I had been able to low-crawl to a newly-excavated five-foot-deep eight-by-eight-foot hole and rolled into it. There were three men already in it. As the fire swept past, four of us cautiously peeked over the unfinished parapet, in the direction of the shooters, but could see nothing. I was the only one with a rifle, for all the good it did. As I've said, there was nothing to shoot *at*.

How those two shit-birds (generic term for this type of nuisance attacker) fired 200 rounds at 200 men in that small field and hit none of them is a mystery to me to this day.

And that's how I was awarded the Combat Medical Badge.

* * *

After that episode, we moved 2/502's FSB to another location, this time on low ground, with what *I* thought were unhealthily-near tree lines. The RSOP was uneventful, except that I got onto the wrong helicopter and was in the first wave instead of the third as had been planned. As we hovered three feet off the ground, I looked around for someone to tell me what to do. Everyone else there was an enlisted man, looking at *me* to tell *him* what to do. So I jumped out onto the ground, shouted "Follow me!" and sprinted to the nearest tree line, where I spread them out there in a line, the men 5 yards apart, and waited for the second wave.

It took them ten very long minutes to arrive.

* * *

Two days later, a patrol following a serpentine, faint, cold trail through the hills came to a straight stretch of about 100 yards. They were moving into the wind. About two-thirds of the way to the point man, a 180-pound tiger (weighed later on the messhall scale) was creeping along behind him, ahead of the main body, chin and belly on the ground, sizing him up as the entree of an early lunch. Every man in the he lead platoon of the main body, including the two machine-gunners, opened fire, killing the big cat instantly, and scaring the unsuspecting point man nearly to death.

* * *

We stayed in that general area for two weeks. Then we were briefed for Plan Zapata, which in 72 hours would become *Operation* Zapata.

It involved all of the 2/502 *parachuting* onto the disused airfield at Bu Gia Map, thirty miles to the northeast. It lay within a few hundred yards of the Cambodian border.

We would conduct a raid in force, and withdraw as suddenly as we'd come.

We might find no one there.

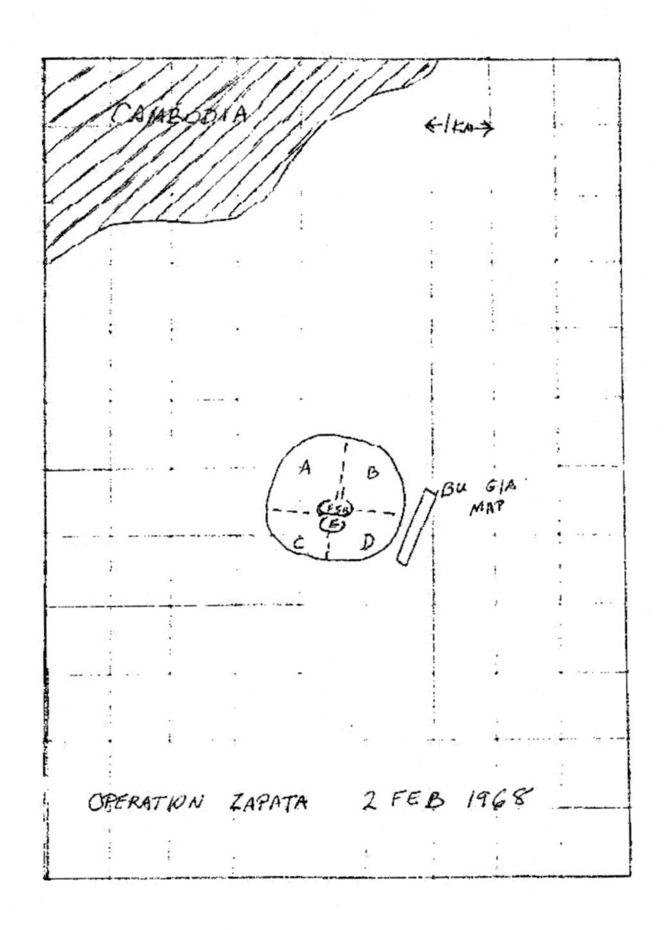

We might also land on the whole North Vietnamese Army.

* * *

Two years later, President Nixon, on the assumption that the National Liberation Front's Central Office for South Vietnam (COSVN) was in this general area, ordered a multi-division incursion into Cambodia. The units involved found evidence that this location was at least a major headquarters of some kind, if not COSVN itself. This operation sparked campus riots all over the United States, Kent State being the best-known.

* * *

Our battalion area of operations (AO) cloverleaf was, instead of the usual nine miles across (see Typical AO Diagram, Bao Lac, p. 272), seven-*tenths* of a mile in diameter. This would stabilize until we got off the drop zone, got organized and sent out the first patrols to see what (and who) was in the surrounding terrain. This should all be completed in the first four hours after the first man jumped.

No time frame was given at our initial briefing, but I doubt we would have stayed even 72 hours, and perhaps as little as 24.

I was thrilled to death, though I hoped not literally, at the prospect. I even missed an outdoor movie getting my equipment together.

* * *

Fresh from Ft. Campbell, the Division Surgeon came into the tent, where three other Medical Corps (MC) officers and I were talking shop, just killing time, really, till the evening meal, or till we were needed for wounded should there be any. I hadn't discussed Plan Zapata even with them; secret *means* secret.

It had been fairly quiet the past three weeks or so. The Surgeon was a lieutenant colonel, Medical Corps, whose name I've blocked, unconsciously but effectively. At first, he asked questions about how things were going, did we have everything we needed, was there anything he could do to help? He was, he said, part of the advance party of rest of the Division. This second increment consisted of two more parachute infantry brigades, which were badly needed, and a Division Headquarters, which wasn't.

When we explained how we handled our jobs, he began to advise us about better ways to do them, other concepts of delivering care, evacuation, etc., etc, all straight from the Fort Sam Houston training syllabus. This, from a guy who'd never heard a shot fired in anger, and who had been in-country less than 48 hours. I don't remember how we put him in his place without being grossly insubordinate, but we did, and he mumbled something about not having come by to argue, and withdrew.

I never saw him again. He was replaced soon after that by a solid gold, real doctor and, incidentally, a leader. He was LTC Bernhard Mittemeyer, who, years later, was made the three-star Surgeon General of the Army, and who deserved it.

This officer's visit was remarkable only because it was the first (and typical) of many that we received from incoming Division Headquarters personnel.

The personal contacts from the two new *brigades* on the other hand were welcomed as opportunities to extend our help and share our experiences with new men who'd need them, just as the old hands at Phan Rang had done for us, when *we* were new.

The divisional staff officers, however, to include all the stateside medical personnel, were mostly higher-*ranked* than we were but they were inexperienced in both military medicine and in combat operations, with a very few exceptions. However, by virtue of those ranks, experienced or not, they were placed in command *over* those of us who'd been in the combat zone, some as little as 3 ½ months like me, or 11-plus months like some of the Class of '65.

In my opinion, then and now, that was sheer madness.

* * *

36.

"Good morning; good morning!" The General said,
As he smiled at his men on their way to the line.
Now the soldiers he smiled at are most of 'em dead.
And we're cursing his staff for incompetent swine.

From *"The General,"* Siegfried Sassoon, 1916

* * *

Major General Becerra, with a truly MacArthur-esque flair, drew himself up to his full height of five feet four inches and saluted General Westmoreland, stating, "The 101st Airborne Division reports for duty!" according to the article in the *Pacific Stars and Stripes.*

No shit? What were we in the First Brigade, chopped liver? For two and a half years, we had been the only part of the 101st that *had* been functioning in a combat zone. The other two-thirds of the Division had been at Ft. Campbell, Kentucky.

Their arrival ended the First Brigade's status as a semi- and occasionally totally-autonomous force.

The Division Headquarters began its activities with what looked to *us* like running in circles; they began issuing orders direct to specific battalions without using the proper intermediate commanders, in at least one instance naming the *company* which was to be used for a given task. It reminded me of the 35th Division (National Guard) on its first day of summer camp. But the Guard is made up of part-timers; these were Regulars, the best we had, and I, at least, had expected better.

Especially in a combat zone, where lives were at stake.

I actually saw the order that came down in the name of command interest, to be sure that every man had a toothbrush. With much of the NVA a few hours' march away.

Someone up-top had entirely too much free time.

At one point in January 1968, the same general diverted all air support away from the 502d, his principal reason being, as I understood it, was to show that he *could.* Had we been in need of rapid resupply or reinforcement. Being squarely on the Cambodian border we could not have waited to have aircraft re-allocated if we happened to step in the shit, which was a likely event in that part of Indochina.

Shortly after that, flying over our AO, his helicopter took a few (U.S.-sized) 5.56mm bullet holes from the ground, exact origin unknown.

I know nothing more about him, first-hand. I heard officers senior to me say, in confidence, then and later, that he was at the very least a little crazy. I'd bet he *would* have presented some interesting answers on a mental status exam, but, as I say, I don't know.

As it was also related to me, he was often wrong, but was never uncertain.

Trying to apply peacetime standards and behavior in a war zone doesn't work. At best, it detracts from the principal mission of a unit. At worst, it costs lives, as it did at the Kasserine Pass in North Africa in early 1943. Over the forty-two years of my service, I've noticed that Americans rarely seem to learn from their mistakes, particularly if there is a generation or two between them. Another example is Mr. Clinton's recent (early 2000) casualty-less, hitless, ineffective air-only "offensive" in Kosovo.

To get back to the General, this officer, and his many, *many* crony-ridden senior staff who were good at wearing starched fatigues, running around shouting "Airborne, airborne!" and jumping from C-130s before an admiring crowd, simply weren't able to understand the paradigm shift. The name of the game in Vietnam was getting down and dirty to go up against some of the finest light infantry on the planet, and nothing less was likely to beat them. To do it, the 101st's two new brigades would have to re-train away from the conventional-war model, toward the empiric and time-tested operating methods of the First Brigade, or suffer the usual casualties and loss of effectiveness entailed in a learning curve.

To state it for the record: In early 1968 we had the power to win the war. The fighting men were sold out by our own leadership at home, by our own upper echelons within Vietnam, and were out-generaled on the ground, though the indomitable Joe Tentpeg was never beaten.

A little before this time the Battalion had been reorganized, adding a fifth, "E" Company which was actually a heavy-weapons unit, and a fourth rifle company, designated "D" Company. Though the companies were smaller, the battalion as a whole was more flexible.

A firsthand expert on Vietnam and the war named John Paul Vann had recommended a similar change *in early 1965,* three years before. Further, his plan was specific in that it would have *had no* division or brigade headquarters except as temporary task force control points. In fact, his projected reorganization would have made our forces' configuration somewhat resemble the NVA's general layout. The Regular Army wasn't interested: nobody makes major general down at battalion level. Gotta make it a large-unit war, even if it costs us a major national defeat and disgrace in the eyes of our allies.

And that's exactly what they did.

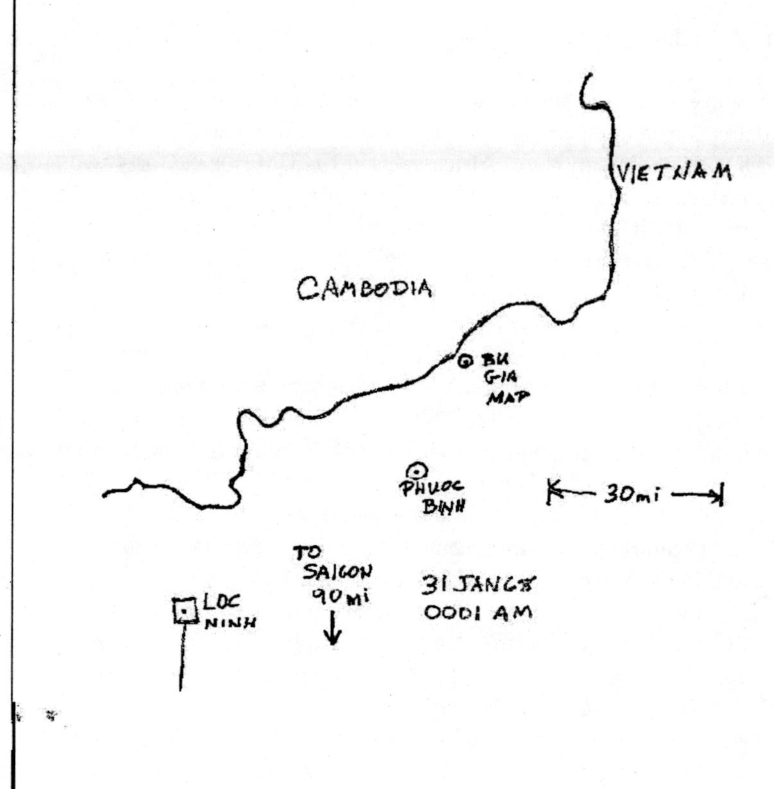

NORTHWESTERN III CORPS, 30 JAN 1968

37.

January 31st 1968:
Tet Holiday, 0520

I woke to the sound of artillery fire, outgoing. To an old "cannon-cocker," that alone wasn't unusual enough to wake me.

What was odd was the *timing*.

It was not our unit policy to use artillery harassing and interdiction fires, the brigade commander's opinion being, rightly, I believe, that it was a waste of ammunition. The guns usually fired a few rounds throughout the night in response to fire mission requests from units in the field, but the enemy always, *always*, broke contact and made off well before dawn, and the howitzers, having no targets, generally were not firing at first light.

Until now.

Also, the gunfire itself *sounded* odd, with a sort of loud "pop" superimposed upon their usual ear-splitting "SLAP!" and I didn't know why, until I looked 75 yards across the intervening clearing at their position. The howitzers' tubes were pointed almost straight up, and *that* got my attention. They were firing high-angle. It meant that the NVA were probably 800 yards or less away from where I was standing, were in defilade, and in large enough numbers that artillery was needed to hold them off, out of Phuoc Binh town, off the airfield, and out of the Brigade rear area.

I grabbed my rifle, web gear and helmet, and headed for the clearing station to treat casualties as they came in.

As I ran, there was a God-awful roar as two South Vietnamese Air Force armed T-38 jet trainers (the commercial export version called the F-5 by Northrop) salvoed rockets from about 100 feet above my head, at targets 800 yards in front of me, toward the town proper. By the time they had come back for a second pass, I was in the medical bunker.

The first wounded man arrived just as I did, hand-carried to us by his platoon. He was dead, gut-shot, and reminded me immediately of the man killed in our own headquarters back at Phan Rang. His wound was very nearly in the same place.

The rest of the men injured were, with a few exceptions, not too severe. Those three or four with serious wounds were stabilized at our station and evacuated by helicopter to hospitals at Long Binh and Saigon (I will *not* ever call it Ho Chi Minh City, by the way). About all that we could do to stabilize the wounded was to stop bleeding, if necessary by invading a major body cavity, to replace lost fluid volume intravenously, to start antibiotics, to splint fractures and relieve pain. All in all, a pretty challenging job that near the site of combat.

Two helicopters were shot down, though the wounded crews were rescued.

Others birds were hit by small arms fire, but kept flying.

The fighting continued into the noon hour, a phenomenon previously never seen. *Why* didn't the NVA break contact? Why were they *purposely* suffering all these casualties? Instead, fighting continued all through the afternoon, then wound down, and by 1900 (7PM) seemed to be sputtering out.

The events leading up to the fight that had erupted at about 4 AM were these, in order : One of our companies was patrolling parallel to, but 100 yards off, a main hard-surfaced highway. They had stopped, maintaining silence, to listen for movement. And they really *did* hear it. The whole god-damned 327th NVA *Division*, 6000 men, was moving southeast toward Saigon, in a column, on that road. The company-sized patrol, outnumbered thirty to one, fired on them from ambush positions on their left and their rear, started mortaring them, radioed for air strikes and called in the beginning of the artillery fire that I had heard earlier. The subunits of the NVA 327th had kept *piling up* on the road, in the dark, their columns telescoping into the ones that were stopped and deployed, and who were in contact with the Americans.

The Brigade reinforced its company patrol-ambush with 800 more men, all the while supporting by fire and directing air strikes, sorry that they had no armor to use to *really* cut them up. Still, though, our unarmored cavalry troop did the best that it could to add to the mobile volume of fire that could be brought to bear.

I will not say that they killed all 6000 NVA, because I don't know. I doubt it. I *do* know, from postwar North Vietnamese reports, that the 327th, as a unit, detailed to take a specific part of Saigon on February 2d, and occupy it, did not even arrive. Perhaps some of them made it, two or three days late, and fought with other units. It's possible. Our actual body count was only 650.

One of my men was killed that day. I won't second-guess him; I wasn't there. But I always told my men, and later, the doctors, under me: " 'John Wayne tactics', running around *in* enemy fire, is unlikely to make a difference to the care of a wounded man. It will most assuredly not help him if *you're* hit and don't make it to him, nor help all the others who might need you later that day. *Low-crawl* to the casualty; and with luck, you'll both get out of there alive."

He was my first loss as a platoon leader. I can see his twenty-year-old face and his nametag as I write. The poor guy wasn't even given the dignity of having his body evacuated back up the chain of command, through the hands of men who knew and cared for him. The remains were whisked away by helicopter to a Graves Registration collection point far to the rear. It was as though he had never been there. Just one more number to be dropped from the Morning Report, which automatically placed a request for one replacement, MOS 91B.

During that evening, 2/502 laid more wire around our positions, and plotted final defensive fires, first around our perimeter, and then onto our own positions. Better to die that way, we reasoned, than to do it being led and prodded north up the Ho Chi Minh Trail.

The next morning, from our position, we could look into the town and see bodies hanging from lampposts. Through binoculars, they could be seen to be wearing NVA khaki or green. Probably they had been stragglers from the units under the 4 AM attack out on the road.

The Montagnard Regional Forces and their families who lived in Phuoc Binh had suffered much at the hands of the Northerners in years past. Their relatives, babies and all, had been massacred with flame-throwers at Bu Dop a month before. Given the opportunity, they had seen a chance for a little payback. And they played for keeps.

News kept coming in on our teletype and on the AFVN- Radio-and-TV news that attacks were being made in force all over South Vietnam, and that the outcomes were still uncertain and even in doubt.

Plan Zapata was cancelled.

* * *

We reorganized for 24 hours and got an ammunition resupply. The artillery and mortar sections. in particular, had been firing steadily for 36 hours, and were running low on their supplies of shells.

Then we were alerted to move by air in 24 hours. Saigon was having trouble fighting off the VC who were all over the city.

* * *

You have never lived till you've almost died. To those who have had to fight for it, life has a sweetness that the protected can never know.

Graffiti, FT Jackson, South Carolina, 1970

* * *

38.

3 February 1968
1203 AM

The Phuoc Binh airfield was a single great roar as C-130s landed and taxied to the west end where we were waiting by chalk. We were loaded in different order than ever before, because we were going, not as we usually did from an improved field to one less so, and then to a landing zone (LZ) that'd be unimproved. Instead, we were headed for what might have been the largest, and was certainly the busiest airfield in the world, Bien Hoa, the same one where I'd entered the country, a long three months before. It was getting dark as we took off to the east, turned first 180 degrees west, paralleling the runway, and then circled further, onto a southeasterly course. Within 20 minutes, we started to descend. We flew over Cholon and western Saigon, with the city lights ablaze, and someone behind me in the dark fuselage bay said, in a perfect Rod Serling voice, "You've gone from Vietnam halfway around the world to downtown Seattle....by way of the Twilight Zone."

We landed and taxied to a stop. The gate dropped, and we unloaded through the same terminal that I described on arrival in-country, but much more expeditiously. There was no confusion; this time we were not individual replacements, but a *unit* with an assigned mission. We were trucked off right away to another part of the sprawling Bien Hoa base, and assigned quarters (with beds, not canvas cots!) in huts, identical in architecture but much newer than those at the 90th Replacement. After a briefing on the current situation in the area, orders were given for individual companies to be detached piecemeal for small operations the next morning. My section wasn't needed, so I stood them down till noon. I told them then I'd meet them in a formation, to be held where we were at standing at that moment.

"Your principal duty is to sleep for the next nine hours," I told them.

The post was locked down and none of us was allowed to leave the battalion's assigned two-hundred-yard-square area.

The concrete-block masonry latrine buildings were brand new, with drinkable water, flush toilets and hot showers. I went to sleep, my nostrils filled with the refreshing odor of fresh lumber.

At the next morning's formation, after breakfast (in an air-conditioned steel prefab mess hall!), the battalion was assigned piecemeal to perform several small missions as a backup to units in contact.

One of those small but highly public missions, thanks to the news media, was the retaking of the American Embassy from the 19 V.C. sappers who'd gotten in, but were having a much harder time getting out. That clearing job took about 25 minutes. No prisoners were taken, but sappers rarely even tried to surrender.

However, like Tet itself, all that the public at home was told and worse, *shown* on the network TV news, was that this demonstrated that the war was going badly for us, and was probably unwinnable. In both cases, it was all a matter of skewed presentation and flawed perception. We kicked their asses, and did it royally.

A fire had been set in one of Bien Hoa's smaller ammunition dumps the day before by a mortar shell. It had seemed to be under control, but then expanded ahead of an abrupt gust of wind, and a couple of minutes later, at 11 PM, 200 tons of TNT and C-4 exploded. No one was hurt by the blast. I must say, though, that I set a personal best record in speed going for the shelter between the huts. Even as little as 0.2 kilotons makes a hell of a bang, a third of a mile away.

Having nothing else to do, I helped count the ripening VC corpses left from the attack on the airfield three nights before, across three lines of barbed wire with many small antipersonnel mines between them. Their losses, percentage-wise, were Somme-like. Even though a significant number of attackers penetrated the defenses and got inside, the Air Police defending just closed the hole behind them, trapping them on a great expanse of concrete with no cover. Then an army tank platoon was brought in and killed nearly all of them, in their final defensive perimeter at the west end of the runway.

Because of the enemy's 33,000 dead in ill-conceived assaults like this one, that was the end of the indigenous South Vietnamese Viet Cong. We'd see a few more, over the next few months, but most of our future encounters, right up to April 1973, would be against regular soldiers, the NVA.

For the first time I understood the power and the whore-ishness of the press. Bad news *sells* better than good news. So, it being more profitable to report the bad news, they never shut up about the twin tragedies of Tet and Khe Sanh, about the war being hopelessly unwinnable, the drug-ridden Army, and so on. Positive events were relegated to page 54, next to the classified ads. Actually, the Tet offensive was, *and should have been reported as,* an American/ARVN triumph, Khe Sanh was, too, and the only druggies *I* saw were REMFs (rear-echelon motherfuckers) who had time on their hands and not nearly enough abject terror in their lives.

The rest of our work around the Capital Military District took two and a half weeks, and was mostly mopping up after the first day. On the sixteenth day after our arrival, we got a 96-hour warning order to move again.

I'd been to Saigon on the seventh day, and wanted to go back, so the next day I took an ambulance and two men to ride shotgun, and the three of us did some shopping in Saigon and Bien Hoa Town. While one of us went inside, the other two covered the sidewalk and the door of the shop with rifles. It was odd to see some of the White Mice directing traffic in whites, just like a peacetime scene, while other squads of National Police were dressed in combat uniforms, digging out surviving V.C. a few hundred yards away.

At lunchtime, we were near the turnoff for the 90th Replacement Battalion, so we stopped there. I dropped the men off at the transient mess hall, told them to meet me back there in an hour and a half, and went to the nearby Transient Officers Club for lunch.

And, lo and behold, there was Pops Macabee, just arrived, with all his baggage piled next to him, at his lunch table.

He told me how he'd fractured a fibula on his fourth jump in the parachute school, so had just finished the course.

We ordered four Bloody Marys as an appetizer. He then said that he bore good news: in view of the DOs' good service so far, the Army was going to open at least some of its residency programs to us. Unofficially, their price was two years' service *first*, one of which would be in Vietnam. He planned to apply for an Army pathology program, once his year out here was over. We had a few beers to chase our earlier drinks (long gone is the O-Club bar that opens at 9 AM. Oh, woe!).

After I picked up Sp4s Ristine and Bates, we headed back to the Battalion for a briefing on our next AO.

There were some surprises in the movement plan. Up to now, I had not left the confines of a rectangle 90 miles long by 80 wide, and I thought that probably that would be our territory for the next year. I was amazed to see that we were being attached to the Marines, north of Da Nang, which the French had renamed Tourane. We'd be going by sea, and would move over 500 miles north, mercifully out from under the Division, who seemed determined to kill themselves, which was okay, and us too, which wasn't.

39.

12 February 1968

We individual self-propelled bipedal Army-green cargo units climbed onto the ever-present 2-1/2-ton trucks again and were hauled down the road to New Port. This was my first visit to the modern seaport area built by the Americans on the west bank of the Saigon River. The 6-lane bridge of Route National 1 (abbreviated QL 1) crossed the river north-south at that point, which made it a bimodal (road *and* waterway) choke point. That had made it a high-priority object for VC seizure on 31 January.

The FLN had, however, underestimated the resolve of the ARVN soldiers and National Police in Saigon. The VC who got to the bridge were counter-attacked almost immediately, and failed to hold their objective for more than a few hours. By noon on 1 February the bridge and New Port were back in government hands, where they remained until April, 1975.

From a rise along QL 1, at a distance of half a mile, we could see two transport ships moored there, an LST and a Liberty Ship, either of which *could* have done the job of transporting us. I hoped for the Liberty, which was twice the size of an LST, but it was not to be. Our taxi up-country turned out to be LST 2124, a dirty, rusting, battleship-gray 3500-ton ship designed to carry a company of 21 tanks and its personnel. The ship was *not* in commission, and was manned by a civilian crew of Japanese merchant sailors. Its official designation was United States Naval Ship (USNS) LST 2124, not the USS *any*thing.

And it showed.

We filed aboard, 499 men in spaces meant for 199. There weren't enough latrines for all the men. Even some of *those* latrines were broken. I couldn't find any showers that worked. *Sanitation trouble*, I thought. We were lucky not to have to crap outboard of the bow while squatting in the forward anchor lines, as was the case from 1492 through 1885, hence the origin of the term "the ship's head" for latrine facilities.

That night we sat and lay on the deck, watching the lines of red American-made tracers criss-cross with the green Soviet ones, to the west, upriver, where the ARVN were clearing the last of the V.C. out of Cholon.

The next day we cast off, and sailed down the Saigon River toward Cap Sainte Jacques and the resort city of Vung Tau, where the river ran into the South China Sea. We ate individual combat rations the whole trip. But, fortunately, that, at least, wasn't to be a problem for many of us.

On our way into the estuary of the Saigon River, and as the odor of Saigon's sewage faded, we broke out the booze, over the objections of the ship's Japanese captain. For the first time in months, we were out of range of the enemy, and could get gloriously drunk without fear or doubt about our personal safety. But, sad to relate, it didn't last.

As we reached the Cape, the ship was taken by the swells, and a long "O-o-o-o-h'" went up from 499 throats. The South China Sea is no North Atlantic, but in winter, it's rough enough, especially for a bunch of non-sailors. The high point of the voyage except its end was the episode with Sergeant-Major Washington, who might have been described as a little tubby, getting jammed in a 24-inch diameter main deck hatch.

That eternal trip lasted 4½ days, and I was seasick fully three of them, tossing my cookies the first day, with galloping dry heaves accentuated by the odor of Japanese cooking the next two.

Still, even seasick, I was struck by the beauty of the landscape of the central coast of II Corps, especially those areas where the mountains dropped straight into the sea, the triple-canopy vegetation of the Highlands stopping only at the high tide line.

We arrived in Da Nang Harbor on the fourth day, just as most of us were getting our sea legs. The 499 of us were dirty-bodied, we smelled bad, and the ship wasn't any better than we were on either count. We had some clean clothes, though. We had dragged them in the ship's wake from a heaving line for twenty minutes, and then let them dry in the wind.

40.

19 February 1968

An admiral's gig with a sideboy in whites, standing stiffly at parade rest while underway, sped toward our floating filth-hole to pass us along the port side. The scruffy paratroopers aboard their scruffy LST hooted, and much more, at the spotless boat and its immaculate crew. Fortunately for them, you can't throw a C-ration can more than 100 feet, and our empty whiskey bottles were long empty and gone over the side

We were bused to and quartered in Navy barracks huts for three days while Seabee work parties built a tent city for us, on a stretch of flat white sand called Red Beach (from the 1964 landings), which lay along the north side of Da Nang harbor. We noticed an improvement in our daily rations, and learned that the Navy allocated 18 cents a day more per man for food than the Army did.

It was noticeably cooler that much further north. It rained *hard* with following gusts from the second through the fifth days after our arrival.

Our mission was initially to have been to support the Marine Corps in retaking the city of Hue. Since we had received that order, and our initial briefing at Bien Hoa, however, the Marines had been successful in reoccupying all of it except the central Citadel. *It* had been designed by one of Napoleon's engineers, and had walls 22 feet thick. Breaching *that* would be a job for firepower, and more men wouldn't help much, so we were attached to the 26th Marines (by chance, my father's unit in 1944).

Their next-most important challenge was keeping Highway QL 1 open between Qui Nhon and the DMZ..

They were a little overextended in the half of that mission that involved keeping the main road (immediately renamed "U.S. 1" or "Interstate-1") open between Da Nang and Hue. It was as rough a 65-mile stretch of road as you will ever see. We were tasked with the southern half of it, which ran north from Da Nang to its high point at the Hai Van Pass. There, it started downhill northward toward the coastal plain and ran along it all the way to Hanoi. The principal towns north of Da Nang were Hai Van village, a few farm hamlets, and then Phu Bai, the site of Hue's municipal (and our military) airport. The southern edge of Hue, the old imperial capital city lay nine miles further north..

The road itself was two-lane blacktop. It was undercut with numerous pipe culverts, and had many hairpin switchbacks, which probably doubled the thirteen-mile straight-line distance from Red Beach to Hai Van. The hairpins were well-engineered by the French, who'd originally laid out the roadway during colonial times, allowing low-powered or even animal-drawn vehicles to make it to the pass. On the other hand, blowing up even one culvert would close the road, and there was no way for a vehicle, trapped between a sheer wall up, and another one down, to bypass any obstruction. Thus, the only way to make ground contact with northern I Corps (pronounced "Eye Corps") on the ground was for the Seabees to keep that road open, first with emergency measures as soon as possible, and follow them with permanent replacement of any obstacles. They also improved the highway by blasting half-turnouts into the uphill walls, and concreting the other half of them onto the downhill sides. I imagine that, like the huge modern ports at Cam Ranh and Saigon, and the 37 hard-surfaced airfields we left behind, the NVA found them most useful, and still do.

* * *

There was a Marine surface-to-air missile (SAM) battery equipped with Hawk missiles located on a high point near Hai Van. The sides of the emplacement were vertical cliffs, probably un-climbable by men coming up from below. The battery's mission was to defend Da Nang Air base against attack from the air. The VC occasionally mortared them, for practice, I think. They seldom wasted more than one or two shells at a time. After all, the Marines were no threat to the VC up there. They could no more come down than the VC could come up. Both sides were stalemated, in a Mexican (or I guess, Vietnamese) standoff, and pretty much ignored each other.

* * *

For most of its length between Saigon and Hanoi, U.S. 1 is paralleled by, and in most cases is visible from, a one-track railroad, unused since 1956. Trains are a terrorist's meat. No moving target is more predictable, and so more vulnerable, than rail traffic.

The first day that 2/502 patrolled off the highway, its "C" Company walked up on 23 VC or NVA, all with rifles.

The soldiers had been seated in a circle, *facing the center*, eating lunch. After spreading out until they covered a third of the circle, the Americans directed their first shots onto the far side of the VC group, progressively firing at nearer targets as the men furthest away went down. Since Charlie Company was well-dispersed, and outnumbered the VC five to one, it was all over in fifteen seconds. The furthest distant VC was only sixty yards away. At that short range, the first bursts of fire killed them all. I suspect the enemy wasn't used to lightweight, fast-moving patrols operating that far off the road. Whatever the reason, like Santa

Ana at San Jacinto, they hadn't put guards out for security.

Perverse as it sounds to say it now, I remember that as an exceptionally good day.

* * *

We dismounted from our deuce-and-a-half trucks to relieve a Marine platoon which had been covering a short stretch of U.S. 1.

We were kept alert by the occasional high or wide rifle bullet fired in our general direction.

It was a foggy, cool, almost cold morning, with poor visibility.

You could smell the mix of fog and fresh-dug earth, where the Seabees had been at work.

Our men got onto the road, and immediately dispersed, fanning out a few meters beyond the shoulders on both sides of the road, to present as non-lucrative a target as possible. The Marine platoon leader walked out to the middle of the asphalt slab and shouted, "GIVE ME A FORMATION OUT HERE!"

Ordering his men to concentrate, when sanity would dictate dispersal.

Brave as hell.

Not very bright, though.

* * *

The next night at Red Beach, we were mortared .

From the rate of fire and the muzzle flash, I'd say that it was a two-man team and one 60mm mortar shooting. The incident lasted for about 20 minutes.

There wasn't much damage done, and no casualties were reported.

An episode occurred during the attack that night that yet again illustrates the difference between the First Brigade and other units. All during the slow, deliberate mortar fire there was a pair of permanent-party Marine guards hunkered-down nearby in a heavily-sandbagged watchtower, armed with an M-60 machine gun.

I shouted up at them, and asked "Why aren't you guys shooting back?"

One of the guards called down: "Orders are to stay under cover if we're mortared or rocketed."

"But, listen," I yelled, "a sixty-mortar only carries 1000 yards, usually less, and if *we* can see the muzzle flash from the ground, you should be able to see it from 20 feet higher."

"Yes," said the sentry, "we *can* see it; it's about 600 yards out."

" Then," I hollered again, persisting, "your gun can hit any target less than 1000 yards away, and even if you don't shoot up the crew, you can sure scare them and spoil their aim."

"Sorry, sir, can't do it. Orders."

I gave up, and went back to a bunker.

I couldn't find my dog-tags after the episode, so I'd probably lost them taking cover.

I'd have gone to the Seabee Officers' Club, but orders closed *it*, too, if we were mortared. It was a beautiful permanent structure, with a great bar, free movies every night, and a big, native stone central fireplace pit, the first I'd ever seen.

Business was slow the next day, so I made a courtesy call to the CO of Headquarters Company, 26th Marines. I mentioned that my father had served in the company. An officer? No, he'd been a PFC jeep driver. He did a double-take, and then roared with laughter. We parted after a great cup of strong Navy coffee.

Da Nang's city streets reminded me of Saigon. They were busy, crowded and bustling. I saw my first children, long-healed but missing an arm or a leg, likely casualties of mine warfare. No prostheses, not even a home-whittled peg-leg, were available to them, so they got by as best they could, one-handed, or on a crutch, whichever applied.

After we'd been in operating around Da Nang for several days, my jeep ambulance was pretty dirty from all the convoying. Driving north on U.S. 1, I pulled into a roadside shop marked "CAR WASH!!!" in three-foot-high red letters. The fact that there was no fresh water source for several miles should have tipped me off that something was amiss. When the four pretty girls came out to be selected, I decided to leave. Had I been alone, or if my enlisted crew had been, might that decision have been different?

Spilled milk, again.

* * *

Two nights later, at twilight, I saw a four-mile-long convoy of civilian trucks, busses, cars, motorcycles and motor scooters coming south from Hai Van, headlights blazing. It was the first civilian traffic to make it south from Hue in two months, even in broad daylight, much less at sundown. The next night, I saw (and was *proud* to see) the first *train* to make it in years. The steam-fired engine looked like the ones you'll see in photos of the First World War, moving supplies or troops. Still, old as at was, it worked well enough to pull 27 freight cars. And our aggressive patrolling had made it possible.

Ten days later, it was time to move again. We were still in support of the Marine Corps, who had, it must be said, gotten over-ambitious and overly optimistic in the extreme north of the country, and were under pressure, from Dong Ha on the South China Sea, west to Lang Vei on the Laotian border. Their ability to hold Khe Sanh was in doubt in Washington, though not by anyone in Vietnam. Their opposition, in that close proximity to North Vietnam, was solidly NVA, backed up by field artillery firing from Laos and from inside North Vietnam.

The First Brigade would set up at Phu Bai, and the Second would reinforce the First Cavalry Division south of Quang Tri. When the signal was given, we, two brigades strong, plus a reinforced regiment of Marines would converge on Khe Sanh from three directions, reopen U.S. 9, and lift the three-months-long siege.

41.

27 February 1968

I flew north to Phu Bai late, and was one of the last to close on our new base at Gia Le, three miles west of Phu Bai. It was located on the east bank of a creek, and at the line where the coastal flats ended, and the first grass-covered inland hills began.

As nearly as I was able to reconstruct it, at about this time United States Army, Vietnam (USARV) decided that, with three divisions of Army forces in northern I Corps, a command and control structure was needed, since the Army mission of supporting the Marines was growing steadily. With that in mind they activated the Twenty-Fourth U.S. Corps (Provisional) at Camp Hochmuth, a large Marine base south of Phu Bai. Our mission in what I later found was Thua Thien Province was continued, but under Army control. The rations dropped by 18 cents-worth a day, again.

XXIV Corps (Prov) was making its influence felt, already.

I hitched a ride to the MSR and, as always, could walk to where the aid station usually was; I found it up and running. All the other sections were located to the inch in the same relative positions as they'd occupied in both earlier base camps. Except they *called* this place Camp Eagle, implying a semi-permanence, and it was unofficially called "Rocket City."

I dropped off my gear, broke out a clean uniform, and went to grab a shower. The shower point was set up in an open-sided 12-foot high pyramidal teepee-pole rig, and about halfway through my ablutions, I noted a silent orange fireball 200 yards away, closely followed by the booming sound of its explosion. I *thought* I recognized the same type 105mm artillery shellburst we'd adjusted in OCS. My immediate impression was that the NVA must have captured some ARVN guns, and turned them on us. We tend to interpret data based on past experience, rather than on what should be obvious.

I dived stark naked into the lowest depression that I could see, but they only fired once more, and stopped. That was my introduction to the ubiquitous Soviet Katyusha 122mm rocket.

I went back to retrieve my soap, and found my shower clogs neatly placed side by side, slightly turned out at the toes, where they'd been when I jumped out of them.

One of our new men was brought in to the aid station later that same day. He'd been shot through the right foot, at the instep, entrance wound on top. That kind of wound always requires hospital care, so I evacuated him. Probably self-inflicted, it usually required 6 months in Long Binh Jail (LBJ, again), too, which was no concern of mine.

2/502 was providing interim security to a rock quarry where a Seabee company was operating a gravel crusher to get material for their various projects in the area. That had been the battalion's first mission north of the Hai Van Pass. Except for one inaccurate mortaring on the second night, that operation had been uneventful. Then, the battalion was alerted to move again.

We'd be deploying west within 24 hours as part of Operation Pegasus, along with the 1st Air Cavalry Division, to lift the siege of Khe Sanh. I was receiving my daily hometown papers about ten days late, but was able to follow public opinion that way. The media were making a great fuss about four thousand marines being surrounded (usually on only three sides, I have to interject) by two NVA divisions. An NVA division at that time would run 6000 men or so. The marines at Khe Sanh were thus outnumbered a little under three to one.

It takes a minimum ratio of *four men* to one to break through a modern defensive line, and the Northerners didn't have it. What they *did* have was round-the clock low-level air attack with napalm, rockets, and bombs, high-altitude B-52 strikes day and night, no air force of their own, rampant malaria, dysentery, hepatitis, inability to resupply, and a medical system right out of the 1860s to treat their sick and wounded. They were also matched by artillery return fire at a ratio of at least four shells received for every one that they fired.

When Pegasus' advance units approached Khe Sanh, they found....nothing. No *one*. The NVA were gone. As I told you earlier, rather than fight when they didn't have the advantage and the odds, they'd pull out and try again later. They are a very patient people, and that patience probably won the war.

Operation Pegasus was canceled.

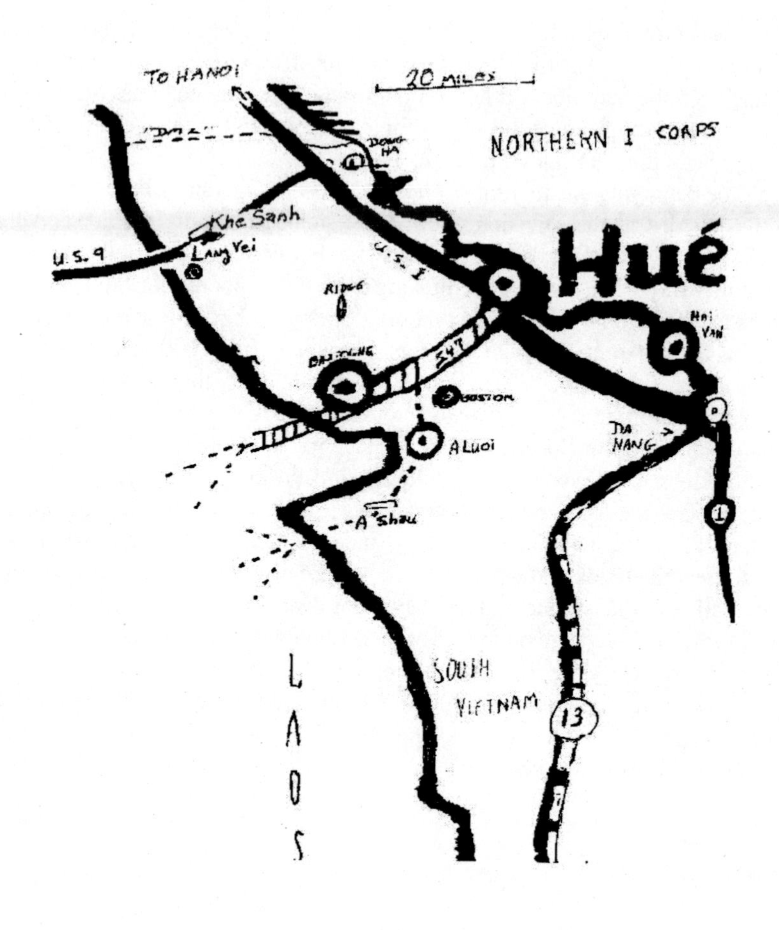

NORTHERN I CORPS

NORTHERN I CORPS

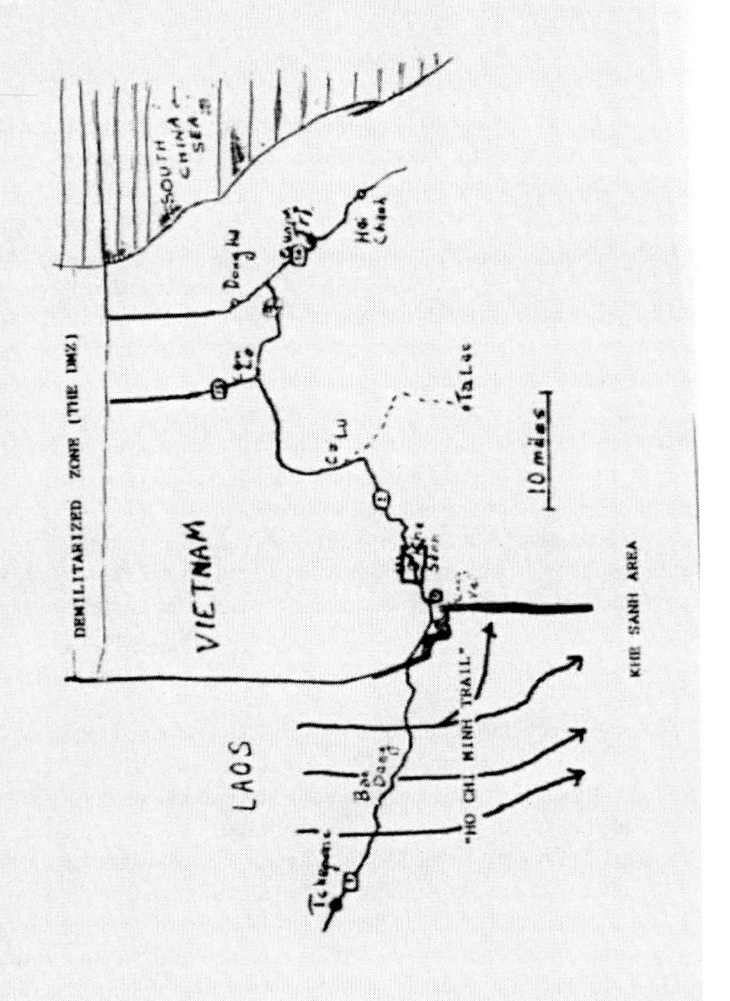

DEMILITARIZED ZONE (THE DMZ)
SOUTH CHINA SEA
Dong Ha
VIETNAM
LAOS
Ca Lu
10 miles
"HO CHI MINH TRAIL"
KHE SANH AREA

42.

1 March 1968

The village of A Luoi lies two miles or so east of A Shau. It was intermittently inhabited, further from the Laotian border, and of less importance to the war than A Shau or any other border ville.

The dirt road, like an American farm road, that ran (and runs) from Hue west-southwest, through A Luoi, to the border village of A Shau, had been abandoned since 1966. We called this road "U.S. 547". In the French times it was Regional Road 547. The road climbed, unimproved, into the hill country of southern Laos, and broke up into branches intended for the use of the colonial European plantation owners who had spent the summers there, growing rubber, tea, and a little coffee. The more affluent of them had wintered in the low, seaside areas such as Nha Trang or Vung Tau. All that, by 1968, was over a decade in the past.

Our first task as a brigade was to re-establish control over the Vietnamese segment of 547, and probably to do it by re-occupying an east-west line consisting of several abandoned Marine Corps firebases running in a rough line along it. We would probably patrol alongside the road to keep it open. Moreover, we'd base long-range 175mm guns at the westernmost base in the chain, which could direct fire into Laos, onto the Ho Chi Minh Trail (*their* MSR), and, finally, we would base secret long-range reconnaissance patrols there, too, going into Laos and coming out.

2/502 was selected to occupy the west end, and renamed the place "FSB Bastogne," after the battle in late 1944 where the 101st had performed well in a last-ditch battle against the Germans. And, surrounded, outnumbered and out-gunned, had held them off till they were relieved.

The other FSBs were located so that no one of them would ever be out of artillery range of at least two others. We'd learned from Khe Sanh.

On my second trip back to Eagle in a CH-47, I heard someone hitting the hull sharply with a stick, from outside. At 2000 feet. We'd been hit in several places, including the starboard engine, by thirty-caliber fire, and the pilot was setting it down while he still had control.

The crew chief leaned over and yelled, over the engine noise, "Hang on, Sir, we're going to hit hard."

He was telling the truth. When we stopped bouncing around, I was gratified to see that no one was hurt. The eight of us aboard jumped out, formed a perimeter, and waited for a response to the pilot's "Mayday." It took about ten minutes for another Chinook to arrive with 25 men to defend the bird, and to evacuate us, no harm done. Scary, but it could have been a lot worse.

FSB Bastogne differed from all the other ones I'd seen so far. It was to be permanently reoccupied. *That* made us a target for shellfire or for ground attack, but the firepower on and around Bastogne was so heavy that only the former was ever tried. Even sniping at Bastogne was risky for the shooter, considering the amount of counterfire that even a single rifleman would draw.

About this time, the weather turned bad. Fog persisted until nearly noon, and heavy rain was common about 4 PM. Air support for personnel transport and for resupply had very a narrow window, to come and go.

* * *

Ten days after we occupied Bastogne, I was in the medical bunker (generically called "The Batcave" because we kept making them successively larger and more elaborate). There was the occasional rifle bullet coming our way, usually high, hitting nothing.

At 11 AM (1100) on the fourth day of our occupation of the FSB, the cloudiest and foggiest one to date, I heard a sentry call out in a manner familiar to anyone who had finished basic training, with its formal guard mounts: "Corporal of the Guard! Corporal of the Guard!" *Corporal of the guard?* Hell, I don't think that we even *had* NCOs of the guard in combat. And if it had been the enemy that the sentry had seen, he'd just have opened fire. Obviously, to everyone within earshot, *something* unusual was happening.

Behind me, I heard an alert mortar section sergeant quietly but clearly, begin the sequence for firing, just in case: "SECTION, Action Left. Range two hundred-fifty yards, do NOT load. Wait."

There was a platoon column of men wearing green fatigues and American helmets coming east on 547, out of Laos. I saw that they were carrying what looked like six wounded on pole litters. I called for a volunteer to help and grabbed an aid bag, heading for the gate-barrier in our wire. I knew that security required that *any* strange armed men not be allowed inside the perimeter. When I got there, I went outside the wire obstacles and began to examine the wounded, laying them out in a line along the north shoulder of the road. I looked up, and saw that three of my men had silently come with me. All three of them were carrying aid-bags and intravenous (IV) fluids in vinyl bags.

The soldiers who made up the column coming toward the gate were native Laotians, fighting as contract soldiers for the CIA, who'd gotten into a spot a little over their heads, and instead of trying for air extraction in this miserable weather, had elected to *walk* out to the east, and had unexpectedly gotten away with it. The officer and the unwounded men were wearing lightweight green muslin facial scarves, against the dust clouds they were causing as they shuffled along.

The men and I started our routine, starting intravenous fluids or plasma albumin, re-dressing wounds, starting antibiotics, and leaving splints alone. We ignored the occasional rifle bullet that was fired in our general direction. They were shooting high and wide of us. I don't think that there was one *real* sniper in the entire NVA, by the standards of previous wars, or even of my peacetime training.

Major Nguyen, our liaison officer, stopped me when we were finished and embraced me, French-style, and kissed me on both cheeks. I was flabbergasted, but stayed cool, and, not knowing the correct procedure, saluted in return.

The Laotians' white officer never fully uncovered his face, nor did he say a word to me. I'd guess it was for security reasons, on a covert operation such as this one.

Our S-4 was able to get the injured men out by aeromedical evacuation and the others in unmarked slick Hueys to an unknown address in Hue. That was the only time in the entire year that I saw any evidence of what later came to be called the CIA's "Secret War" in Laos.

* * *

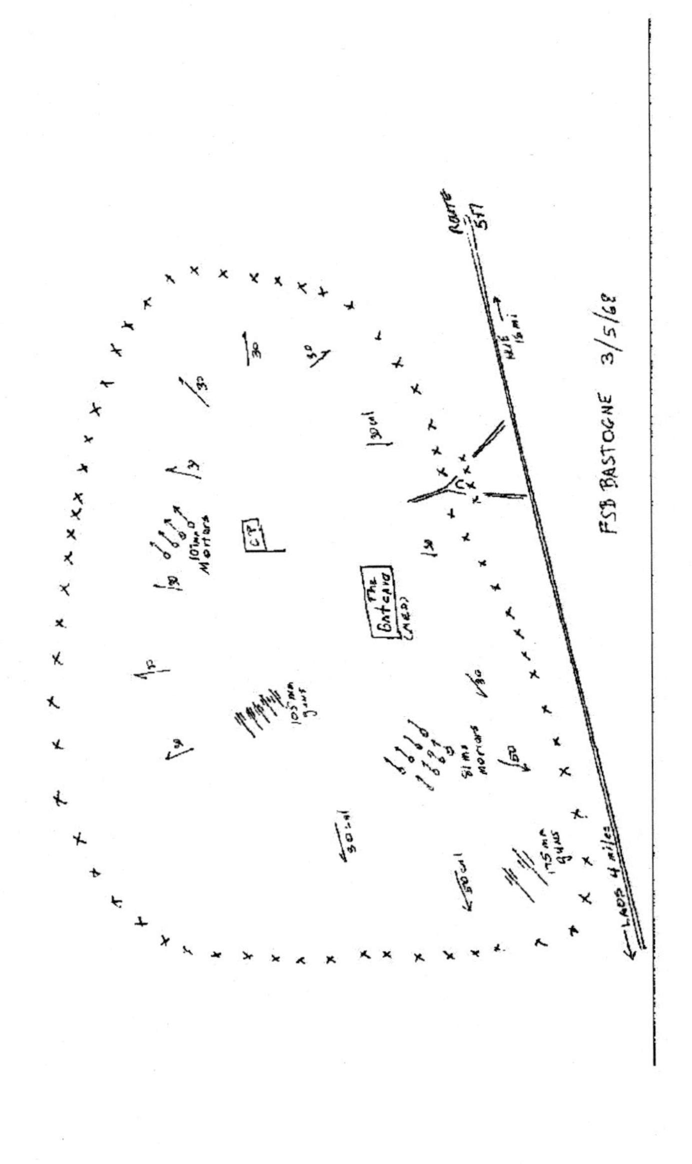

I heard no more about the incident, except that it resulted in my being awarded a Vietnamese medal for gallantry, months later, as recommended by that ARVN major.

* * *

We heard on the radio news that Martin Luther King had been murdered in Memphis. *He* was dead and no one could help him; we tried to stay alive.

We kept doing our jobs.

* * *

The Ho Chi Minh Trail ran north-south to the west of A Shau village, which lay on the edge of an abandoned PSP airfield. The NVA had taken it from the Special Forces "A" Team who had garrisoned it, in 1964. They had controlled, occasionally occupying it outright, it ever since. Aerial photographs taken later that same day, in 1964, showed uniformed men digging three trenches across the runway to make it unusable by airplanes.

Our next operation was to be an incursion into A Shau and the surrounding area. Ours would be the first American (or ARVN) units to set foot there since the NVA had arrived. The purpose of our visit was to see if we could interrupt traffic in men and materiel significantly, and to inflict casualties.

The operation would begin forty minutes after a B-52 strike, which would lay down a bomb line half a mile wide and six miles long between A Shau and the Laotian border, roughly parallel to the trail of mud ruts christened "U.S. 548."

Exactly twenty minutes after the last bomb fell, our artillery and mortars, directed by our brigade Artillery Liaison Officer (ALO) would begin a slow, steady fire onto likely enemy positions. The last targets to be shelled, at a more rapid, crescendoing rate of fire, would be the landing zones. The fire would be lifted no more than two minutes before the assaulting troops touched down.

The first wave, a battalion force of 800 men, jumped off by helicopter assault from FSB Veghel. a few miles west of Bastogne, and landed in the village of A Shau itself.

The second wave, a force of similar size, left Bastogne to arrive next to A Shau airfield, opposite the village, five minutes after the first wave touched down

Another battalion would air-assault onto a hilltop a mile east of A Shau at the same time that the second wave landed.

The three groups would then move west and recon in force, the rearmost linking up with the force ahead, to further reinforce the more forward elements.

The first company-sized waves met determined resistance, and it included a high percentage of anti-aircraft or dual-purpose machine guns laid along all axes of approach from the east and south. In fact, we lost nine Hueys the first day, though most of their crews and passengers were rescued.

Once our units were on the ground in force, though, the picture changed rapidly. There wasn't much infantry in place, and the NVA's transport and support troops seemed more inclined to run and to rally later than to fight. After all, their job was to move cargo, not to fight the Americans, especially if they were locally outnumbered two or three to one. As usual, the speed and surprise of a multi-focal large-scale helicopter assault, coupled with overwhelming simultaneous artillery fire and air strikes swept the defenders off their hilltop positions, many of their antiaircraft positions, and the ditched-across airfield. Then, even with the ditches, that runway and its grassy aprons then made a perfect large-scale *helicopter* landing zone (LZ) for the second and third echelons of troops to close upon, and to receive the reinforcing waves of light artillery, signal and medical personnel.

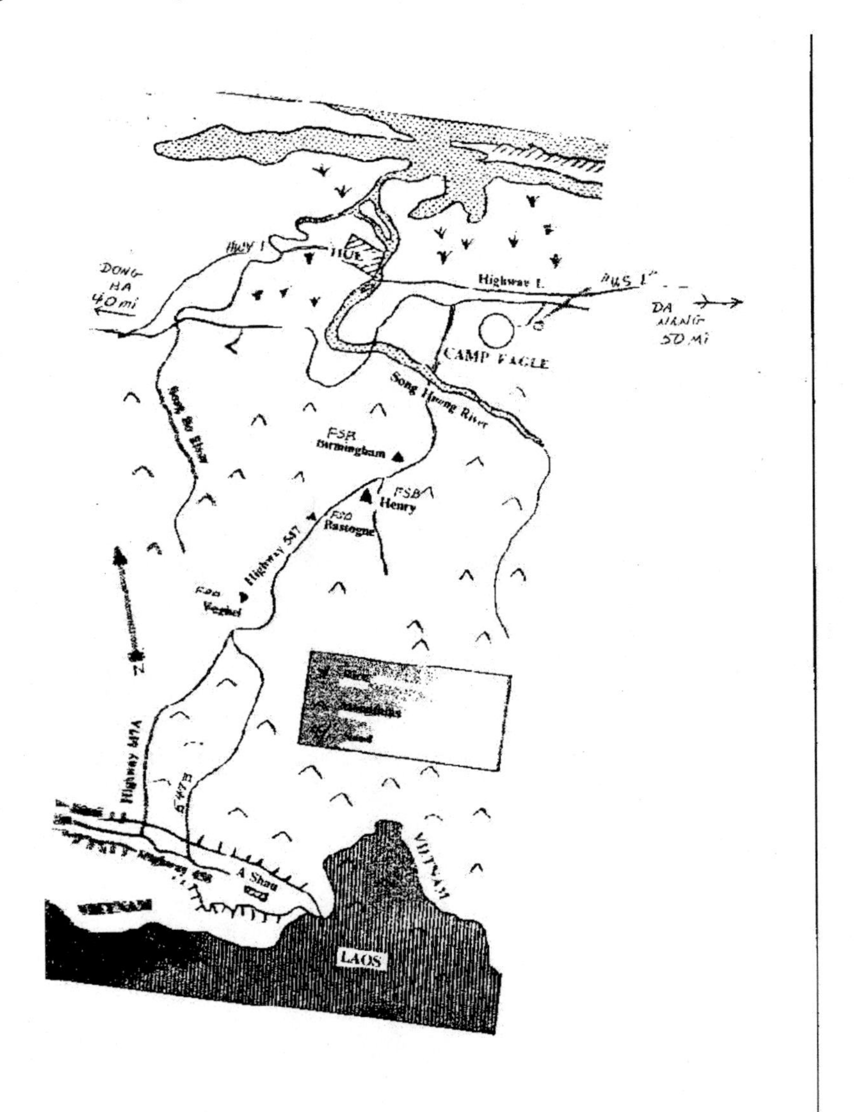

Patrols quickly fanned out north, west and south. Almost all of them, within the first tree lines, began to capture dumps of long-range artillery pieces, trucks, spare parts, rations, and so much ammunition that it took three days to count it all. As the second and third waves came up to the airfield, they reported having found similar caches on their way in. Evidently, the NVA thought that we were *never* coming back.

I have always hated to be the bearer of bad news.

For a loss of 37 American KIA, we found 381 Northerners dead, most killed by bomb and artillery fragment wounds.

My battalion had been in the second wave.

By noon on the first day of the operation, the battalion commander released Company B from patrolling. It was detailed, instead, to police up as much enemy equipment as it was possible to retrieve.

Working as separate platoon task groups. B Company hitched all eighteen of the Soviet-made 130mm guns we had found to 18 Russian trucks, with full loads of ammunition. Seven other trucks were filled with as much high-trading-value loot, such as AK-47s, that the could carry. Then this convoy (the equivalent of a field artillery battalion), with Marine M-48 tanks at the front and rear for security, drove east along 547, past Bastogne, past FSB Veghel, through Hue, and on into Camp Eagle. Anything that we couldn't move was destroyed.

The morning after the captured gear was brought in, the Soviet trucks were apportioned out to the Brigade's battalions. For once, the airborne units had nearly enough transportation. The guns were lined up, hub-to-hub near Brigade Headquarters, and all their ammunition was fired back onto the Ho Chi Minh Trail at odd hours of the night, when the NVA was likely to be moving, safe from air observation. After their ammunition was exhausted, the guns were shipped back to the United States, one to a post, as long as the supply lasted, with the caveat that two (naturally) were reserved for our home post of Ft. Campbell, Kentucky.

One of the 130mm guns, painted green, can be seen in the Artillery Museum at Ft. Sill, Oklahoma today.

* * *

I was able to get some time off, enough to make a day-trip into Hue. It was my first exposure to the civilian culture this far north, and it was quite different from that seen in the southern regions of the country. The Chinese influence on the architecture was much more noticeable. The tiled roofs of even the most humble dwellings were turned up, pagoda-like, at the corners.

Bhuddist culture does not dictate the use of cemeteries, as do most Christian sects. All along the road (U.S. 1, formerly Route Colonial 1, then Route National 1), just off the shoulder, I saw the foot-high stucco walls that demarcated the usual six-by-three-foot outlines of individual graves, laid out in no particular order, location, or density. My impression is that those were the graves of rural ancestors of the current occupiers of the tiny farms that lined the road. The better-kept graveside walls were painted blue, the traditional Oriental color denoting death and mourning.

Near the intersection of U.S.1 and the MSR to First Brigade was a small temple. It was unique in that it served *all three* of the religions found nearby. The altar across the back wall of the nave (for want of a more specific descriptor) was laid out, left to right, with a life-sized Virgin Mary behind a bank of votive candles. A one-and-a-half-times life-size gold-colored Buddha sat in the middle, in front of a painted backdrop showing a sacred banyan tree. On the right was a mosaic-tiled column, which I understood was used by the Cao Dai segment of the congregation.

Before the altar was a glass-topped library table, with photographs of the departed parishioners, mostly young, mostly casualties of the war.

The interior color scheme was of a cheerful red and gold, bright against the off-white walls.

Eight miles up the road, on the south edge of Hue, was an *art moderne* French-designed Catholic cathedral with a single 12-inch-diameter hole in the front face, the result of a 90mm tank cannon's shell, fired into it during the Tet Offensive.

The city is roughly circular, split into north and south sides by the Perfume River, which runs west to east, widening rather precipitously, then becoming an estuary, then opening onto the South China Sea, all in no more than four linear miles from the center of Hue.

The city of Hue itself was a pretty knocked around. The Tet attack/occupation and the US-ARVN counter-attack had torn things up badly.

The Perfume River at that time was crossed north-to-south by a four-lane highway bridge, and further to the west, by a railroad bridge. Those were the first two structures that the VC had blown up, to drop into the river, when they saw that their Tet Offensive was lost, and that they would have to leave. They'd have to try to escape to he west, perhaps as far as the highlands of Laos, sixty miles away.

They did a better job of destroying the larger four-lane road bridge, though civilians still were able to wade across the fallen center span, in single file, at its narrowest point above water. I think their pathway was the top of the west-most concrete bridge rail.

Our engineers had filled in enough around the dropped end of the railway span to pave it over and allow for one-way alternating vehicle traffic, though at any speed over ten miles per hour the exposed railroad ties made pretty rough riding.

There was a *faux*-French four-lane boulevard along the river banks both north and south of the Perfume River.

Along the landward side of the broad avenue on the north bank lay the south wall of the Citadel, the huge, mile-and-a-quarter square Napoleonic (or the earlier 17th-Century Vauban-like?) fortress I'd heard of, but not seen, until this trip.

* * *

A six-week-old letter from Bill Anderson, my 1954 fellow-recruit in the Kansas National Guard, caught up with me after our four moves in the past 45 days. In it, he advised me that he was writing from Camp Carson, Colorado; the old Second Battalion had been mobilized and called into Federal service a couple of weeks after the Tet Offensive had begun. As infantrymen, none of the men doubted they were headed to Southeast Asia. He also said he'd look me up when he arrived in Vietnam, if he could.

I wrote his wife, Marcia, and asked her to keep me advised of Bill's mailing address, so that I could get in contact with *him*, once he had "APO San Francisco" preceding his zip code.

* * *

43.

18 March 1968

The battalion was moved seven miles straight north to a north-south ridgeback position, well-covered by the artillery on FSBs Bastogne and Veghel. It was an odd type of firebase itself, because of its shape, and the almost cliff-like slopes on both sides and both ends of the elongated "goose-egg." The unwary trooper who mis-stepped might roll a hundred feet downhill before being able to stop himself. Any attempt to drop a mortar shell onto it would probably miss the narrow crest, and hit far down the slopes. An attempt to assault the position would be like trying to climb a cliffside while 200 men fired down at you, while under artillery fire from other firebases. Not a promising prospect, either way. The only downside was that our companies on patrol would not be able to walk in for refit and recuperation, as they had previously. They'd have to be airlifted like everything and everybody else on the ridge (called FSB Ridge, logically enough). I once heard it described succinctly as "hard to land on, hard to stand on, hard to drop a shell on, easy to fall off of."

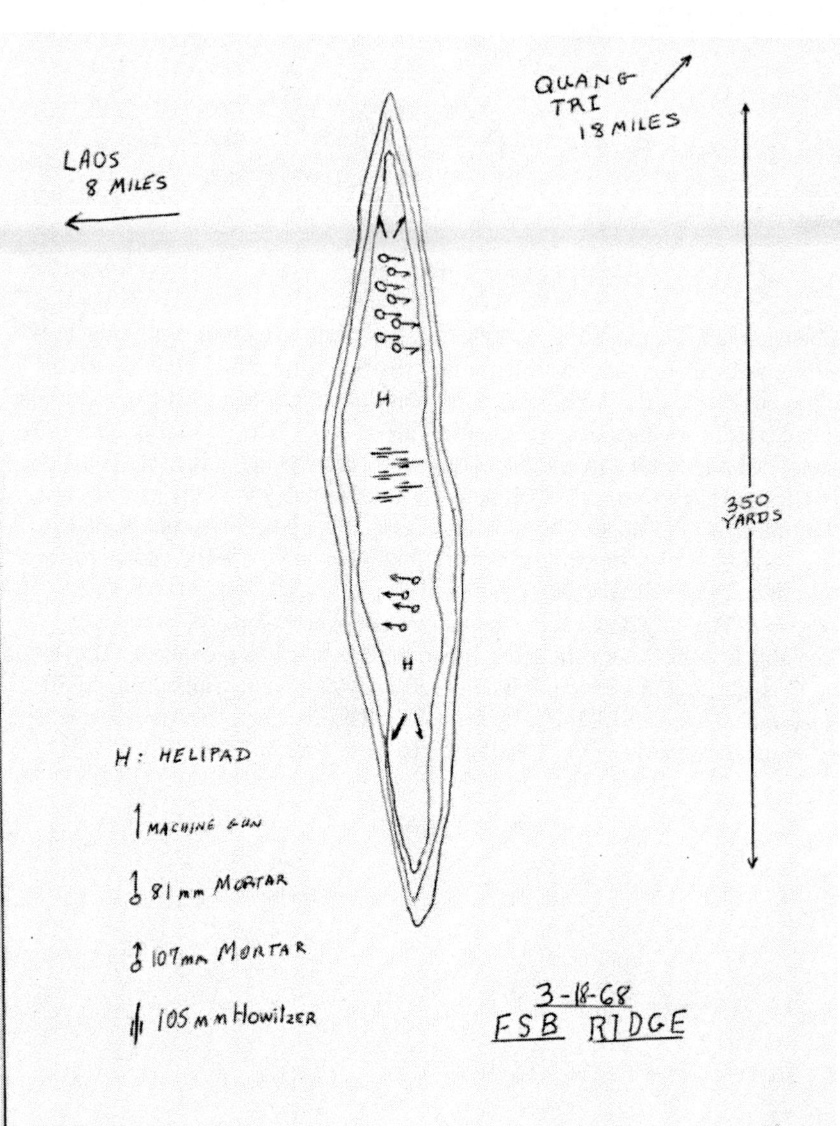
QUANG TRI 18 MILES
LAOS 8 MILES
H
H
350 YARDS
H: HELIPAD
MACHINE GUN
81mm MORTAR
107mm MORTAR
105mm Howitzer
3-18-68
FSB RIDGE

* * *

On a resupply mission to "A" Company, I was shown a cache of small arms in a base area that they had overrun. It had been covered with rubberized canvas and then *that* covered with six inches of earth. I spotted what looked like a brand-new Chinese SKS rifle, and appropriated it. What was one out of over a hundred weapons? Anyway, it was OK to bring small arms home, as long as they were legal to possess in the United States. No automatic weapons allowed, but the SKS is a semi-auto, and there must be a couple of dozen of that category manufactured commercially, for hunting.

I later found a thirty-caliber bullet gouge on the left side of the pistol-grip, but that was easily fixed with a little Plastic Wood, and some judicious sanding and staining. Otherwise, overall, if the piece had ever been fired, I couldn't find any evidence of it. It was spotlessly clean.

Weapons Cache, Uncovered by 2/502, 21 March 1968.

* * *

The second day at Ridge, one of our companies patrolling in the surrounding low country walked into an ambush, and CPT Bill Anthony, the company commander, was killed outright. He had been a superbly-trained consummate professional, was well-liked, and his future had seemed promising in the extreme. His loss cast a kind of pall over 2/502 that day. Most of us had looked up to him. If he could be killed, then the chances of life and death in combat had to be about

80% sheer, dumb luck, and that, do what we might, anyone's luck could run out.

* * *

Two other episodes occur to me, as clearly as if they'd happened yesterday, that illustrate the influence of luck as opposed to preservation of life and limb by superior training.

In the first incident, a man on FSB Ridge was struck by lightning, and all five of the grenades that he had been carrying on his belt exploded, leaving only his legs and his head and shoulders recognizable. It would have been almost impossible for the NVA to have harmed him, but lightning......Well, if you can figure out a way to avoid it on a high bald hill, the Army would like to know about it. Electrical storms form fast, and if you are living outdoors, as the old saw goes, it never rains in the Army. It rains *on* it.

The second event occurred later, after I got my command. I was taking sick call when a low-pitched loud roar went up nearby. It had been a 155mm howitzer shell, fired 100 mils off deflection, landing on *us* instead of several thousand yards to the west. Eight men carried in a marine lieutenant, dead as a stone, exsanguinated from a high abdominal large-fragment wound that probably involved the lower chest, posteriorly. The questions pile up in my head as I write: Who *was* this Marine? Why was he in our area? Who could say why the gun captain didn't catch the error, and above all why the hell did all of those factors coincide *in the same time and place*, to produce a corpse who had certainly expected to live out this day in a rear area?

* * *

"(They are) doubly dead because they died so young."

Harvey Cushing, M.D., on his
companions who were killed, 1917-1918.

* * *

44.

24 March 1968

On the battalion's sixth day at Ridge, Company A was patrolling four miles to the west when it came under fire from what they thought were three four-round volleys of artillery shells, probably the 85mm caliber used by the Soviet bloc. The explosions had been marginally larger than those made by an 81mm mortar shell, and smaller than those of a 122mm rocket. The men of "A" Company had heard them coming in; the shells had *sounded* like artillery projectiles rattling in flight, not mortar rounds. Their impact zone had probably been pre-registered; the shells in each volley had all struck close together, and no attempt had been made to adjust them. That argued against observed fire.

The company's attached artillery forward observer (FO) (better him than me, I thought) had run to the impact site, and done a rapid crater analysis on four of the shell-holes. They all showed that their point of origin lay on an azimuth of about 270 degrees true from the point of impact.

By chance, the forward air controller (FAC) of a neighboring unit had seen and reported a fine blue smoke plume over the upper canopy of jungle in the windless air to his west, at the same time that the shelling was reported.

The battalion operations officer plotted the smoke's location on his map. It lay 270 degrees (dead-on west) from "A" Company, and was roughly five-and-a-half miles from it. He wasted no time in forming his plan, and alerted Company "D" and the Recon Platoon (its hepatitis cases now recovered or replaced) to prepare to air-assault in twenty minutes. He cleared his plan with the battalion commander, and called for a shuttle force of six Hueys. He got five.

He planned to assault directly onto the gun position in three waves, hitting hard and fast, the entire operation taking an hour an a half or less. The gun crews themselves weren't likely to be much of an obstacle, and hopefully they would have no infantry support. If the attack didn't go as planned every man was told, going in, that the rally point was a stand of wild banana trees 200 yards south of the suspected NVA battery position.

The only real drawback to the plan was that the guns were located nearly three miles inside Laos.

The C.O. chose to ignore the border, remarking that even on the map it was marked as "Unmarked and Poorly Surveyed, Demarcation is Approximate." So off they went.

It worked like a charm.

The magic probably lay in the elements of surprise and rapid response.

Under local control, the helicopters flew at treetop level to the LZ. When they arrived, the M-60s on the slicks laid down covering fire, while they hovered just off the ground. The men jumped off, and as soon as they were on the ground began to fire along the long axis of the gun line, moving slowly behind their own fire, sweeping along the battery position from end to end. As they came to bunkers and fighting positions, they would shoot into them, sometimes throwing a grenade in if there were any blind spots inside. Once the gun line was cleared, the men went into a perimeter by squads, and waited for the second wave.

There had been no resistance. Not a shot was fired at the helicopters or the men.

The place was deserted, though from the evidence of still-burning fires, and wet laundry still in buckets, it had been occupied until very recently.

The guns, four American-made 75-mm pack howitzers, were still in place. The NVA had not had time to take them, or much else, when they'd evacuated a few minutes before. They hadn't had time to booby-trap either the guns or the position.

The Artillery Liaison Officer came out from our firebase with the third wave. He had brought four thermite grenades along. After directing eight men to bayonet the guns' tires beyond repair, he pulled the pin from each grenade, let the handle pop away, and loaded the grenade into the breech of each gun, quickly closing the breechblock before ignition of the thermite. A few seconds after the metal filings began to burn, the temperature in the howitzers' firing chambers rose to several thousand degrees, welding the barrel, rifling, and breechblock into a single solid mass of junk.

Those guns could never be fired again. They were each now just a ton or so of irreparable old iron that had probably been captured by the Chinese Communists from American aid supplies to the Nationalists in 1949, shipped by rail or truck into North Vietnam, and then hand- and bicycle-carried three hundred miles through the jungle, down the Ho Chi Minh Trail.

Company "C" had ben the last unit to arrive on the battery position, and was the last to be withdrawn. Before they left, they mined and booby-trapped the battery and its approaches to a fare-thee-well.

Everyone left by reverse shuttle. Not a man was wounded in the operation. And not a word was ever said, to my knowledge, about the incursion into Laotian territory.

*

45.

30 March 1968

Our battalion briefly traded places with another, and was airlifted to a camelback hilltop a few miles away. It was reminiscent of our position at Bao Lac, and had been christened FSB Boston. During our time there, Brigade placed a Forward Supply Team there, too, to provide rapid supply to the four battalions operating in the immediate vicinity. That, in turn was necessary because of the incessant rain and fog, which only cleared consistently from about 10 AM to 2 PM.

The increased supply levels at Boston inevitably led to a degree of accumulation of materiel. That, in turn, led to an also-inevitable amount of small-time pilferage. One morning I awoke to the sight of one of my men unloading a stolen 64-ounce can of prime boned chicken from under his poncho. Boiled up with my last half-kilogram of rice and three onions, with five GI supply-issue salt tablets added, it was delicious when served with a few drops of someone else's Tabasco sauce.

Since CPT Anthony's death, we had been meeting very little resistance, and our casualties were correspondingly light.

I took advantage of the lull to return to the rear in Rocket City, pick up some medical supplies to bring forward in the morning, as well as to catch up my overdue paperwork.

That was the night the North Vietnamese attacked Boston.

Most of us in the battalion rear stayed up all night listening to the radio traffic from Boston, the surrounding FSBs, and the Air Force night intruder flights trying to follow the action.

I was on the first reinforcing helicopter flight to take off at first light. All the way to Boston, I kept kicking myself mentally for choosing that night to come in (but how do you predict the right one?), and for not being there when I might have been needed.

The sun shone from behind us as we flew west toward the firebase. On the hilltop ahead, I was able to see what looked like a huge spoked wheel, or perhaps a sunburst, with the hub roughly corresponding to the location of our concertina wire.

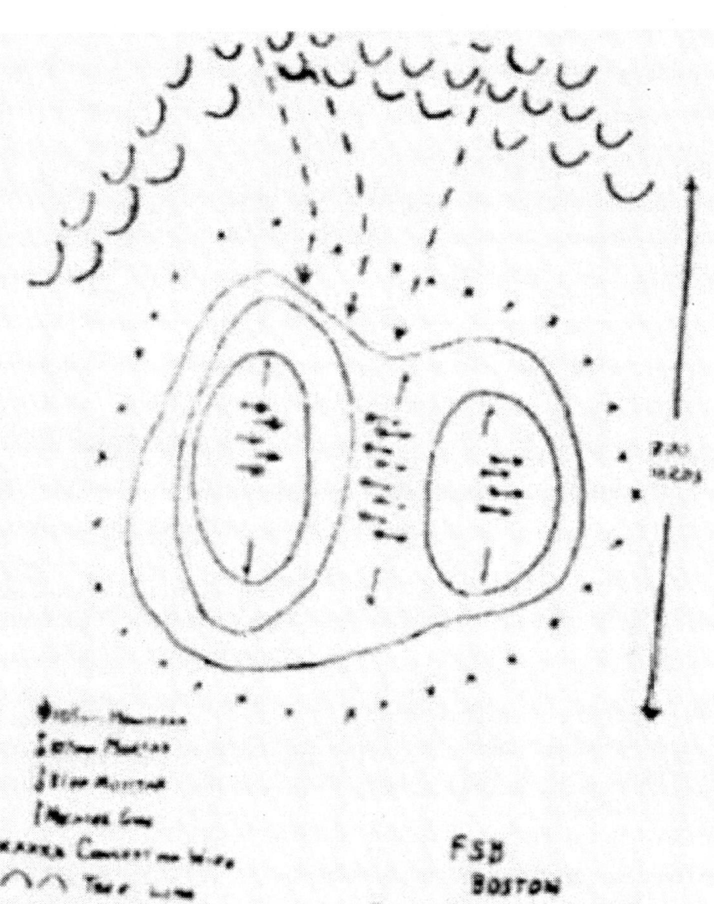
NVA ATTACK
FSB
BOSTON
3-30-68, 10 PM

My Huey let down, casting a long shadow, and I jumped down while it was still a foot off the ground. I walked to the medical bunker, where the senior medic/sergeant was in charge. Fortunately, he told me, I *hadn't* been needed during the night attack. Our wounded were few and minor. The dead had been beyond help from the moment they were hit, and there'd been only four of them. Only four.

Hearing that, I reported to the S-1 to offer any help that I could, but all dead and wounded were accounted for, and evacuation had been arranged, so no further action was necessary. Finally, I went to the S-4 team to help out there if I could. With nothing better to do, I helped to count and stack North Vietnamese dead. There were 147 of them. The pattern of NVA routine was that there'd probably be about an equal number more dragged away and buried in pre-dug graves. That would explain some of the blood trails. They'd also drag or carry away *another* equal number of wounded, who, when subjected to their Civil-War-Era medical system, would either die or be invalided out of the army as totally disabled. The number of walking wounded, or those who would recover from their injuries, could not be estimated with any degree of accuracy.

The NVA had attacked and tried to overrun Boston at 10 PM. Their intent could be deduced by the relative earliness of the first strike. That would give them time to open a hole in the concertina-wire perimeter, insert a sizable force, kill all the Americans they could manage to, in the dark, and still have time to reorganize and march away into the surrounding forest before first light. All this would be accomplished before the arrival of the inevitable air power and reaction force. It had been tried, and had worked, before.

Instead, the sentries were alert, and they'd run straight into a storm of razor-sharp flying steel, cutting into them at just over half a mile a second. Our mortars, firing from inside our wire onto the wire itself was particularly effective, as was the artillery firing a box barrage from two *other* FSBs onto Boston's most likely approaches. This allowed the NVA neither a pathway for reinforcement nor an exit route, isolating them on the battlefield until the very end of the night.

No prisoners were taken by either side.

* * *

It is a mistake for a soldier to live too long a life.

Robert Clive, 1760

Sixth Hand:

The players are about halfway through the 6-deck shoe. First chair: queen and jack. Second: four-three. Third: six-two. Fourth: pair of sixes. Fifth: five-six. Dealer has a four up. One sticks on twenty. Two draws a deuce, a trey, and an eight for twenty, also. Three stays with eighteen. Four splits his sixes, drawing a five and ten for 21 on the first of the sixes. On his second six, he draws a four, and a seven for seventeen. The dealer turns up a six in the hole, draws a six, and another six for 22. The Count now stands at 13.

* * *

Robert Kennedy was in Los Angeles capaigning for President when a Palestinian Arab refugee shot him at short range with a "Saturday Night Special" .22 revolver. He was dead in a few minutes, as is the usual case with multiple head wounds.

We took note of the event, and tried to keep breathing, ourselves.

* * *

46.

17 April 1968

At about this time, CPT Bob Phipps, commanding Company D, 326th Medical Battalion was due to rotate home. None of the other Medical Corps officers in his company was interested, so I was asked if I'd take the job.

I jumped at the chance. Command experience (or "command time") is all too rare in the Medical Corps. If I'd learned nothing else in the seven years since OCS (and MSU), it was never to waste an opportunity.

The 326th Medical Battalion was commanded by LTC Ronald A. Allen, who'd be my immediate superior.

The Company itself was in great need of some changes. The only thing that made it mission-capable was the low level of the missions required of it.

It *was* the organic (permanently assigned) medical support of the First Brigade, and had deployed to Vietnam with it in 1965, as part of its provisional four-company Support Battalion.

I began to spend time around the Company before the actual change of command, to try to get a feel for what I was getting into, and what needed to be changed.

The mens' morale was low. Officers generally performed their medical duties creditably, but had no interest in any other areas of responsibility. As a whole, the non-commissioned officers (NCOs) were kind of a bust, with a few exceptions, due to conditions beyond the control of anyone on-site.

First, Army-wide, the old NCO Corps had been gutted by assignment of any significant tasks to junior officers. Secondly, the decision to draft all the 18-year-olds at once meant that there were few older men with the maturity or combat experience to be considered promotable, to be corporals or sergeants, By the time they were twenty, they were also out of the Army. Any exceptions to these crippling deficiencies were repaired, quite rightly, from the front first; the line (combat) units got almost all of them.

And, to keep myself honest, I must express an impression I developed at the time: a high percentage of the enlisted medical personnel in airborne units were able to hold their ratings not because they were especially competent in their primary Military Occupational Specialties (MOS), but because they would jump. Their careers rotated them from the 101st Airborne to the 82d Airborne, then perhaps to Special Forces or XVIII Airborne Corps headquarters, and back to the 101st or the 82d, around the cycle again and again.

Still, with all D Company's faults, a command is a command.

Another, newer, captain, MC arrived to take charge of the medical platoon of 2/502.

I packed and headed south along the MSR, to my new home, the one I'd been waiting for since 1961 and OCS.

47.

30 April 1968

My new company was housed and worked in tents pitched over cuts in the ground, each to the width of a bulldozer blade. They were deepest in the center, sloping upward toward each end. Water tended to accumulate at their deepest or muddle points, and there was a lot of wasted space at both ends. They had been hastily dug on the Brigade's first day at Rocket City, and had never been meant to be permanent housing.

Two months later, as an example, the kitchen tent (covered trench?) was never able to get out more than one hot meal a day, and sometimes not even that. It was C-rations the rest of the time. There was no mess hall, which was understandable initially. However, once it became obvious that the Company was going to be there for weeks, if not months, there was no acceptable excuse not to have one. In fact, it was unforgivable not to, for the sake of morale alone.

Bill's First Sergeant was an older (forty-five?), small man, quiet and introspective. He was carried in rank one level below that of company first sergeants. He wasn't like any first sergeant I'd seen before, and for that matter, haven't since. He was, to say the least, ill-suited to the job.

The Ambulance Platoon Sergeant was sort of a loud, Victor-McLaglen-type character. Bill didn't have the authorized MSC officer platoon leader. Thus, no supervision.

The Clearing Platoon Sergeant was a schemer. His platoon leader was a doctor due to DEROS in ten days. Useless.

I can't help wondering (in all honesty, it didn't occur to me at the time) if these three senior NCOs, who should have been the Company's backbone, hadn't instead been the bottom of the 101st's barrel back at Ft. Campbell, hence their presence in South Vietnam. The Motor Sergeant and Mess Sergeant were good at *their* jobs, but they were climbing a "down" escalator. I remembered only too well how that task could be.

But, I hear you say, how is this situation avoided in most medical units? Easy. The answer is that almost any unit in this shape, to have any hope of being mission-capable would be salvaged by the executive officer, a captain, MSC, whose jobs ran something like this:

1. Keep the MC officer nominally in command out of trouble, if necessary by forceful, quite directive, not-necessarily-asked-for advice.
2. Either directly supervise the first sergeant or strenuously advise the C.O. how he should do so.
3. Keep an eye on *everything* else.
4. Provide continuity between successive commanding officers.

I suspect that Phipps's exec (or XO) might also have been one of Campbell's bottom-of-the-barrel men. Fortunately for me, he succeeded only in the last task of the four that I've listed, by leaving for another assignment before Bob did.

So, before I arrived, CPT James Scott did. Most of the success with Company D (sort of like President Truman's 1918 Battery D) that was to follow, we *all* owed to him. He, for example, had sized up the NCOs and their relative strengths and weaknesses before I arrived. Alone, I might never have figured it out. And without definition, a problem cannot be solved.

Scotty came from Baltimore, a light-skinned African-American six feet five inches tall, who wore a size 14 ½ combat boot. He had piercing, medium-green eyes. His ultimate goal was, after passing the Advanced Course at Ft. Sam Houston, to be trained as a hospital administrator under the auspices of the Army.

The men called him "Pinky." I was known as "The Man."

He gave me more advice than I wanted, and probably less than I needed.

He could also play my favorite free-form parlor game, which was to feed out the first half of a line of movie dialogue, to see if I could finish it. Or vice versa. Preferably in the voice of the actor, or even act*ress* (Bette Davis' "Fasten your *seat*belts. It's going to be a *bum*py flight."). As an alternative, we'd greet each other with a similar line. For example, if it was time to mete out company punishment, he or I would opine that it was time to "Round up the usual suspects."

What I later came to think of as "the MSC Mafia" of the Division was almost entirely careerist and crony-ridden to its core. Scotty was not part of it, thanks be to God, and when he left the 101st, it didn't matter to him. The 326th's Battalion Operations Officer and its exec, both majors, weren't involved in it either; those three were truly miraculous exception.

Scotty, and those two superior officers were career *Army*, not career Airborne, and that made all the difference.

A few days after Scotty arrived, so did a new first sergeant. The old one was sent to the Division Surgeon's office (more cronies from Ft. Campbell), never to be seen again. He meant well, but he just wasn't a first sergeant.

His replacement, 1SG Thomas, was everything he hadn't been.

1SG Thomas spent the few days before I reported in getting the orderly room knocked into shape.

He was a big man. He had been a medic in the Korean War. He was about five feet eleven, stocky, not fat, and I'll bet he weighed 240 pounds. He could (and did) handle the two platoon sergeants. With CPT Scott's guidance, I'd tell him what I wanted done, and he'd see to it. That's the way a company is supposed to operate.

With those two, CPT Scott and 1SG Thomas as my right and left arms, I would even have time to take my turn in the dispensary and the holding ward as Medical Officer of the Day (MOD), sort of like a Navy watch officer. That would make it a little easier on the two other MCs I had on hand (we were supposed to have four).

We didn't have X-ray capability, and missed it less than I'd have predicted.

My two-man lab section did the best microbiology work I've ever seen, before or after Vietnam, military or civilian. If a man had a fever of undetermined origin, it was likely to be malaria. Routinely. they'd do a thick blood smear, find the parasite and make the correct diagnosis of the three possible varieties (there *is* a fourth, but it was not found in Asia) in an hour or two. The same held true for their accurate identification of the country's endemic infectious gastroenteritides. As an example, I have since depended upon labs *in civilian teaching hospitals* which couldn't isolate or identify amoebae or pathogenic bacteria in the stools of a patient with dysentery. My two lab techs in he company could and did do it accurately several times a week with no problem whatever. In a tent.

The company also had a male second lieutenant, Army Nurse Corps, who was a qualified nurse-anesthetist, assigned to the unit. Airborne units are designed to operate independently of ground evacuation for up to 72 hours, so that particular personnel spot is unique to them. Regular line units' medical support didn't have that capability. I was fortunate in that he was willing to take on added administrative duties. I made 2LT Wallace a *de facto* preventive medicine officer, in charge of the mess and inspector of the five whorehouses and three restaurants that I designated as "approved" for the company's personnel in nearby Phu Bai village.

For the same reason, Airborne medical units also have organic dental support. CPT Joseph Palermo was our dental officer, who was also, like Wallace, willing and able to help the unit to function, even if it called for duties outside those of his MOS. He treated minor wounds alongside my MCs, and did it well. And with head and neck wounds, he was priceless.

Again, I was attempting to prevent or at least control those things (like VD, or a shortfall in medical capability, or food-borne illnesses) that could *be* headed off at the pass.

Something happened a little later that might have *added* to our overall medical capability, but, as it turned out, that didn't.

At about that time, two weeks after the unit's makeover, of which more later, Company D got another General Medical Officer (GMO) who was with the unit less than 24 hours. Hell, it was less than *twelve* hours. His saga is one of those many things that, when I cogitate over the incident, and I often do, I don't know whether to laugh or cry.

Dr. John A. Smith (believe me, not his real name) had graduated from a West Coast medical school, interned, and gone directly to work in a state psychiatric hospital, an unchallenging and dead-end career path. He had been drafted in December, 1967. I don't believe that he was jump-qualified. I know nothing else about his history. He arrived, dropped his gear, took one look around, evidently didn't care for what he saw, and asked to see LTC Allen.

He was shipped out within two hours of his return from battalion headquarters.

I have no idea why or where, to this day. What had he said to Colonel Allen? Was he unable to live under primitive conditions? Just spooked by likely combat? And the possibilities of his next assignment are nearly infinite. A job separating watermelons from jelly beans at Dugway Chemical Warfare Proving Ground, Utah (be careful: some of the jelly beans are the same color as the watermelons)? Counting dead nerve-gassed sheep at Dugway? Toole Chemical Weapons Depot? Fort Polk, Louisiana as Permanent Recruit Sick Call Officer? The Convalescent Center at Cam Ranh Bay? As a doctor or as a patient? And on, and on.

Anyway, as a poker dealer will say, all too often, "No help there."

48.

LTC Allen, the commander of the 326th Medical Battalion, was present within the first hour of my reporting to the company.

Only then did I find out that he and his principal staff had transferred themselves forward and had co-located with First Brigade headquarters. This was done to give themselves experience *while exercising command under combat conditions*. Incidentally, they would all also qualify for the Combat Medical Badge, a career-enhancing award for a Regular Army officer or NCO. In fact, those old-Fort-Campbell-crony officers and principal EM left behind at Bien Hoa were scheduled to be *rotated in and out* of my company for that express purpose. The practice is now called "ticket punching."

Medics assigned at levels higher than that of infantry brigade do not qualify for The Badge. Not one of the MDs at Nha Trang, later, wore it.

A short change of command ceremony was held the next morning, and the orders appointing me commanding officer (CO) were read aloud to the Company in ranks. Bob Phipps left the same day.

I then sat down with Scotty and between us came up with what he called "Plan A," which 1SG Thomas embroidered with Plan B. My contribution was to try to do *both at once* in three 12-hour working days, with the help of both Army and Navy engineers. It went this way, in order:

PLAN A.

1.We'd close the company to in-patient treatment and use Phu Bai's Navy medical teams instead, for three days, supplemented by our own "tail-gate" ambulatory medical care.

2.Fill in the holes in the ground, compact the dirt back into them, and roll them flat.

3.Pitch the same tents over the filled-in holes, kitchen tent first, Admissions and Dispositions (A&D) next, with patient wards to follow. Extra men were to start filling sandbags.

4.Build and install plywood floors in the tents, wards first, while 2/3 of the men filled sandbags.

5. Pitch a T-shaped mess hall using two attached GP mediums tents, floor it, and sandbag it up, thigh-high, two bags thick (that width will stop a bullet or shell fragments).

6. Bag up all personnel tents thigh-high and two bags thick. The first hot meal in the new configuration would be breakfast on Day Three. Iced water, iced tea and/or Kool-Aid would be available at the kitchen tent no later than 2 PM on Day One of construction (medical units can draw 130% of the ice ration allocated to

other unit types).

Thereafter, unless I agreed in advance, there'd be three hot meals a day for the company and its in-patients.

PLAN B

1. Simultaneously, Plan B would be started by a section of Seabees:First, they'd dig a circle of trench line, using an engineer ditch-digger,around the company perimeter, 2 feet wide and 4 ½ feet deep with staggered segments connected by short saps.

2. Our men would follow behind, and two-thirds-cover the segments with corrugated iron half-cylinders of culvert six feet long, separated by 3 feet of open fire parapet. Then, the trailing edge of the detail would sandbag the iron roof, three bags thick (enough to stop an 81mm mortar shell). A single layer of sandbags covered the parapets. That left us with a zig-zagging overhead-covered perimeter trench, with an open two-manfiring position every twelve feet.

* * *

We finished The Great Makeover on the second day, at 8 PM. It's astounding how much men will do to help themselves.

The next morning, I made my first speech to the whole company, officers included.

"Look around you," I said, "and compare what you see with what was standing on the very same spots four days ago."

I went on: "This is the first step in welcoming you back into the Army, from which this Company has evidently strayed.

"While I know that we are in a combat *zone*, we, ourselves will rarely, if ever, be fighting. For that reason, I expect you to look like what you are, the best soldiers in the world. That means as a minimum, a non-dirty uniform worn with baseball ("lifer") cap, polished boots and a clean shave. Traditionally, paratroopers don't wear mustaches, so if any of you have them, they'll have to go.

"You can expect quarters inspections at irregular, unpredictable intervals.

" You've all heard the old saw: 'A new broom sweeps clean.'

"I was an enlisted man for seven years," I continued, "and I understand that this *is* a new broom, and that any change in routine is difficult, but as an officer, I can promise you that you will feel better and work better if you *look* better and are proud of it, as part of a clean sweep *with* that new broom."

It's a good thing that we accomplished all those changes early, because two days later we were warned to expect a full-bore peacetime-type Adjutant General Inspection (AGI).

In a war zone.

I have no doubt that some careerist at Division volunteered us for it, for the sake of his advancement, or at least to curry favor at a higher echelon.

I know that AGIs are required annually under peacetime conditions. God knows, I've stood enough of them *since* Vietnam.

They are, to put it mildly, and as my old mother would say, fucking impossible in a combat zone. Hell, just accounting for the daily casualties and combat equipment losses would invalidate the procedure. But we *were* gonna have one, just the same.

* * *

I was required to contribute three men a night for a 24-hour guard detail. Three or four from each company made up enough of a task force to at least put up some resistance and sound the alarm if Brigade Rear was attacked. Then, everyone in the area would form company-sized perimeters, and the MPs and our light cavalry troop (mounted not on horses, but M-151 Jeeps) would engage the attackers. The new trench line was D Company's internal perimeter, literally our last ditch. As 1SG Thomas put it, the only way they can get you *out* of a trench is to get in there with you, and that's not the NVA's style. The Vietnamese are mostly too small for rough-and-tumble with Americans.

My eighth night in command, I was wakened by an explosion, and far-off firing from the outer guard posts. We'd been probed at 3 AM.

Dejectedly, I got to write another letter home, because the man who had been killed by the satchel charge I'd heard was one of my three. He was the seventh and last I'd lose in Vietnam. Seven too many. How did I (and *do* I) feel about them? I can't improve on this:

In Memoriam

**Private David Sutherland, killed in Action
in the German trench, May 16th, 1916,
and the others who died.**

So you were David's father,
And he was your only son,
And the new-cut peats are rotting
And the work is left undone,
Because of an old man weeping,
Just an old man in pain,
For David, his son David,
That will not come again.
Oh, the letters he wrote you
And I can see them still,
Not a word of the fighting
But just the sheep on the hill
And how you should get the crops in
Ere the year got stormier
And the Boches have got his body
And I was his officer

You were only David's father,
But I had fifty sons
When we went up in the evening
Under the arch of the guns,
And we came back at twilight-
O God! I heard them call
To me for help and pity
That could not help at all.
Oh, never will I forget you.
My men that trusted me,
More my men than your fathers',
For they could only see
The little helpless babies
And the young men in their pride
They could not see you dying,
And hold you while you died.
Happy and young and gallant,
They saw their first-born go,
But not the strong limbs broken
And the beautiful men brought low
And the piteous writhing bodies,
They screamed 'Don't leave me, sir!'
For they were only your fathers
But I was your officer.

Lieutenant Ewart Alan Mackintosh

* * *

The peacetime-style, stateside-fashioned AGI came and went. It wasted a day of my company's time, or about 24 X 5 X 200= 24,000 man-hours, counting 5 full 24-hour days for 200 men to prepare, to no useful end.

We passed the AGI, but I'm not sure that you can *fail* one under those conditions.

* * *

With the Company living and working up on the surface, and what Scotty called "the Days of the Mole-Men" (also the title of a really bad movie) behind us, the mens' morale was noticeably better. They were able to keep cleaner, and their uniforms looked sharper.

But those bottom-of-the barrels NCOs were less than happy. Leaders like them almost invariably manage by crisis, and thrive on disorder. I was trying to *end*, or at worst control crises, and substitute routine for daily confusion.

I actually caught SFC Griffith, the Clearing Platoon Sergeant, urging a collective work slow-down, but could only count on one witness who'd testify against him. A charge of mutiny takes two, so all I could do was transfer him out of my company, back into the briar patch where he'd thrived for 16 years.

SFC Bryant, the Ambulance Platoon Sergeant left Vietnam with over $13,000 cash in his pockets, that he declined to even *try* to account for. I still can't figure out where he got it. He didn't gamble, and hard as I looked to find it, nothing was missing from the inventory.

49.

The change in the company's appearance and the policies initiated resulted in a visit with the (new to us) battalion Sergeant-Major. My three senior NCO low-lifes had been complaining to him. I heard him out, enough to come to the conclusion that he had probably been a middle-of-the-barrel NCO, had survived in the Army by staying on jump status, and by currying favor with the Fort Campbell Crony Mafia.

"Generally, Sir," he said, "new COs don't make many changes until they get onto their feet, and evaluate their commands a little longer. I wonder if you haven't moved ahead a little too quickly, and changed too much?"

I took a deep breath, exhaled, and silently counted "three."

Then I told him: "I think that you've been had.

"Sergeant-major," I continued, "you just arrived here late last night.

"This is your first sight of D Company. You were never privileged to see this unit during its first nine weeks here. All that time, it was living in damp holes in the ground, eating cold food out of cans three times a day, running its vehicles, when they ran, dirty and unmaintained, and was plagued with discipline, payroll and promotion problems on a daily basis.

"So," I went on, "now that it *looks* like a company of soldiers, it is easy to look for faults. And probably to find them. But, performance-wise, if we aren't up to snuff," I concluded, "I am ready to step down, any time. *I* think that we've bottomed out, and *now* we're starting to move in an upward direction."

I don't recall that he ever came back, unless he was carrying LTC Allen's briefcase.

We finally fell into a predictable routine.

Monday was Malaria Pill Day.

Friday night was Monopoly Night.

Saturday was Poker Night.

Thursday evening's meal was an outdoor barbecue instead of a mess hall-prepared meal.

Tuesday, Thursday and Saturday were Outdoor Movie Nights, weather permitting, showing first-run movies or two hours' kinescopes of recent TV shows.

There was discussion about the officers forming an investment club (the men already had one).

We ordered delicacies by mail from the United States, since postage to Vietnam was free. Ashley's Mexican Food of El Paso, Texas, refused to accept our check, sending it back with their thanks, along with our full order of canned tortillas. A popcorn company did the same thing. Several magazines sent us complimentary subscriptions, for the asking.

* * *

I took advantage of this lull to utilize the Pacific Post-Base Exchange (PX-BX) Mail-Order Catalogue to order a moonstone bracelet and some pearl jewelry for Joan, as well as an Akai high-fi reel-to-reel tape recorder, all to be delivered to my home after my DEROS.

The *Overseas Weekly* newspaper was barred from newsstand distribution in Vietnam as a scurrilous scandal sheet (and it was), but they couldn't stop a U.S. Mail-ed copy going to the Commanding Officer, Co. "D", 326th Med. Battalion, which then was mysteriously circulated from tent to tent. Same for *Ramparts*, a virulently anti-war magazine, and *The Realist*, a newsletter published by the Yippie Underground.

You will always find it useful to keep a close eye on what the enemy is thinking.

* * *

I was able to make several more half-day trips into Hue. It was reasonably safe now that the Citadel had been retaken, and the highway to the north and south cleared of the NVA. There are some scenes that will always remain with me:

- A modern Shell station that would'nt have been out of place on any corner in the U.S. facing the main highway on the south side of town.
- ARVN soldiers dropping grenades from the top of the Citadel wall into the surrounding moat, to catch the stunned fish.
- The rambling red-and-gilded-wood Imperial Palace, last occupied by the French-puppet Emperor Bao Dai, with its gleaming outdoor blue-and-white porcelain flower pots the size of a bushel basket, and sporting a couple of 81mm mortar-shell-holes in the roof.
- Ornate columns in the extensive Imperial Palace grounds that looked like solid polished stone from a distance, but turned out to be only mosaics of porcelain fragments pressed into wet mortar before it had set.
- Many villas and hovels within the Citadel walls. Who lived in each? How was it decided who got the villas, and who the hovels?
- A short-tempered water buffalo cow (with a calf I didn't notice) butting my jeep, tilting it up, trying to gore it to death *while I was in it*, hanging on to the steering wheel, trying not to fall out.
- The bullet-and rocket-pocked walls of the MACV Compound, on the south side of Hue, across the highway from the Shell station.
- where the file clerks and finance officers had stood off the NVA for six days before its siege was raised,
- The stone building at the junction of U.S. 1, the North-South railroad and

our MSR that looked several hundred years old, until I saw the date "1956" cast into its lintel.

- Crossroads gas stations consisting of little old ladies squatting in the shade, beside pyramids of one-liter bottles of gasoline.
- Two hand-in-hand columns of seven-year-old uniformed schoolchildren, herded along the sidewalk by Vietnamese nuns in blue habits and the wide-swept white headgear of their French order. I have since seen similar scenes all over France, with no obvious differences.
- The presence of wild birds, which I had been missing (I had taken ornithology at Central Missouri State) for six months. I suspect that even in the jungle our presence caused them to flee or to at least be silent.
- My stopping to pick up an Australian sergeant while he was walking north along U.S. 1, *alone,* wearing one of their unique, pinned-up-side-brim campaign hats, carrying a British-army-issue self-loading rifle (SLR). When I asked him if he wasn't concerned about the possibility of his being ambushed, he said: " No, Sir. I'm an advaasor to the First ARVN Division, and all the civilians heere-abouts are their families. They all know me. I wouldn't try this at naaht, but it's safe enough now. Plenty of daylaat left. And I can walk ten miles in three hours. No worries." He was optimistic about the war. The Aussies, probably the best jungle fighters in the world were, I reflected later, doing something right, perhaps something that *we* weren't doing. I think it had to do with their advisory people *identifying* with the men of their assigned units. Advising indigenous troops was their major contribution to the war, rather than fighting the NVA and also trying to train the ARVN to do it, using our conventional-war tactics, our first-world supply/support system, and not considering that niether could be simply grafted onto an ancient Asian culture.

* * *

1SG Thomas adopted a stray puppy, mostly white with brindled tan highlights. It was a hoot to watch this big, tough NCO about the size of a 55-gallon oil drum, playing with a frivolous dog the size of a beer can.

He supported me in my efforts to eradicate drug use in the company. The first unannounced show-down inspection turned up some marijuana and an opium pipe, which were publicly destroyed.

"I have to equate the use of drugs," I told the company one morning, "with extreme alcohol intoxication, but involving an *unpredictable* detoxification period. Neither can be allowed this close to a hostile force, which could hit us at any time, and when every man will have to function predictably."

At Scotty's suggestion, the Company began to undergo frequent drills to test its alert procedures. My tent's position had the best field of fire in the company area, so it was reserved for our one stolen M-60 machine gun, which would increase our defensive firepower dramatically, unauthorized though it was. It would have been quite a surprise to an attacker, after having penetrated the outer perimeter, to run into our trench line, covered by the fire of a well-sited light machine gun.

Between drills, we hid the gun under the floorboards of the supply tent.

We were probed again after I'd been there three weeks, one night at about 11 PM (2300). The company automatically went into its alert posture, moved to their defensive positions and waited for me to fire the first shot, from my position at the left end of our firing line, all as we'd worked out in our Standing Operating Procedure (SOP). It was a beautiful thing to see my own creation at work, and really an ego boost, even as I recall it, now.

Then, two brand-new UH-1G gunships came in from Brigade, flying in from the east, and fired thirty or forty 2.75-inch rockets into our wire. Whatever was perceived as feeling us out stopped right there. The probe failed, and we in Company D didn't fire a shot.

Throughout the night, an AC-47 gunship (called "Spooky") circled at 5000 feet, and strafed the approaches to our positions with mini-guns. Recon patrols the next day found no signs of casualties, just a lot of footprints and broken-down grass trails.

Nearly every day at irregular times, two self-propelled eight-inch howitzers would quietly pull into place on the reverse slope of the hill where we were camped. They'd fire two to eight shots over our heads, to land 8 miles to our front. Having finished, they would drive away (they were quite mobile, on their tracks). Then, the NVA would *return* the fire with six or eight of their 122s, much less accurate than a gun, at the now-empty 8-inch position. The scattering rockets came uncomfortably close to us, more often than not.

Afternoons, about five-thirty, we would get a shower out of the west. You could see it coming, rain falling below the low clouds, passing over the deforested blue hills, across the creek, and then onto us. A purple- or red-clouded sunset usually followed. If we got a morning rain shower, there'd usually be a much larger rainbow (closer to the equator?) than I had ever seen back home.

* * *

LTC Allen was given a sudden lateral transfer to command a non-airborne separate medical battalion down on the coast of II Corps. That cost him $110 a month in lost jump pay. I don't know to this day *why* he was transferred out. And it's probably just as well that I don't, or I'd probably spill it now. Generally speaking, you don't get laterally transferred within a theater of operations if your boss is satisfied with your work.

Then, I think of General Becerra, and wonder how anyone *could* please him predictably, short of doing so by sheer luck.

One afternoon that summer, as a Huey flew overhead going whop-whop-whop, I heard a sharp *WHAP!* interspersed with the rotor's beat. The bird started down in a long arc, and landed *hard* 300 meters outside our wire. In a few seconds, as the crew scrambled free, the helicopter began to burn, and continued to do so, right down to the skids. The crew didn't even have time to remove the two M-60s (or leave them for us to steal) before the flames got to them.

2LT Wallace, the nurse-anesthetist, grabbed an ambulance and driver, and started, unarmed, toward the point of the impact with him, crossing the creek at the ford in front of our position. 1SG Thomas sent my jeep with three armed men to follow it, for security. However, all they had to do was to transport the crew back into our lines; none of them had been injured in the crash. I was gratified at how rapidly that all the men concerned had acted, without orders, to handle the unexpected situation.

The cause of the accident was that a field jacket had been blown out of the crew cabin and had been pulled back into the tail rotor, breaking it away, and thus rendering the aircraft very difficult to control, especially if it lost headway. A controlled crash was about the best that the pilot could do, under those crippling circumstances.

Every company has a few men who cause 95% of a captain's problems. I had two men who kept going to the Brigade's Red Cross representative, to get emergency leave or compassionate transfers home (granny died, house burned, children lost or with relatives, etc, etc, etc. Upon investigation of at least three requests apiece, no family *or* emergency could be identified.

Nice try, fellows.

Then, there was my doper, an ambulance driver who tried to drive a malaria case to a nearby Navy hospital for further evacuation. The patient was found standing beside U.S. 1 by Marine MPs holding his I.V. bottle over his head, trying to hitch a ride back to his unit. The driver, stoned on hashish, had rolled the ambulance, and was *still in it.* Not hurt, he just couldn't figure out that he needed to get out, now. I busted him back one grade, to Private First Class, and fined him the cost of repairs to the ambulance, the leniency being due to his having paid his dues by serving six months as a rifle platoon medic before transferring to Company "D." If it, or anything like it, happened again, I advised him, he'd do six months' jail time.

During a heavy rain, our 3-year-old tent housing Admission and Disposition (A& D) split and collapsed, its canvas so rotted that it couldn't be repaired. It took four days to get a replacement; I borrowed two smaller tents from the nearby Navy Shore Party on a temporary basis, till then.

During the time that the Company was using the borrowed tentage, we coincidentally began to receive overflow patients on an almost-daily basis from the local Naval Medical Company in support of the 23d Marines. I treated my first armored-vehicle casualties, caused by hits on Marine APCs or tanks by B-40 rockets.

If the crew or passengers were not killed outright, the most significant medical challenge was to assume and treat for thermal burning of the respiratory tract (that kills 'em about 24 hours after wounding) due to the just-short-of-incandescent gasses released by a shaped charge's hot-gas-penetration of armor. If the patient's nasal hairs or tongue are scorched they're going to develop it, so *right then* was the time to start treatment. If we waited until respiratory distress developed, it would be too late to help the patient. And, there were always multiple tiny fragment wounds, resulting from spalled-off supersonic pieces of the armor itself flying around inside the stricken vehicle. Their removal was not difficult, but was time-consuming. And, since all war wounds are contaminated, antibiotic treatment (as in-patients) was mandatory; my SOP was to hold and treat for 72 hours after arrival.

When we got our new A&D tent, I was gratified to see that the World War II cotton canvas model had been replaced by one with a much thinner, lighter, 65%-nylon fabric. We overhauled the interior, using telephone wire stretched seven feet above the floor to add a homemade suspension system for I.V. fluids, freeing floor space and moving I.V. standards to the wards. Using surplus artillery ammunition boxes, we built shelving for the multiple small items needed for patient care out *in plain sight*, for easy location. For the design, I had to thank my Clearing Platoon Leader, CPT Jerry Tarsney, who had had only to be asked, to let his imagination solve the problems.

So, over a period of 4 ½ months, I experienced all of it: low morale, management by crisis, crisis resolution, losses, mutiny, personnel turbulence, influence peddling, probable grand larceny, high morale, winning, and perhaps even triumph.

Evenings, I would listen to the Chinese Communist news broadcast in English from their powerful transmitter on Hainan Island, beamed to Southeast Asia. It was mostly propaganda. Naturally, when I heard their description of the Chicago riots of July 1968, I didn't believe a word of it, until I got my ten-day-late copy of the *Kansas City Star.*

That company command was the best job I ever had, before or since.

Then, once again, opportunity knocked.

* * *

Eighth hand: There are about 100 cards left in the shoe. The Count is now five. Fourth seat, who's doing the counting, doubles his bet, catches an eight and a three. He doubles down again; his total bet is eighty bucks. The dealer tosses him a king for a total of 21. The dealer has a twenty. The Count is now seven, indicating that a preponderance of low cards has been played. Fourth seat looks at the $160 in front of him, takes a deep breath, and without touching his chips, says, "Let it ride."

* * *

Present Day.

Serving in combat in a paratroop unit must be sort of like having been in the SS.

If people, like ODESSA, want *to find you, they always can.*

Even people who want to organize jump tours with foreign armies, and invite you to go overseas with them, and jump with the Airborne troops of other countries.

Or gray, quiet men who are covertly organizing mercenary units, whom I turned down each and every time.

Anyway, the former approach explains how I became a qualified Israeli paratrooper at the age of 54.

The Israelis remind me of us, in the Fifties, before America turned inward, became soft and fell apart.

* * *

50.

15 August 1968

An intra-theater opening was announced for a general medical officer at the 8th Field Hospital (a misnomer; it was easily the size of a 500-bed general hospital, grown by accretion, one small detachment after another, since it had arrived at Nha Trang in 1962).

I said, writing through channels, that I'd like to have the job in exchange for the favor of allowing me to hang around the headquarters of the 43d Medical Group in my spare time, to see how a medical group (a command and control headquarters) worked in a combat environment. I felt, I said, in explaining this unusual request, that my Army Reserve career of 13 years was just beginning. I intended to stay in the USAR after I got out of the active Army, and I thought that whatever level of experience I could return *to* the Reserve from Vietnam would be useful to the Army. The 43d Medical Group commander agreed.

The 43d was located in the same compound as the 8th Field.

For the same career-exposure reason, I also wanted to see how an Army hospital operated under conditions of limited war. I thought then, and still do, that for ten and a half months I had been paying my dues, and now it was time to *get* a little career enhancement for myself, instead of providing it to everyone else.

It was the Medical Department's policy to rotate officers, six months forward and six months back. I'd been forward for almost ten months, already.

In World War II and in Korea, the methods of dealing with the wounded were pretty much the same, and were closer in overall concept to the 1918 war than was Vietnam to *them.* I wanted to see first-hand how this was being accomplished. Much of the difference was made possible by aeromedical evacuation, not just dramatically by helicopter from the site of injury, but by rapid turboprop and turbojet air ambulance flights out of the combat zone, to intermediate hospitals in the Philippines, Japan, or Okinawa. Or, as a planeload of those requiring it was assembled, they might be sent straight to the United States from Nha Trang.

I was to depart the 326th on 25 August 1968, with no delay in route (DNR), and report to the 8th Field that same afternoon.

I said my good-byes the night before, and left on schedule on a C-123 hop from Phu Bai to Nha Trang, with an intermediary stop at Cam Ranh Bay.

* * *

THE PARTING OF THE COLUMNS

A RESERVIST LEAVES HIS REGULAR ARMY UNIT FOR DEMOBILIZATION

(SOUTH AFRICA, 1900)

We've rode and fought and ate and drunk as rations come to hand,
Together, for a year and more around this stinkin' land:
Now you are goin' home again, but we must see it through.
We needn't tell we liked you well. Good-bye--Good luck to you!

You 'ad no special call to come, and so you doubled out,
And learned *us* how to camp and cook an' steal a horse and scout.
Whatever game we fancied most, you joyful played it too,
And rather better on the whole. Good-bye--good luck to you!....

Our blood 'as truly mixed with yours, all down the Red Cross train.
We've bit the same thermometer at Bloeming-typhoid-tein.
We've 'ad the same old temp'rature--the same relapses too,
The same old saw-backed fever-chart. Good-bye--Good luck to you!

We'll never read the papers now without inquirin' first
For word from all those friendly dorps where you was born an' nursed.
Why, Dawson, Galle, an' Montreal--Port Darwin--Timaru,
They're only just across the road! Good-bye--good luck to you!....

Rudyard Kipling
Barrack-Room Ballads.

* * *

I left the First Brigade then, but it has never left me for a day since.

The flight from Phu Bai was as thrilling as a C-123 ride always was.

That rather old-model aircraft had been retro-fitted with a jet engine under each wing, and takeoff and climb-out felt something like a cross between a fast express "up" elevator and a blast-off into space, the sensation being one of going *straight up*, fast.

We had been warned at the pre-flight passenger briefing that we'd be taking a twenty-mile detour out to sea, to dump three steel-strap-reinforced weighted footlockers full of classified material. When we reached the drop point, the under-tail ramp was partly lowered, and the crew chief, safety strap around his waist, shoved the boxes out from 3000 feet.

The remainder of the flight was uneventful. I arrived at the Nha Trang terminal at about 2 PM.

I hitched a ride in the back of a ¾-ton truck from the Nha Trang Airfield to the 8th Field Hospital Headquarters just across the boundary road, but halfway around the field (and four miles) from the only gate.

The coastal plain was about twelve miles wide at that point, with the mountains, a dramatic shade of blue, standing off to the west.

The security gate at the 8th Field Hospital was decorated with a pagoda roof, turned upward at the corners.

When I went into the Orderly Room to sign in at 1500, the Company Commander, First Sergeant, and Company Clerk were already gone for the day. The place smelled of clean dust and of furniture polish. The CQ didn't know where (or what) the sign-in book was. I pointed it out to him, and asked for it. I signed in, left three copies of my orders *in* the book, and threatened the CQ with serious consequences if he (and here I conspicuously took down his name) didn't press them directly into the hand of the First Sergeant, first thing in the morning.

I then asked him where the officers bunked, and walked over to the area that he indicated.

It was a line of white-stucco, red-tile-roofed villas, each with four double bedrooms, a bathroom in the French style, and a central conversation-TV room with dry bar.

I buttonholed an off-duty officer, and asked where I could spend the night, until I was officially assigned quarters. Temporarily, I was doubled up with a neurosurgeon, who was never there. I dropped my gear and looked around the bedroom.

And there it was, a real wooden bed with a three-inch thick mattress on solid wood underboards. No springs, and I didn't care. A ceiling fan right out of *Casablanca.* My very own gecko who spent his time clinging to the wall near the ten-foot ceiling, eating hapless flies, gnats, and mosquitoes.

I skipped dinner, took three showers and went to bed.

26 August 1968

The next morning, having no assigned duties yet, I grabbed a civilian Lambretta motor-scooter/taxi, and asked the driver to take a couple of hours and show me the city. He agreed, for Vietnamese piasters equivalent to eight dollars, American.

The hospital compound was located three blocks inland from the most beautiful beach I've ever seen. It was white sand, ran north-south, and was fifteen miles long, with a gentle inward curve. There was a large island called Hon Tre two miles out, which had the effect of breaking up any rough seas, and making an ideal bathing beach.

A white forty-five-foot-high statue of the Buddha overlooked the entire city, sitting on a prominent hilltop, looking out to sea. It was not the usual chubby little Buddha that we see in souvenir shops in every Chinatown in the United States. It was tall and thin, carved to match a Vietnamese somatotype, and had the narrow face so frequently seen in the population. At its foot was a large, ancient temple and an attached monastery. The polished gray stone base was marked at the cardinal points of the compass with two-foot square shined brass plaques. I couldn't read their Chinese ideographs. Each of *those* was faced by a bushel-basket-sized white pottery sand receptacle to hold burning joss sticks. Except when extinguished by the occasional offshore wind, the incense burned throughout the daylight hours, and filled the air with its unique smell. I wouldn't know about the night-time hours. I almost never left the base after dark. After dodging the NVA for ten months, I had no doubt that God's sense of humor would be tickled by my being mugged by civilian criminals and left dead in some alley.

The whole monument was lighted at night by eight street lamps, and in clear weather its bright white reflected color was visible for several miles out to sea.

The top of the hill was reached by any one of four long stairways, with fifteen-foot-long porcelain dragons serving as stair rails, and set at 90 degrees from each other to the Northeast, Southeast, Southwest, and Northwest. The dragons' scales were outlined in a bright yellow, and were blue at their peripheries, fading inward to turquoise centers.

Below the monument and its monastic hilltop, the architecture was radically different. There were many old French villas, also with the ubiquitous red-tile roofs, set well back from the street on the landward side of the four-lane beach-front boulevard. They ran on and on, block after block of them, for several miles. Some were still owned and occupied by Frenchmen who'd stayed on after 1954, who'd accumulated enough money to invest it safely in France, and live on its income.

Francs or dollars, hard currencies went a long way in Vietnam; for all I know, they still do.

The sidewalks along the boulevard were shaded by seventy-year-old plane trees.

It was an awesome sight.

I hope that it still is.

There were several seafood restaurants on the beach itself, built up on stilts, and called, in order from right to left "Beach House Number One," "Beach House Number Two," and so on. They were reputed to harbor seafood crawling with hepatitis A, Salmonella, Shigella, and maybe cholera. I tried Beach House Number Nine a few days later, and lived.

The favorite hospital officers' hangout in town was La Frigate, which was probably also less risky health-wise than its reputation implied. Its name had been changed to the colloquial "Faggot's" years before by long-departed members of the hospital medical staff. I really liked the pseudo-French atmosphere. Also, I'd never had spiny lobster (as opposed to the New England species) before. At La Frigate, it was served split in half lengthwise and broiled. They served it sizzling on a hot steel plate. It came with French baguettes and with a large bowl of steamed rice, and it cost $2.55, U.S.

They also had a specialty consisting of two of the biggest prawns I've ever seen as an entrée, with the head, eyes, and whiskers still on, poached whole. As one of the less-classy MDs said, if you *can* bring yourself to eat a bug, they were delicious. That cost $2.50, American.

For atmosphere, there were still lines of bullet holes across the façade, from the Tet Offensive five months before; the VC had tried to take Nha Trang, too.

Six blocks north and six blocks west of the hospital was downtown Nha Trang. It featured traffic jams, multi-storied buildings, three nice hotels and a lot that were less so. The Colombe had a French restaurant next to its penthouse. I have yet to taste the equal of its onion soup, even in France.

The Colombe also had a group of three French whores who did a lively business there, or so I was told, in those glorious pre-AIDS times. Their competitors were the Vietnamese girls in downtown Nha Trang ("GI, you buy me Saigon tea, I love you too much"). There was a little lacuna of safety on Hon Tre Island, where there was no VC activity. The sex industry was a little more genteel there, involving dinner, dancing, and relaxed. If professional sex happened, it took place without wondering who might be outside getting ready to toss a grenade through the open window onto your back.

The only way onto or off the island was by boat, and all traffic was closely monitored.

Next day, COL Pillsbury, who'd taught us at Ft. Sam Houston, and whom I had never expected to see again, interviewed me. He was coincidentally assigned to the 43d Medical Group, too. He sent me to the 43d Medical Group Sergeant Major, who *did* (at last!) know what to do with me.

At the end of the day, I was quartered officially, assigned duties, and introduced to Major Dave Dennison, the Chief of Medicine at the Eighth Field, who'd be my immediate superior.

MAJ Dennison explained that I'd be filling in at several locations. From eight AM to 10 AM I'd do sick call at the 128th Medical Detachment (Dispensary), supporting three rear area battalion-sized support units which had no organic medical support. That job would include inspecting their mess halls and latrine facilities for proper sanitation. After that, I'd report to the emergency department and help with sick call there, assisting the two internists who were now doing it and were overloaded.

The Sick Boat for those fortunates stationed at he radio and TV repeater stations on Hon Tre Island would land at 10 AM, and their treatment would mark the end of morning Sick Call. That shift would continue till 5 PM.

If wounded were received, *everyone* reported in to treat them, *whatever* time it was, in response to a sounding siren.

I'd further be expected to coordinate with the medical staff of the Fifth Special Forces Group, which was also based in Nha Trang, in the event that they required anything medical outside duty hours, usually to consist of a few small items of medical supply.

As might be expected from the workload as described, illnesses and on-the-job injuries were to be the rule in my patient load. *Some* combat casualties were still seen, but nothing like the numbers encountered in a forward medical company. And my coworkers would be indistinguishable from those I might have had in the United States, five years before, who had no idea of what warfare was like, except at second-hand.

During any slack times, I could hang out at 43d Medical Group and watch it operate, day or night, as agreed.

The Hospital was made up of dozens of the frame buildings that I'd first seen at the 90th Replacement Battalion, Camp LBJ. They were connected by covered open-air walkways, which kept out the rain in wet weather and provided shade from the blazing sun.

The Americans' work areas were air-conditioned.

The wards where the inpatient Vietnamese were treated by American nurses and doctors were screened-in but were *not* air-conditioned. They were clean, and certainly adequate, but austere.

The mess hall was three times as wide and three times as long as the Mark I Vietnam barracks building. It, too, was air-conditioned. It stood 75 yards from our orange-and-white checked seventy-foot-tall water tower, and had a small, well-kept lawn around it. The lawn was lined with small but well-manicured flower beds.

It made a nice change from the jungle.

51.

That second night, I finished unpacking, took three more showers (it was still hard to believe), and after an early dinner at La Frigate, settled in for an early evening. It felt truly luxurious to take my boots off at bedtime, which would have been a suicidal act anywhere that enemy attack was likely.

At exactly 1245 AM I was wakened by a PFC duty CQ and told we were being mortared, and that I'd have to go to a shelter. I had reached under my pillow as soon as I was disturbed, and gently grasped the stolen hand-me-down .45 that went with the villa, but then, when I realized there was no danger, let it go.

"Listen," I said, "I've been dodging mortar shells for the last ten months, and *I* don't hear anything. Go away and let me enjoy my third night in a real bed."

"No, Sir," he replied. "Anyway, he persisted, you *can* hear them; listen."

Far away in the tropical late September night I heard a *faint* "b-o-o-o-m." And silence. Then, an even fainter "b...m-m-m...m...m...m."

"Listen closely to me," I said softly, in the dark, "I am in a real bed under a real roof, in no danger for the first time in ten months. No, *look* at me. Those shells are at least two miles away. The shells are also *getting further away.* That means that the gunner is walking them in a pattern and direction *away from us*. If they start back this way, and start getting close, I'll be in that shelter before *you* are.

"Until then, *go away.*"

I heard nothing directly, but the appellation "The Animal" began to be heard at a distance in daylight, or close-by in the dark.

Most of my fellow quacks at this post had never been in action. They had come into-country, served in Nha Trang, and had never been posted anywhere else. They'd probably have been in more danger at Ft. Lewis from civilian traffic than they were at the Eighth Field Hospital. No one in unit memory could remember being fired on, except for the occasional stray round, aimed at the airfield, but that fell a little wide. The enemy never shot at us deliberately. After all, we treated them, too, as POWs, and their families, in the civilian care wards.

Our compound's perimeter was guarded by an overstrength company of 240 Nung mercenaries. Being professional soldiers, they did their job well. I would occasionally speak for a few minutes in Pidgin-English to their captain, who told me about the Nungs' history, their origin in the North, near the Golden Triangle where Laos, Thailand, and Burma approximate, and their forced evacuation by those governments, as well as the Chinese nationalists in 1945-1946. They took pride in their tribal trade of being mercenary soldiers, made all the more effective because that was their *family* occupation also.

Bad military behavior (if it ever happened) reflected not just on the soldier involved, but upon the individual's family honor.

I had remarked or responded (I'd had a few drinks) to some poor MD captain crying in his beer (I remember that he had a large, turnip-shaped head.) about being in Vietnam: "You dumb son of a bitch, you're not *in* Vietnam. Vietnam starts about half a kilometer beyond that fence, goes all the way to Cambodia, and is full of some very bad people who'd love to get their hands on you. Be happy that you're on *this* side of the fence. And hope that you never have to go outside."

That episode got me some directive counseling from our chief of professional services. He was a sawed-off little pussy of a Regular Army urologist (a major) who felt that the comparison had been aimed at him, too.

It wasn't, but it should have been. The description fit him like O.J. Simpson's gloves. Plus, he had the short-man complex if I'd ever seen it. I've been looking for him for 33 years, to catch us, both in civvies, off post. No luck so far.

This place was so full of self-centered, self-pitying wimps that the it didn't even *have* an Officers Club or an EM Club, after being there for over six years.

I suggested opening an all-ranks lounge to the same hospital sergeant-major I'd met the second day. He got behind it, and it was open in ten days. It was a hit from the first night. How they got a juke box, pool tables, a beer bar, card tables, booths, a dropped plywood ceiling with inset fluorescent lights, and slot machines, on such short notice I don't know. But, hell, that's what sergeants-major are *for*. On my second day in the ER, I noticed that the two internists I'd been supposed to help had not come in that morning. Nor the next, nor the one after that. I asked MAJ Dennison where they were.

He mumbled a vague: "I can't make them do it," and left.

He was a genuinely good man, and a gentleman. He was a good doctor. He just wasn't a good officer. The joker is that those internists had never *been* overloaded. I handled the patient load (not all that heavy) alone for two months, and turned out for incoming wounded seven nights out of 55. Got some odd glances, too, wearing the Combat Medical Badge and a 101st eagle patch on my right shoulder. Hell, I was 31, had been in the First Brigade, and could do anything.

For example, one evening one of our wounded patients who hadn't been properly frisked by his unit medics dropped a grenade onto the E.R floor, which panicked most of the personnel, who weren't used to things that go "Bang!" up close. I picked it up, taped down the safety handle, taped the pin in, and took it down to the beach the next day followed by a group of five MSCs and one MC officer who wanted to see a grenade explode.

There was no one around except a native mama-san selling domino bananas. I motioned for her to stand back, but it wasn't necessary. After living through 26 years of war, she knew perfectly well what that object was, and stepped back about ten meters. I untaped it, pulled the pin, let the handle fly off, and threw it into eight feet of water, where it sank to the bottom and exploded harmlessly.

The upshot was that I moved into the MSCs' villa as soon as a vacancy occurred. There was a limit to the little doctor-on-doctor one-upmanship games that I *could* handle. I wasn't missed by the MCs, and was welcomed by the MSCs and by the lone Veterinary Corps (VC) officer.

What, you may ask, does a vet do in a war zone? Local food inspection. Lots of it. All over II Corps. This guy spent more time in the air than a SAC B-52 pilot, clearing local produce and even some meat for purchase by the Army (much cheaper than shipping it 11,000 miles)

One day, AFVN-TV showed a video. It depicted newly-hatched baby sea-turtles running for the water across a beach, trying not to get eaten by circling gulls. One of the MSCs said: "It's too bad Coe isn't here. He'd enjoy this." Guffaws all around.

I visited the Fifth Special Forces Group Dispensary, touched base with their surgeon, and most importantly with their Platoon Sergeant. I offered him anything that I could supply, any time; after all, I understood what it was like to try delivering medical care out in the bushes, too. He, in turn, offered *me* anything I wanted in the way of souvenirs or government property, within reason, if I could give him a few days' notice.

I asked for some captured ammunition for my SKS rifle. Who knew how likely it was to be available in the States? Answer: *then*, not very; *now*, extremely common.

Another week went by. Two. Then, one morning at six, the gates were secured and we were told it was MPC Trade Day (you see, there *were* just enough corrupt Americans to make it possible for Vietnamese to get away with trading in MPC after all. So, these trade-outs on no notice were necessary). Whatever MPC the Vietnamese or anyone else possessed became worthless immediately after the announcement, since no legal exchange was possible, and all Americans were locked inside their bases throughout Vietnam simultaneously, out of reach of the civilian traders. We exchanged our MPC one-for-one, old for new, all personnel, no exceptions. It occurs to me now, after he fact, that possession of more than 12 months' pay might have been a little difficult to explain.

I realized that being wounded was unlikely now, and I started wearing jockey shorts and a white T-shirt again, *a la* stateside Class C uniform.

Late that afternoon, I met the Hospital Commander, though the conditions were less than ideal. In fact, it almost qualifies as accidental; certainly it happened under unusual circumstances. My ER was set up for *wounds* of every type, and for most *illnesses* known in this part of the world. We were *not* set up for obstetrics, however.

A Vietnamese woman was brought in by our administrative Officer of the Day (AOD) in her 13th hour of her third labor, a complication in itself. A third delivery usually proceeds rapidly over no more than six hours.

It turned out that she was the wife of the local Province Chief, sort of like one of our State governors, hence her presentation to us, and not a Vietnamese civilian hospital.

I examined her, verified that she was in the second stage of labor, had weak contractions, was exhausted, and wasn't progressing. I then did what I usually do, when I've run out of things I *can* do, which was scream bloody murder for HELP!

There was but one obstetrician on the staff, and the nurse called him. He was a huge, *really* black full colonel, who re-assessed the patient, and arranged for her admission. While we waited for lab work, we talked, as doctors do. He hated the command job he had, and he hated the war. As a board-certified obstetrician-gynecologist, with a special interest in oncology, the *last* thing he'd expected as an assignment, even in wartime, was commanding an overgrown field hospital in a combat zone. But, he was a Regular, and having been treated well by the Army *until* this turn of events, felt he owed *it* his support now, so here he was. In short a good doctor, and a good man.

Good soldier, too.

52.

CPT Larry "Moon" Mullins, our veterinarian, decided to enjoy one of his infrequent days off, and go downtown. I didn't ask if he would be stopping by the Colombe. As it turned out, he came as close to serious injury or death that afternoon as any infantryman on an average day. He and I took a Lambretta mini-cab down, and he started away while I paid the driver (I owed Moon a few dollars). I was slow in paying because I was carrying a bundle of dirty laundry.

As Moon was walking away from the cab along the sidewalk, an adolescent boy passed him at a run on his left. When they were abreast, in a fraction of a second, the boy had reached down and snagged his watch, planning to stretch the expansion band and skin it off over his wrist. Not a bad plan, except that Moon wasn't *wearing* an expansion band (it was leather), and that he'd quickly grabbed the kid's right wrist with his left hand. In about a third of a second, he'd delivered a short right that probably broke the delinquent's jaw. However, then he had to turn and run back toward me, to stay ahead of six more of the gang who were chasing him. I grabbed the money back from the driver, got out of the way, and yelled for him to take us back to the compound. As soon as Larry's first foot hit the rear doorjamb, he peeled out, turned around on two wheels, and cut off a gray Navy 2½-tonner in traffic. We'd made it, but it had been a near thing.

* * *

53.

The wounded NVA soldier was in bad shape, with a stabilized chest wound and probable slow bleeding into the abdomen. His left forearm was broken, compounded by a bullet wound. Still, the treatment team was pulling ahead of his wounds, he didn't seem to be deteriorating, and was answering our translator's questions by nodding his head "yes" or shaking it "no."

Because he had an endotracheal tube in place, he couldn't talk. I turned away for a moment. When I turned around I saw one of our medics intermittently pinching and obstructing his tube, so that the patient couldn't always breathe, and, since he was conscious, he could feel every second of asphyxia.

To my knowledge, what happened next was about as close to a court-martial as I've ever come.

I didn't hit the medic.

I *did* lift him off the floor by his shirt front, and slammed him hard into the concrete-block wall behind him, making a half-turn left to avoid a possible knee, and yelling that maybe the patient *was* an enemy, but while I was present, once he got to us, we *would* treat him as humanely as we would one of ours. *If,* I shouted, he was really interested in some action against the NVA, I was sure that my old unit could use him in 24 hours or less; medics were always getting killed there (an admitted exaggeration for effect). A replacement would be more than welcome. I then ordered him out of the ER.

The Protestant chaplain, a sniveling weasel if I ever met one, advised me the following day that I should consider an apology. I told that godly man to get lost, and to stay out of my way for the four weeks I had left in-country.

I heard no more about it.

Having lived another lifetime since then, I'm not sure I'd be as judgmental if I saw the same incident happen today, not because I think it's any less reprehensible, but because now the depths to which the average person can sink do not surprise me. Another illusion gone.

* * *

I went into the city and visited a small mens-wear shop to buy a short-sleeved sport shirt to wear off-duty.

I spoke to the owner:

"Do...you...speak...English?" *Very* slowly.

"Indeed I do, Captain," he answered in Oxford-accented English, probably better than mine.

I can be a real chump if I'm given half a chance.

* * *

Two A.M., 29 April 1975.

I had been back from Vietnam for well over six years.

Mentally, for me at least, the war was over, though it actually was anything but. It had been alternately smoldering and raging the whole time, till today.

I had been drinking beer alone, and watching the television coverage of the fall of Saigon for fourteen hours, straight.

There they were, the crowd filling the street at the Embassy in Saigon, watching us, their allies and protectors, cut and run.

They stood single file up a narrow stairway, to a small platform, first us, then as many of them as was....ah....convenient. As many as could fit onto the all-too-small Marine Hueys, until it got too risky to fly at all, plus a few more missions, too dangerous or not.

There it stood: most of our Vietnamese allies would be abandoned to the re-education camps if they were lucky, or to permanent disappearance into the jungles to the west or north if they weren't.

After America's stand in Korea, its word was solid gold.

After today it became debased, devalued, and dishonored. It lay at the bottom of those stairs up to nowhere, trampled into the dirt of the Vietnamese Republic's grave.

Perhaps we should have left the flag behind, too. It was (and is) no less than we deserved.

54.

20 October 1968

I had taken three years of French in college.

I was, and still am, intrigued by the unique love-hate relationship between the French, who virtually enslaved the population of Indochina for 80 years, and the natives. Those natives' restaurants were often rightly famed for their French cuisine, their bakeries turned out baguettes every morning, nearly all of the Vietnamese spoke French, and dressed, at least on formal occasions, in French-tailored Western clothes.

The Vietnamese absorbed and retained those things French that they regarded as positive. They had *not* developed what would have been an understandable reactive francophobia, as the Burmese had done after the departure of the hated colonial British.

* * *

55.

It was turning cooler, November 16th was coming, and it was nearly time to go home.

I finally completed the final subcourse of the E-24 Course a year late; a diploma would be forthcoming once the Medical Field Service School in San Antonio could process the paperwork.

I can remember reflecting on the changes I saw in myself over the past year. There was, for example, the way that I, and most men, looked at the future:

Phase One: I haven't got a chance. I will be killed in the next few hours or days. And, most men who *are* killed die during this time frame. It lasts about three months.

Phase Two: Maybe I'm not doomed after all. A few men have DEROSed (*d*ate of *e*stimated *r*eturn from *o*ver*s*eas) home during the past three months. *They* survived a year. *Perhaps* I have a chance of surviving. This phase, too, lasts about three months.

Phase Three: I *do* have a fair chance of living through this. After all, I'm surrounded by men who have survived. One or two DEROS every two weeks or so. (This time frame takes another three to four months). There's every reason to think I'm going to make it out of here alive. It's been six months, and I'm halfway home. If I don't take any stupid chances, that is. Toward the end of the first nine months, I at least began to feel as if I *belonged* in Vietnam, and that others, outside the circle of my close associates, were regarded as The Americans. Vietnamese stopped registering as foreign. They were part of the scenery in this new, if temporary, home.

Phase Four: (60-90 days to go)I am invincible and unkillable. I'm going to make it. A very dangerous time, obviously, due to false overconfidence.

* * *

2 November 1968

Officers were allowed to send home no more than 124 pounds of "hold baggage," which would be crated up and sent home through postal channels, in the hold (hence the name) of a surface ship. It would take between six and ten weeks to arrive. You could send it not earlier than two weeks before your DEROS.

The army post office had American civilian carpenters working to order.

You'd walk up to a two-foot-high counter with your gear bundled up, and they'd ask you one question: "Are there any flammables, detonators, explosives, drugs, or government property in there?"

You said, straight-faced, "No."

The carpenter would then, measuring your pile of possessions by eye, make a crate from scratch, from rough lumber and plywood, that couldn't have *been* a closer fit, nail it shut, plaster your own label on it and off it went to The World. My whole family were master carpenters, and I don't think they could have done that. They were slow, methodical, and exact. This was more like pop art.

* * *

I paid a last visit to the Buddhist monastery, and talked with a few of the monks there. We were able to communicate in French (my Vietnamese was impossible). My impression was that they were waiting out the war. When one thinks in units of centuries, what do a few years of political, or even military, unrest matter?

* * *

56.

The afternoon of November eighth was cold for coastal Vietnam, probably 62 degrees or so Fahrenheit. The weather was staying cloudy most of the time, and it had rained most of that day.

Just before the evening meal, a clerk brought a message to me at work. It said, in effect, "Pack up and be ready to go to the Helipad at 6AM tomorrow. You're being given a five-day drop, and will probably fly out of Cam Ranh on November 11th." Signed by the Chief of Professional Services, he of the sterling personality described above.

Armistice Day, I thought. How appropriate.

Four of us went to La Frigate to celebrate. By happenstance, in the next room another officer, this one from USARV, an advisor to the District Chief, was being given a farewell dinner, hosted by the Chief, that same evening. His dinner was more formal and *much* more sober an occasion than was mine. The proprietor even had the largely-decorative fireplace lighted.

Outgoing personnel were held at Cam Ranh for Out-Country processing for two or three days, then flown out. Maybe they were waiting for our VD to show up.

Which reminds me: what about a sex life in Vietnam? I've spared you a description, so far. Well, there *wasn't* one. That doesn't make me the world's oldest Boy Scout. When I wasn't too tired to think about it, I was too scared to. One morning of VD sick call, made up of patients with two or three diseases simultaneously, would make a believer of anyone.

* * *

At six A.M., I was at the helipad.

I followed the asphalt path, out to the LZ itself, onto the bird, a Huey D-model, with two EM who were also going home. We took off, and flew across the Geneva-Red-Cross-marked hospital roofs, south along the coastal plain, circling past the huge white Buddha, past the fishing villages, farm hamlets and rice paddies, river mouths and fishing weirs, and were dropped off (the pilot didn't even shut down his engine) at the Cam Ranh helipad.

The clearly-marked pathway out of the country first took us before a well-drilled team who did the usual paperwork (could we have fought this war, or any war, without it?) check, and did a cursory review of our medical records. We traded our MPC for U.S. dollars. We were offered medical attention if we thought we needed it, and showed to barracks, one for officers and two for enlisted men. The mess hall was in the next hut.

There was a built-in box in one corner of our temporary barracks. It was six feet square, and three feet deep, marked "Usable Items of Uniform." It was nearly full, and probably due for a visit by the recycling detail. Being the world's foremost scrounger, scavenger and cheapskate, I inventoried it and found a few useful items, such as a commercially-made boonie hat, and a set of nearly-new tiger-striped camouflage (*not* solid green) jungle fatigues in my size. Anything else would have only duplicated what I'd already declared and packed falsely in my hold baggage crate.

I packed those items away in my duffel bag, leaving out only a set of khakis to wear in flight, a green wool fore-and aft cap, black socks, and shiny black shoes.

On top of my packed gear was a roll of Army-green duct tape and an easily-concealed proscribed eighty rounds of 7.62 X 39 mm ammunition for my SKS, which I was carrying in a padded canvas Vietnamese-made gun case.

I had registered the empty rifle, and planned to send it as checked baggage, but the ammunition, then as now, was forbidden aboard a commercial aircraft.

At long last, an orderly came into the officers' barracks, and called out four names from a list that he was carrying. Mine was one of them. We had three hours to report to the Company Orderly Room for transportation to the airfield and our Freedom Bird.

We were a subdued, oddly somber lot as we were called out for our final chalk.

I quickly duct-taped 40 rounds of rifle ammunition in clips around each leg at shin level, and dressed in my travel khakis. The drape of the trousers hid the clips nicely.

As we walked toward the plane, again in a single line, we were each issued, gratis, a field jacket, against the winter weather awaiting us at home.

There was minimal muttering as we loaded onto the Seaboard Airlines stretch DC-8. As an aside, in those few months before the introduction of the Boeing 747, it was the largest plane in the world. As we took off, at 10 PM local time, most of us looked silently back, over our shoulders, toward the country we were leaving, and would never leave behind entirely. However, because it was pitch-black outside, and because the first leg of our flight was straight east, we could see nothing of it, not even a light.

Our pilot changed course northward, along the coast of China, toward Yokota, Japan. I had hoped to see the lights of the Chinese mainland, or of the island of Hainan, but we were out of sight of land. We were also bucking a severe storm, with thunder audible *inside* the plane. I had a sudden recurrence of chronic Vietnamese diarrhea, and seat belt signs or no seat belt signs, elderly stewardess or not, I *was going to the john. NOW.* And I did, hanging onto its interior bulkheads with both hands against the plane's bucking and yawing, driven by the storm.

At daybreak, we made landfall in Japan. I was seated across from one of those little six-inch portholes in the plane's hatches, and, looking west, saw Mount Fuji centered perfectly, illuminated by the morning sun, against a cloudless blue sky.

We dismounted during fueling at Yokota, which took over four hours (I don't know why it took so long). The air was thick with the odor of jet fuel, outside the terminal. Again, as the cargo waited, its members men spoke in low tones, or not at all, gathered in twos and threes. Unlike the flight *to* Vietnam, there was no buying or drinking of any liquor that I could see.

You couldn't see much of Japan, and first-world airports all look pretty much the same.

We finally reloaded onto the plane: Next stop, Fairbanks, Alaska.

Five hours into the flight, as the sun was getting low, the pilot announced that we had picked up a 120-mile-an-hour jet stream, and would not need to refuel in Alaska, so he'd be able to get us in to McChord AFB, Washington, late that night. The cargo gave an approving murmur.

Throughout the flight, every time a meal was served, and then the trays picked up, each of the three runners-up for World's Oldest and Sloppiest Airline Stewardess brushed past my aisle seat. I finished my flight lightly coated on the left side with bread crumbs, drops of orange juice, more drops of water, and the remains of two pats of butter.

We came into U.S. airspace north of Seattle. Looking down through the fog and clouds lighted *from below,* I could only stare in awe at the *volume* of the civilization below me. The engines' volume diminished as the flight deck crew cut power preparatory to entering the landing pattern. We banked, turned, and started down. The silence was broken only by the rush of air and the low rumble of the turbines on low power. No one spoke. The landing gear dropped. The pilot leveled off, put his plane onto final, and in a few minutes more we touched down.

The plane exploded with whoops, cheers, and loud cries of "Made it!" and "GoodBYE, Vietnam!" It was deafening. And, looking back, I recall having to hold back tears, for all the men I'd lost, for all the friends I'd left behind, and for the thousands more who'd have to go in the future. Looking around, I saw that I wasn't alone in being seriously choked up.

* * *

One of the saddest lessons for a warrior, usually not learned until a war ended, was that you'd never live anything quite so intensely again. This didn't mean you wouldn't enjoy life. Looking death in the face meant you'd enjoy everything *a little more. But the biggest moment of your life, when you were the most frightened, the most focused, and the most alive, would have passed.*

William Martin,
"Annapolis" *Warner Books, 1998.*

57.

13 November 1968
1230 AM

I got off the plane and was bused along with all the others to SeaTac Airport.

I just stood there, outside under a marquee and stared at my condensing breath, at the rain, the traffic, the massive number of lights, and *at a population that had not changed at all,* though I had. We all had, and would always stand apart, some more than others, from the rest of the American public.

A Good Samaritan saw me and said "Sir? Captain?" I turned and answered in a mumble.

"Where are you trying to go?" he asked, trying again.

I managed to croak: "Kansas City," and he put me into a cab to the right terminal.

I was able to get a ticket home for a laughably low price, one- fifth or so of full fare, in uniform and on orders. The USO Lounge took me in, fed me sandwiches, apple danish and coffee, and got me through my first five hours back from the war.

As I sat in the USO Lounge, I saw three officers walk past the USO doorway wearing new khakis, carrying new duffel bags and wearing no combat decorations, evidently on their way from their home stations to McChord, via SeaTac. They looked uneasy, and a little frightened, staying together as new men tend to do. My cue, I thought.

I walked over, sunburned and wearing seven decorations, with the 101st patch on my right sleeve.

"Headed to Vietnam?" I asked.

They nodded "Yes."

"Relax," I said, after introducing myself. "It's not going to be nearly as bad as you think it will be."

And I walked back into the USO Lounge to await my Kansas City flight. Perhaps, I thought, in a year they will do the same thing, and make life a little more bearable, in turn, to three or more replacements on *their* way out.

On the 727 home, a nun, the first I'd ever seen in a m habit, as opposed to the 14th-Century model of my earlier life, asked me about the Church's current activities among the displaced peasants and orphans of South Vietnam. I told her as much as I could remember, not omitting the Catholic leprosarium near Dalat.

* * *

"(We love) not war, but ourselves in *war, the men that we become. A kind of personal best."*

Gordon Kent,
"Rules of Engagement," *Putnam.*

* * *

Joan met me at the plane, and drove me home to Platte Woods.

I promised never to go more than a mile from home again.

The homecoming was truly memorable. So was the reunion with our son, now 18 months old.

I went to see Mel Frank three days later, with a certified check for the $6000 tuition that I owed him. He thanked me, and wouldn't take it.

Mel was never well-liked or much respected within the profession. But no one had better say that in *my* presence. The man was a saint, and too decent for his own good.

* * *

I visited O'Riley, now ensconced as an associate pathologist at St. Luke's Hospital in south-central Kansas City. That was where he'd always wanted to be.

I met with Johnny Moreland, and a select few fourth-year students from KCOM, but did it too soon; I hadn't given myself time to get used to being in a safe area. As I remember that November evening, I couldn't concentrate enough to answer questions (and there were plenty) coherently.

* * *

During my reacclimatization to America, I listened to AM radio most of each day, especially during long drives. All the music seemed to be new: *"Witchita Lineman"* and *"Both Sides Now,"* were the most moving. I cannot hear them now without being instantly returned to November 1968.

58.

I was, had been, in fact, assigned at my own request, to serve out the remainder of my two-year military commitment at Munson Army Hospital. It was the post hospital for Fort Leavenworth, Kansas, eighteen miles from our home in Platte Woods, an easy commute. It was a singularly uneventful tour of duty. I *did* receive a second Army Commendation Medal in June 1969 for designing and implementing an appointment system to replace the traditional military clinics' first-come-first-served "cattle call" routine.

Our second child, Kiersten Elizabeth, was born at Munson on 22 July 1969.

I received my diploma for the E-24 Course in September 1969. It had been mis-sent to my Vietnam address. That was why it had taken so long to arrive.

Bill Anderson had returned from Vietnam to Fort Levenworth in June, 1969, so for a few months, he and I, two old recruits from the defunct 137th Infantry, served together again, even though our jobs were at opposite ends of the post.

My release back to the Active Reserve was effective 5 October 1969.

From then on my day job (plus a lot of nights) was as a civilian family doctor. After several false starts (remember my remarks about the hopelessness of trying to start a practice in Kansas City?), we finally settled in southern Arizona, not far from the Mexican border. My old study partner, Frank Hawkins, had steered me there, to the hospital where he was a practicing radiologist.

However, I also went on to serve in the Active Reserve, always in Troop Program Units, for a total of forty-two years, retiring only when progressing chronic arthritis made it impossible to pass the Army Physical Readiness Test (APRT) at age sixty. I was sorry to leave; I'd miss it. But after a few months I realized that what I missed was the USAR (and the Army) *of the Cold War years.*

The Clinton Department of Defense was not for me.

I'm not sure it was for anybody.

* * *

These are some of the things that made the Army a good place to be, now gone, probably never to return:
*The Officers Club bar that opened at 9 AM, with happy hour from 5PM to 7PM,where drinks were so cheap, they might as well have been free
*The guesthouse that always had an extra room for the unexpected overnighter.
*Men-only combat support and combat-service support units, though the performance of women in the latter has admittedly been promising.
*Really classy, posh officers' clubs, with NCO clubs not far behind.
*The ability to buy package liquor before 5 PM, on the assumption you'd act like an adult about its use.
*Gay soldiers (homosexuals, that is) excluded from service as "detrimental to good order and discipline" in the *perception,* whether real or not, of favoritism of like for like. Homosexuality had been rife and notorious in the peacetime Army and Marine Corps of the interwar periods of 1919-1941 and of 1953-1965, and we'd learned from the experience.
*The financial wherewithal to support and train the Army, albeit with 1% or so waste, that included enough ammunition to fire our weapons for qualification every six months, and to fire for familiarization on the calendar quarters between. We were *good* shots.
*Getting a Delinquency Report (DR) for appearing off-post in fatigues.
*Unusually good quality and quantity rations served in mess halls (see "wherewithal," above).
*Elimination of drivers in mobile units, and, rather, making this an additional duty of some technician in the unit. At first, that sounds like a pretty picayune example, *but* drivers require considerable experience to competently handle a five- or ten-tonner with a three- or seven-ton trailer attached, respectively. If he or she doesn't *get* that frequent practice, accidents become more common (and they have) often totaling the vehicles involved. How much did we save by eliminating that driver-and-first-line-maintainer's slot?

Well, when a driver is needed *now,* one has to be *detached from his/her important primary duty* (which then doesn't get done) so that he or she can be used as a driver.

Military vehicles are designed to be kept clean and maintained by their operators. How thorough would *you* be in this area if it weren't your primary duty? So, the trucks wear out, and have to be replaced *more often.* That's another example of false economy.
*Elimination of Company Punishment, which gave NCOs (remember them?) a chance to straighten out a soldier before he got enmired in the Military Justice System. And once he's court-martialed, he's a man with a federal conviction on

his record, which will then follow him throughout his working life.
*A five-day work week, slowly increasing to longer and longer work days, then on to a six-and-seven day week, leading incrementally *but logically, even predictably,* to the over-commitments of today, in Haiti, Bosnia, Somalia, Korea, Germany, Taiwan, the Sinai, etc., etc., etc.

The net loss has been a coarsening and cheapening of the military "that guards you while you sleep," as Kipling put it, and represents (or should) all of us. Shame on us all. Again.

* * *

When I reflect on Vietnam, and there's rarely a day when I don't, I ask myself if it all could have really happened?

If so, the most of the visual and auditory images are as fresh, and as intense as if they'd happened yesterday.

If not, could it all be a fantasy chimera, based on a few experiences, and embellished by books, movies, television, and endless old soldiers' tales, all mingled so as to seem to have been real?

And how could thirty-plus years have passed so quickly?

And *if* it happened as I remember it, is there anything I could have done differently? Something I might have done that resulted in even one less death?

* * *

*** * ***

Ninth Hand: The shoe is really low and *has* to contain a high percentage of high cards.

The dealer has a five up, and Mr. Fourth Chair has a ten down and a six up, the absolutely worst hand possible in blackjack, that any player *can* have, unless it's a *three-card* sixteen.

*** * ***

10 November 1945

I can remember listening to a radio commentator (in those pre-television days) on evening describing the effects of nuclear weapons (still called "atom bombs" at that early date). I was eating canned dark red Bing cherries, a special treat, from an ivory-colored dessert dish.

I was nine years old.

Particularly alarming, the news-reader opined, was the possibility that future testing of larger bombs might well start a chain reaction in the earth's atmospheric gases, and "destroy all life on the planet."

I was terrified.

* * *

For the next 45 years I lived under the constant threat of nuclear war, admittedly more likely at some points than others, but always there.

Then, for a glorious decade, 1989-1999, it was lifted.

Coincidentally, I moved to the Pacific Northwest. Now, that area is Ground Zero for Chinese or North Korean ICBMs.

* * *

I still can't eat canned Bing cherries.

Colonel Pillsbury

He was a small man, thin, wiry, and dark-complexioned, as well he might have been, burned by the sun of a hundred battlefields. I'd guess his age at fifty-five. He had stayed in the Army after World War II through preference; he could have been a successful surgeon in private practice anywhere in the world. He seemed sad, as though the tragedy of each wounded man he'd tried to save had whittled away at his life. That's not to say that he was depressed. He had a sense of humor, and a ready laugh.

He had been at Fort Sam Houston as a training officer on the faculty when I went through Basic.

In 1968, when I transferred to the 43d Group in Vietnam he was there, and remembered me. We talked informally for half an hour. He asked me: "Now that you've been in Vietnam for ten months, can you think of anything we should have taught you that we didn't?" He was the only senior officer I'd met who seemed to care, or to be willing to accept, and even solicit criticism.

The next time I saw him was in 1972 at Camp Bullis, Texas, when my reserve unit was there, being tested for proficiency in its performance in a field environment. After four years, and teaching hundreds of MC officers, he was able to call me by name.

He was training and certifying combat-readiness of medical units, *this time, not just individuals.*

God knows why he wasn't made Surgeon General of the Army. I've never known a man who was better suited for the job. A young Medical Corps captain could do a lot worse in choosing a role model.

* * *

Fall, 1989

It was noon; I was in my car with an all-news station on, and heard that the guards were off the Berlin Wall.

I flashed back to that night during OCS when The Wall had gone *up*. Merciful God, how could it have been 28 years? Is this what people mean when they say "closure?"

I find it downright scary.

During the next 14 days, Soviet troops were reported to be packing up, preparatory to moving back to areas within the borders of the USSR.

Joan asked me about it one afternoon, when the stand-down was being reported on the TV news. What had happened?

"I think that the war is over," I said, "and I believe that we won."

It had lasted, for both of us, from the ages of nine until we were 54.

The country went back to peacetime business as usual.

For about thirteen months.

* * *

01 May 1991

200 men and women dressed in desert camouflage, stepped off on their collective left foot on the count of "one," moving off, back in our home town, proud as Satan of what we had accomplished in Iraq and Kuwait.

There was something else we had achieved that only four or five of us, out of the two hundred total, realized, or at least verbalized: America is *back.* We're a credible world power again, because *this* time we kept our word, and held firm. This was the parade down Main Street that I *should* have had in 1969.

The wraith of Vietnam that had clung to us as a nation for nearly twenty years dissipated, and was gone for good.

* * *

01 June 2001

At this time, the United States is continuing to rotate fighting men and women into the Balkans, to "keep the peace," where there is no peace to keep.

We have had units on the ground there for five years, with no defined end-point to limit our involvement. No one from The Family has deployed, however. We are not, by nature, peacetime soldiers.

At the risk of being pedantic, I can't decide whether this is a replay of Vietnam in 1964, of the Germans' anti-Yugoslav-partisan campaign of 1941-1945, or a waiting game, expecting a 1914 Sarajevo incident, again.

The First Commandment of Military Strategy is this: "Never, never, however tempted you are to do so, march on Moscow.

Though I've never heard it iterated, the Second must *be: "Never send troops to intervene in the Balkans."*

Retirement Day, 9 October 1996

Personal Involvement versus Gutless-Wonder-Hood

My limited personal experience in Washington, D.C. and its environs during interwar intervals of peacetime service taught me one more thing about war: Hell hath no fury like that of a non-combatant.

My prior-service stepbrothers (Korea) and cousins (Vietnam and Desert Storm) all agree, to a man. And it has proved to be true. The only men who've ever *been* shot at who took this country into wars were George Washington, Harry S. Truman, and George H. W. Bush.

So, the next time that you hear some latter-day doctrinaire Cato urging us to take up arms against some new Carthage, chuck the son-of-a-bitch *out* before anyone can hear and believe him. *He* won't be doing the fighting. *You* will. The validity of his opinions about war will be inversely proportional to his likely distance from an armed, angry, enemy soldier.

And never listen to a Memorial Day speech from this twit. He doesn't *know.*

Fathers, excuse my pedantry, but if *you* enlist, by all means take your sons with you. If you *don't* serve, then respect and support your sons' decision to do the same. If your son elects not to accept military service, hide him out, arrange an international flight to a country without extradition, and at worst, visit him regularly in Federal prison.

Fathers and sons, if you're conscientiously opposed to war, report in, refuse to be sworn in, suck it up, and take your two years in Leavenworth to bear witness to your belief (though you can elect to be a medic based on Conscientious Objector status). Anything less is just cowardice, rationalize it and call it whatever else you will.

* * *

My father died during intra-infarction cardiac balloon angioplasty in the autumn of 1988. He was just short of his 74th birthday. He told (only) those close to him how proud he was of me. He never once hinted it *to* me; he was a Richards to the end.

* * *

59.

20 April 2001
(26th Anniversary of the Fall of Saigon)

Why did we get involved in Vietnam? Well, from the vantage point of 2001, with most of the people who can sue me dead, I'd say it went something like this:

- LBJ wanted to be a wartime, and therefore *great*, president, and he believed the Army when they told him it would be an easy conflict to win, partly or primarily because he *wanted* to believe them.
- The Army, and World War II's also-rans then in charge of the Army, wanted a war in Vietnam because that's where promotion lay, especially in a large-unit war.
- The idealists and intellectuals, many of them carryovers from the Kennedy cabinet, wanted war in Vietnam so that they wouldn't be perceived by history, understandably, as having made the same mistake that the democracies had made in the 1930s, in dealing with *that* generation's regional aggressors, Japan and Germany.
- The people of the United States had, at least initially, supported the war. The martyred JFK had *told* them that they must, because it was their duty to do so.

* * *

The Increased Lethality of the Modern Battlefield
(2001)

This subject was discussed as such on a theoretical basis starting in the mid- and late-seventies by both the Command and General staff College and the Infantry School.

I have had some training from each of them, over the past four decades, and have great respect for both. That means, in short, that they usually don't fuck up and get Little Sonny from down the street killed, if it's possible to avoid it by prior planning. Now, if Sonny's luck has run out, that can't be avoided.

We should have been warned, if not have concluded, earlier *that the addition of high-tech to the battlefield after 1965 would produce an unexpectedly-high level of fatal casualties, like that seen in 1914-1915. The old killed-to-wounded ratio of one to four, more or less constant since 1862, would also probably adjust upward to around two to four, perhaps even three out of four, in a ground war against the USSR.*

We missed the boat for several reasons:

1. The small numbers of men in active combat in Vietnam at any one time and place was so small that valid conclusions could not be reached, due to questionable sample size (what has since been called "fourth-generation warfare.").

2. Superhuman efforts were made in support of rapid casualty evacuation to support the field Army. This would be unachievable in the absence of absolute control of the air space above the battlefield, as was *the case in Vietnam and Desert Storm. That benign circumstance is unlikely tohappen so fortuitously in a future war.*

3. The same inability to over-assign medical treatment assets as was done in Vietnam, would apply in the future, too, *due to simultaneous requirements for medical support elsewhere.*

4. We did not then and do not now *know the* quantitative *effect of B-52 strikes, TAC air, or even long-range field artillery strikes triggered by infrared and sound sensors, as well as by agent reports, that took place along the borders of South Vietnam congruent with those of Laos*

And Cambodia. I had serious doubts about the earlier claimed total of 340,000 North Vietnamese/Viet Cong dead in the entire war, and I further doubted that the North Vietnamese would ever release the actual, much higher figure, until, in mid-2000, they claimed a revised number of 1,400,000 dead.

One of my most vivid memories of the war is of flying at 2000 feet over a solid forest that had been hit by B-52s a week before, and for a timed two minutes being subjected to the strongest odor of rotting animal tissue I've ever experienced. That's an area over two miles across. Was that just one company of men? Too few to account for the size of the area we crossed. A battalion of three companies? Nine companies? And was that a unique event?

I doubt it.

* * *

60.

What are the lessons learned from Vietnam? Volumes have been penned about that. I can only present a worm's-eye view, based on personal experience, one of The Family in the generation that won the Cold War:

*First and foremost, do not send armed forces in harm's way unless the vital interests of the United States, *to include its credibility as an ally* are in danger of being compromised.

*Call up the Reserves, *all of them*, as fast as the force structure can absorb them, as we did in the Desert Shield mobilization of late 1990. If nothing else, it shows the enemy that we are not fooling around or bluffing, and are determined to kick ass.

*Avoid committing any kind of cohort to combat. Units are stronger if they are *heterogeneous* in as many aspects as possible, e.g. ages, colors, regional origin, etc., etc., etc. A glaring example of how *not* to do this is to draft all the eighteen-year-olds and send them off as replacements, so that all the private E-2s are the same in every significant way. The members of a cohort can learn little or nothing valid from each other.

*Don't have an individual rotation policy. *Units* should rotate in and out of the combat zone together, *as units*, and should stay active, intact, until the war is over. The increased financial expense of this strategy would be offset by greatly-enhanced unit effectiveness.

*Draft men *and women* for the duration plus six months as was done in World War Two. Have no more two- and three-year enlistment policy if there's any American in action, anywhere in the world.

*Don't be afraid to engage in low-intensity, fourth-generation (see Glossary) or guerrilla war, but don't try to do it with 18,000-man divisions. You have to fight small units *with* small units. Remember Ferguson's Law: The effectiveness of a force is a function of the *square* of like units *versus* like units. Cousin David's unit and mine, as separate brigades, usually deployed as four-company battalion task forces, wreaked utter havoc on the NVA. So did the Special Operations Group, Vietnam, in even smaller autonomous task groups.

* * *

Savannah, Georgia, Memorial Day Weekend, 1996
(Momento mori)

On Memorial Day Weekend, every even-numbered year, the Brigade assembles again.

The appearance of the survivors of the First Brigade varied tremendously. I was unrecognizable; my facial features had changed too much, as had those of many others. Amazingly, though, many had not. Some hadn't even grayed.

These were the men who'd been corporals and above in 1965, and served together as twenty- and thirty-year men, before, during, and after Vietnam. To me, they were more of those cues I sometimes see in life, cues to instant time travel, carrying me back to the one thing we all had in common: "Gone for a soldier, 1967."

* * *

61.

I started packing for Desert Shield as soon as I got back from a biological warfare course at Fort Detrick, Maryland on 12 August 1990, once I heard President Bush say that "...this (aggression) will not stand," in describing Iraq's invasion of Kuwait.

Bill Anderson had warned me to get ready via a long-distance phone call.

I had been through a refresher course, and accepted as a graduate Israeli paratrooper (on a tourist visa) exactly 71 days before. Had the Israelis known something that we hadn't? Our briefing officer in Tel Aviv had said that a Middle Eastern conflict was very likely in the near future, but in that area, it *usually* is.

In August 1990 my unit was alerted for call-up.

I was activated for the Middle East (what I call the Second Gulf War) effective the day after Thanksgiving, 1990.

My unit of Reservists flew out of its home station on a leased Southwest Airlines 737, and assembled at Fort Sill. It was my first time there since 1961.

A travelling team from Fort Sam Houston arrived a week later to present the Advanced Trauma Life Support Course (ATLS) to the doctors. I spoke to the Team Chief and made the point that it should be opened to *anyone with a patient-care MOS, officer or not,* because I thought it would augment our unit's capacity to triage, and that's what we did.

Some Medical Corps officers took the course and didn't pass. Some enlisted medics took it, and did. Make what you will of that.

* * *

I had a stash of Darvocet that I took for my chronic back pain, hoping that the war would end before my dope supply did. A sixteen-hour day, seven days a week, is a little rough, on the wrong side of age 54. Oddly enough, I took half-a-dozen unannounced drug screens and was never called on what *had* to be positive results on every one of them.

I was released from Active Duty (again) 31 March 1991, after a pretty un-distinguished five months' service. And I was awarded my fifth Army Commendation Medal that same morning.

That was medal number twenty-four of my career; none of the few that I deserved were awarded; all that I got were undeserved, in my opinion, at least.

* * *

Through forty years of twilight struggle,
You balanced firmness with patience.
Readiness with restraint
And gave us, at last, victory.

David Poyer
"Dedication" (to the men and
women who fought the Cold War);
The Circle, *1992, St. Martin's Press.*

* * *

62.

By 1995, I had recovered financially from Desert Shield, and developed a successful, well-established family practice.

I had also had resumed a fifteen-year avocational interest in a local medical school, where I was an office preceptor to some of its third-year students. In an ironic turn of events, based upon recommendation of the local American Academy of Family Physicians chapter, I was offered a position as an assistant professor, *full*-time, in the Department of Family Medicine at West Arizona University's School of Medicine.

Me, teaching in an *M.D. school*? After the Debacle of 1960? It was, it *had* to be, one of God's jokes, I thought.

I didn't volunteer the information about MSU and my fiasco there. First, WAU might already have known. The AMA *does* keep track of medical students who don't complete their course of study, voluntarily or otherwise. Second, they came to *me* with an offer; I didn't ask for it. And, third, I think that what you are now is more significant than what you were over a third of a century ago.

So, to the faint sound of the whirling in their graves of the dean and faculty of Midwest University State Med, I smiled broadly and accepted Western Arizona University's offer.

I stayed there for three years, and every day of my tenure there I looked into the mirror in the morning and said aloud: "Don't be like *them*, whatever else you may do today."

And I never was.

* * *

Binion's, eleventh hand, hit-or-stick phase:

It's down to the dealer, second chair and fourth chair. All the other players have left.

The shoe is low, with probably 75 cards left to play, and according to The Count, rich in high, ten-value cards.

Fourth chair stands with sixteen, having maintained The Count, and gambling on the dealer to bust. The dealer, with a king down and a five up, for a hand total of fifteen, draws a ten, and *does* bust, as Mr. Four had predicted he would with about an 80% certainty.

Life *is* uncertain, but it sure helps to know the odds. Like your chances of hitting a 31-to-one three-bet series, and, knowing that, your ability to influence life's inevitable changes.

It *can* be done, if you pay attention to detail, and *never* give up.

* * *

SHALLOW: . . . .certain she's old . . . .
SILENCE: That's fifty-five year ago . . . .
SHALLOW: . . .Cousin Silence, that thou hadst seen what this knight and I have seen. Ha! Sir John, said I well?
FALSTAFF: We have heard the chimes at midnight, Master Shallow.
SHALLOW: That we have, that we have, that we have; in faith, Sir John, we have.

Shakespeare, *Henry the Fourth.*

* * *

That about wraps it up.

My point has been and remains this: In spite of adversity and change, if *I* can succeed, anyone can.

You can.

R.T. O'Riley retired to a snowbird's life in 1996, spending six months in the Colorado Rockies and six months in Kansas City each year.

Johnny Moreland died of lung cancer in 1997. He is greatly missed.

Frank Hawkins had left our clinic for greener radiolgic pastures in 1973 and evidently found them; he had been able to retire in 1986.

Bill Anderson is still in the Army, a command sergeant major, E-9.

Prince Henry retired from the Regular Air Force as a full colonel in 1994.

Pops Macabee got that Army residency, retired a full colonel in 1993, and has been teaching pathology as a second career since 1994.

Paul and Connalee Howard are still living and working in San Antonio.

Roy, my stepfather, my son's beloved "Grandpa Roy", died in 1993, slowly and painfully, of arteriosclerosis obliterans due to cigarette use for sixty years.

For all of them, for generations of The Family, or for any individual, adversity is the engine that drives personal change; ask any survivor of the Great Depression. In addition, war changes you in a penultimate way. It is *the* ultimate adversity.

And no one who hasn't experienced it can even begin to understand it. In expressing their opinions, they should, in fact, do the world a favor and shut the hell up about it.

The only civilian analogy that I can present is that war's effect is like the change that occurs in a Ph.D.-in-English-Literature-candidate who discovers that most of the poetry of A.E. Housman can be sung to the tune of "The Wabash Cannonball." Forever after that revelation, he *cannot* see Housman's work in the same way as he had before.

War does that, with every experience you will ever have afterward.

Old soldiers thus stand apart, the movers of history, living survivors of a lifetime series of personal changes, the result of shared hardship, shared mortal danger, and loss of friends as close as brothers, the possessors of a quiet, unshakable dignity.

THE END

GLOSSARY

AID: Agency for International Development.

AIT: Advanced Individual Training. Completion results in awarding of a Military Occupational Specialty. 11B is the MOS of a light weapons infantryman (See Joe Tentpeg).

AC-47: A 1938 model heavily-armed DC-3 (also called the C-47, or "Gooney Bird"), heavily armed as a gunship to support ground troops.

AK-47: Kalishnikov 7.62mm assault rifle, used by the Soviet bloc's armed forces.

AO: Area of Operations.

ALICE: Army Load-bearing Improved Cargo Equipment.

APC: Armored Personnel Carrier.

ARVN: Army of the Republic of Vietnam, now defunct.

B-40: Shoulder-fired antitank rocket, carried and fired by one man. Earlier models are called RPG-7 (rocket-propelled grenade).

Battalion: A tactical unit of three rifle companies and a support company. Normally, it has an artillery battery of six guns attached to and co-located with it. It is commanded by a lieutenant colonel. Strength: approximately 800 men.

Brigade: A tactical unit of three or four battalions, a support battalion, and attached support units. Strength: 4000 or so.

C-123: Obsolescent twin-piston-engined light-to-medium-lift transport plane. Very reliable.

C-130: Medium-heavy-lift transport plane powered by four turbo- prop engines. The real workhorse of the fixed-wing airlift fleet in Vietnam.

Cam Ranh Bay: Excellent natural harbor about midway between the capitol and Da Nang. Massively improved by the U.S. in 1965 and 1966. Will be operational for at least 400 years more, with minimal maintenance.

Capitol Military District: a 20-mile diameter circle centered on the Presidential Palace in Saigon.

CH-46: Navy/Marine twin-rotor light-to-medium lift helicopter.

CH-47: Army twin-jet-engined twin-rotor helicopter, half again the size of the CH-46.

CH-53: Army and Air Force heavy-lift helicopter. These are the model lost at Desert One in 1980.

Cholon: The Chinese west side of Saigon.

Claymore: A command-detonated mine consisting of 750 quarter-inch ball bearings imbedded in one surface of a two-pound slab of C-4 plastic explosive about the size of this book. There is a fool- (and GI) -proof label on the ball-bearing surface that says "Front. Toward Enemy," in half-inch-high raised letters so that it can be aimed in the dark. It even has a pistol-like open sight for more accurate aiming of the projectiles. If you've ever seen a man shot several times at close range with 00 buckshot, you have an idea of what a Claymore does. I think that it was the world's first command-detonated directional mine.

Company: 187 infantrymen organized into three 50-man rifle platoons, plus a 37-man command/support element.

Corps Area: the four major military zones comprising South Vietnam, e.g. I Corps, II Corps, etc.

CQ: Enlisted man in Charge of Quarters, who mans the Orderly Room after duty hours, all night long. In the pre-answering-machine days, his principal duty was to be there to answer the phone, and to relay telephone messages to the Commander, Duty Officer or First Sergeant.

Da Nang: Medium-sized city with perhaps the best natural harbor in South Vietnam. Generally marks the southernmost boundary of Marine Corps responsibility, plus the area to its south needed to secure it.

Defilade: Masked by terrain feature(s).

DEROS: Date of Expected Return from Overseas.

Division: Two to four brigades. An airborne division has about 13,000 men assigned to it, at full strength.

DNBI: Disease and Non-Battle Injury (patient).

DZ: Drop-zone.

Eight-one: The standard Army infantry smoothbore mortar, caliber 81mm.

Four-deuce: Heavy World-War-II era 4.2-inch (107mm) *rifled* mortar used by airborne units because of the portability-heavy shell tradeoff.

Goose-Egg: an oval on a map denoting a unit's position.

GP Large: A Tent, General Purpose, Large, floor area 45 X 22 feet. There are also GP Mediums and GP Smalls. Any combination of like tents can be buttoned onto others to form a double-length, double-wide (tricky), T-shaped or cruciform floor plan, depending on the task at hand.

GR: Graves Registration, a branch of the Quartermaster Corps.

Heat-tab: A pellet of one ounce of solid trioxane, which burns for eight to nine minutes, i.e., just enough to heat one individual can of C-rations.

Hooch: Field living space, perhaps dug-in, probably with a temporary fabric or plastic sheeting roof to keep off the rain. *Not* designed to be a fighting position.

Huey: The UH-1 Iriquois, a single-engined jet-powered helicopter, used in many configurations ranging from that of an unarmed medical evacuation type to a rocket-firing, tank-busting gunship, with many variations between.

ICBM: Intercontinental ballistic missile.

IRBM: Intermediate-range (2000 miles or so) ballistic missile.

KIA: Killed in action.

LBJ: The stockade called Long Binh Jail for serving sentences of less than six months confinement. Longer sentences were served at the U.S. Army Disciplinary Barracks located at Ft. Leavenworth, Kansas. The sentence was called "bad time," because it did not count towards time served in Vietnam or against their term of Army service. The author knew one private E-2 who had physically been in Vietnam for three years, but who, because of several terms in the stockade hadn't been able to accumulate twelve months' good time, so that he could go home. I wonder if he's still there?

Lifer: A career or Regular soldier.

LOH or "Loach": a light observation helicopter; minimal to no cargo-carrying capacity, unless modified.

Lyster bag: A canvas 20-gallon bag that supplies drinkable water to a company-sized unit; if hung in shade, some cooling of the water occurs by evaporation from the canvas walls of the bag.

LZ: Landing zone.

M-14: 7.62mm U.S. assault rifle very slowly phased into the Army inventory between 1958 and 1965.

M-16: 5.56mm U.S. lightweight assault rifle issued fairly rapidly to troops in Vietnam after 1965.

M-60, or "pig": a one-man-portable light machine gun, borrowing freely in its mechanics from the German MG-42 design, though *not* in the M60's much slower rate of fire.

Mini-Gun: 30-caliber motor-driven Gatling gun that fires 6000 bullets a minute.

MOS: Military Occupational Specialty. Expressed as a three-digit number. 11B denotes Light Weapons Infantryman; 11C is a heavy-weapons infantryman. 91B is a basic medic's MOS.

NVA: North Vietnamese Regular Army, as opposed to the native South Vietnamese insurgency that we called the Vietnamese Communists, or Viet Cong (V.C.). Excellent light infantry, brave and well-motivated.

OAC: Officer Advanced Course: intended to qualify captains for company command.

OBC: Officer Basic Course. Administered to ROTC graduates after they are commissioned, as practical preparation to be functioning lieutenants. OCS graduates don't have to take it.

OCS: Officer Candidate School. A road upward (see Chapters 4 through 7) from the ranks. Fairly uncommonly utilized in peacetime.

One-oh-five: The 105mm howitzer. Range, ¼ mile to nine miles, depending on propellant charge increments used (from one to seven), elevation of the tube, terrain, and other variables.

POV: Privately-owned vehicle.

PSP: Perforated steel planking. It interlocks with ingenious tab-in-slotted-hook fasteners, and makes a lovely airfield surface overnight, given enough men to assemble it.

R&R: Rest and recuperation: A short furlough to a non-combat zone, not charged against annual leave.

RASH: Rear-area-shit-head.

Rations, Class "A:" The same as you buy at a supermarket, issued in units of sufficient quantities to feed 100 men or percentage thereof for one day.

Rations, Class "B:" Bulk, nonperishable rations (e.g. gallon cans of tuna, or of sliced bacon or of flaked, dehydrated potatoes) designed for areas where refrigeration was uncertain or non-existent. Also issued in units per hundred men or in fractions for less than a hundred.

Ration, individual, combat: Three small tin cans encased in a cardboard box, containing various types of main dish, starch dish, fruit and dessert, intended to be one meal for one man.

REMF: Rear-echelon-mother-fucker.

ROTC: Reserve Officer Training Corps. Two years' instruction in military science was once required of undergraduates at land-grant universities. Since 1973, it's been optional. The third and fourth years were never required, unless one wanted to be commissioned a second lieutenant upon graduation. The four-year course still provides over 60% of the Army's juniormost officers.

Seabees: Navy Construction Battalions (CBs), consisting of engineer personnel.

S-1: Staff officer who's responsible for personnel actions, pay, leave, DEROSs, discharges, and after 1970, *coordination* of medical services with all three. At division and above, called *G*-1.

S-2: Intelligence officer.

S-3: Operations and training officer.

S-4: Supply, maintenance, and non-tactical transportation/movement officer.

Shell Oil Company: An international conglomerate operating many crossroads

gasoline stations, and running its tanker-trucks over every road throughout Vietnam, without obvious interference by the V.C. I suspect that they paid protection money (called "taxes" by the VC) to the local insurgent units.
Sixty-mortar: 60mm smoothbore mortar.
SKS: a Soviet-bloc semi-automatic 7.62mm ten-shot rifle.
Strategic Air Command (SAC): That part of the Air Force concerned with delivering nuclear annihilation, internationally.

Tentpeg, Joe: Archtypical U.S. infantryman.

V.C.: The insurgent South Vietnamese Peoples' liberation Army.
Vung Tau: Beach Resort 40 miles East of Saigon. Used for in-country leave site for U.S. troops, and I suspect by the Viet Cong (V.C.), too. There was no military action in this area for the entire duration of the war in Vietnam.

Wadi: A low-lying dry stream-bed in arid or desert terrain.
Wait-a-Minute Vine: A tropical bush that has a three-pronged, claw-shaped protuberance about every six inches along its entire length. Sort of like a domestic blackberry vine on anabolic steroids, making it bigger, stronger, and meaner.
War, *First-generation*: Wherein victory is attained by masses of men pressing in and stabbing each other with spears or bayonets (Thermoplae, or Blenheim, 1703), in a theory first described by Colonels John R. Boyd, USAF, and Franklin C. Spinney, USMC (q.v. on The World-Wide Web).
War, *Second*-Generaton: Firepower, not shock action, determines victory (Western Front 1914-1917, or the last half of the Napoleonic Wars' battles).
War, *Third*-Generation: Large forces are attacked in an unexpected spot, and beaten through superior strategy of a possibly smaller power or organization (Pearl Harbor, perhaps, and the first six months of World War II in the Pacific).
War, *Fourth*-Generation: Wars won *not* by attacking an adversary's armed forces, but civilian targets in the enemy's homeland (e.g., the Weather Underground, 1967-1973).

***NOTE:* The generations are *NOT* sequential**. One step may or may not follow another in numerical order. The dispatching of V. I. Lenin to Russia by the Germansis a fourth-generation act--but it was carried out in *1917*, while *firepower* (second-generation tactics), if not a war-winner, made winning by any *other* means impossible.

WIA: Wounded in action.

CERTIFICATE OF RECOGNITION
JOHN COE RICHARDS, JR.

4 January 2001

In recognition of your service during the period of the Cold War (2 September 1945-26 December 1991) in promoting peace and stability of this Nation, the people of this Nation are forever grateful.

William S. Cohen
SECRETARY OF DEFENSE

If you enjoyed this novel, you will also want to read *ARMY GREEN,* by Walter D. Rodgers, due for release by Trafford Publishing in mid-2002.

ISBN 155369338-8

9 781553 693383